Mathematics 3

Foundation Skills for 11-14 year olds

Michael Ashcroft BSc

Head of Mathematics,
Berry Hill High School,
Stoke-on-Trent

Charles Letts & Co Ltd
London, Edinburgh & New York

First published 1986
by Charles Letts & Co Ltd
Diary House, Borough Road, London SE1 1DW

Illustrations: Andrew Birch; Tek-Art

© Michael Ashcroft

All our Rights Reserved. No part of this publication may be reproduced, stored in a retrieval system, or transmitted, in any form or by any means, electronic, mechanical, photocopying, recording or otherwise, without the prior permission of Charles Letts Publishers

ISBN 0 85097 671 5

Printed in Great Britain by
Charles Letts (Scotland) Ltd

Acknowledgements

The author and publishers are grateful to the following organizations for permission to reproduce photographs for which they hold the copyright:

Clem Haagner/Ardea London: p47; B.P.L./Barnaby's Picture Library: p82; Central Press/Barnaby's Picture Library: p99; Alan R. Smith/Barnaby's Picture Library: p75; British Aerospace: p82; Daily Telegraph Colour Library: p15; Maggie Murray/Format: pp10, 13, 42; Laurie Sparham/Network: p103; John Sturrock/Network: p74; Trustees of the Science Museum, London: p17

Preface

Although many parents do not realize it, probably the most traumatic happenings in a child's school career take place during the transition from Primary to Secondary school at the age of 11/12/13 (depending upon the organization of their Local Education Authority).

Whilst most children take the upheaval in their stride, inevitably some children experience a very difficult period of adjustment. Coming from the much smaller Primary schools into the far greater populated Secondary schools, is a daunting prospect in itself. The changeover from a general teaching system to a strange system involving many teachers handling their own specialist subjects, can also lead to confusion and have an unsettling effect on the child.

'Tell-tale' signs are often evident to parents – such as sleepless nights, slight character changes, mystery illness on a morning before school, and even truancy in extreme circumstances.

More often than not, the root cause of the problem may appear – on the surface – to be quite trivial when it is eventually unearthed and, frequently, the problem can easily and painlessly be dealt with at school. However, in order for this to be done, parents must feel free to contact the school and enlist pastoral help. Most schools are only too pleased to be of assistance regarding such problems and, as parents, it is our duty to help not only the child but also the school who are, after all, not always aware that there is a problem.

As parents, we should also be aware of a large problem faced by the teaching staff of the Secondary school. My own school, for instance, admits 'new-intake' 11-year-olds from as many as ten different 'feeder' Primary schools. Imagine the problem of the teacher of a 'new-intake' class of thirty pupils who may have arrived from any of the ten 'feeder' schools. Whilst not in any way wishing to be critical of some 'feeder' schools and their differing 'systems', we have the very difficult task of moulding the class into a single unit rather than the fragmented unit as presented to us. Children are used to different teaching styles, methods and even variations in subject matter covered in their Primary Education. Liaison between 'feeder' Primary schools and their Secondary schools is improving all the time, and some of the problems in this area are gradually being overcome.

Due to the continuous nature of a subject such as Mathematics (probably more so than in any other school subject) most Secondary schools adopt a levelling and consolidation period of teaching, whereby the children are taken over the 'common ground' arithmetical work, in order to ensure a reasonable consistency amongst the group. Having achieved this consistency level, on which the whole of Secondary Maths depends, we then proceed to introduce new work built upon the child's previous arithmetical knowledge.

It is easy to see that, without these basic arithmetical concepts and skills, the foundation for further development and future success in Mathematics would be missing and would lead to recurring problems in the learning processes forthwith.

In conclusion, whilst it is fair to say that some of the arithmetical work in Volume 1 is quite basic, it is of extreme importance as far as the rest of the course is concerned, and we must always be mindful that the best buildings are the ones laid on good solid foundations. Volume 2 built on these foundations and extended the mathematical concepts further.

Having completed Volume 3 and its assigned Activities, one should be adequately prepared for a GCSE Course in Mathematics.

Mike Ashcroft 1986

I wish to thank the following people for their help in producing these books: my consultant, Ray Williams (second in Maths Dept, Berry Hill High School) who has given tremendous assistance with the assigned Activities and for his general help, advice, criticism and encouragement; my wife Norma for her marvellous support and the professionalism of her typing; and the staff of Charles Letts & Co. Ltd, for their excellent assistance. My special thanks go to my Copy-Editor Eileen Jarvis, for her superb help and advice that she has offered and in particular for the hard work she has contributed to all three volumes of *Foundation Skills–Mathematics*.

Contents

Introduction

and guide to using the book

As already mentioned in the Preface, in order to achieve success in Mathematics it is very important to acquire basic concepts and skills. This first volume is designed to 'bridge the gap' between Primary and Secondary school Mathematics, whilst at the same time developing the subject matter to greater levels, thus providing the basis for the first-year Secondary Mathematics course. The second and third volumes are designed to be a natural progression from Volume 1, dealing with the basic skills at a higher level and introducing slightly more difficult follow-through skills, in Mathematics, thus widening and enlarging the pupil's Mathematical vocabulary.

Most teachers would accept that much assistance and practice at home can be invaluable in the acquisition of mathematical skills. However, the order in which subject matter is tackled is not necessarily as shown in this volume. Other Secondary schools may tackle the different skills and concepts in a slightly different order but hopefully, whatever the order, the subject matter will be found somewhere in the book.

Volume 1 is basically aimed at the 11-year-old child.

Volume 2 is basically aimed at the 12-year-old child, and;

Volume 3 is basically aimed at the 13-14-year-old child.

Again it must be emphasized that, because of the follow-through nature of mathematical study, there will be slight variations from school to school.

Much research has been done in recent years into methods of learning and much discussion has been directed at deciding what should constitute a Mathematics course up to 16+ years of age. The Assessment of Performance Unit (APU) was set up in 1975 as a branch of the Department of Education and Science (DES). The Unit aims to provide information about the levels of performance that pupils achieve in different subjects and how their performance changes over the years.

The terms of reference of the APU are: 'To promote the development of methods of assessing and monitoring the achievement of children at school, and to seek to identify the incidence of under-achievement'.

To this end, the APU, based at Chelsea College, University of London, and at the University of Leeds, has carried out a large number of tests of pupils aged 11, 13 and 15 years. The analysis of the results of these tests has enabled the researchers to identify the levels of understanding which we can expect pupils to have at different ages. *Foundation Skills–Mathematics*, in its three volumes, has been compiled along the broad outlines laid down by APU, which categorizes mathematics into five specific areas – Number, Measure, Algebra, Geometry and Statistics. Hence, the three volumes are designed with units devoted to each of the five specific areas.

In Mathematics, the APU has developed both written and practical modes of assessment. In its reports, entitled *Mathematical Development*, published by HMSO, some very interesting results have come to light concerning mathematical 'under-achievement' – a problem to which we, as teachers and parents, should pay great attention.

It is also interesting to note that, in November 1981, Dr W.H. Cockcroft and his research team submitted a report entitled *Mathematics Counts,* published by HMSO, dealing with an Inquiry into the teaching of Mathematics in Primary and Secondary schools in England and Wales. It is the most authoritative document concerning school Mathematics to be published for many years. Known to most as the *Cockcroft Report*, it puts forward recommendations which call for 'early' action by all involved in mathematical education.

At this time, many teachers of Mathematics are greatly aware of the Cockcroft findings and of our own shortcomings, and are attempting to implement as many of its recommendations as possible. These include such things as enthusiasm and enjoyment for the subject and its 'rub-off' effect, discussion between teacher and pupils, the introduction of activity/practical work, consolidating and practising of fundamental skills and routines, problem solving relating to everyday situations, and investigational work.

The report also makes reference to the role of parents in a child's mathematical development. It does this along the lines that parents can exercise, even if unknowingly, a considerable influence on the attitudes of their children to Mathematics. The encouragement to make use of aspects of Mathematics during normal family activities can assist with the development and understanding of the number concept. Sometimes a negative attitude by parents in failing to understand the nature of the work which their child is doing, can result in the child adopting the same negative thoughts and hence developing poor attitudes in general towards Mathematics. It can also happen that parents can expect too little or too much of their children. Total backing and encouragement from parents is a vital ingredient in assisting the teaching of Mathematics.

Most schools would be only too delighted to enlist the help of parents, by explaining the approaches to Mathematics which they are using and the purpose of mathematical activities – which parents, themselves, may not have undertaken while at school.

With this particularly in mind, these volumes have been designed carefully to explain to interested parents the concepts and skills of the Mathematics taught to 11- to 13-year-olds in our Secondary schools.

As a result, parents may then feel in such a position as to be able to offer their children positive help and advice with most problems which the school Mathematics curriculum may cause them.

It is important to view these volumes not as a school textbook, but more as a back-up source for schoolwork, which can be used by the family in the confines of its own home.

The book can be used as a whole course, i.e. worked through from start to finish, or by selecting particular problem areas. By use of the Contents (at the front) any particular skill/concept can be easily located. The analysis table (at the front) can be particularly helpful when matching a particular topic to its constituent skills and concepts. Assignment activities follow on from the sections in each unit. Answers to activities in some detail can be found at the end of each volume. There is also a list of some school textbooks which may be helpful in further follow-up work, particularly in the area of further activities/exercises.

Finally, having used Volume 3 to good effect, it would be most fitting to follow the basic ideas extended therein, through the *Letts Study Aid–Revise Mathematics* (Duncan Graham), which concentrates on the Examination side of Mathematics in the 4th and 5th years of the school Maths Course.

Remember, Mathematics, well taught and understood, can be one of the most enjoyable subjects of the Secondary school's curriculum. My hope is that these volumes will enrich and enhance the users' mathematical prowess.

SKILLS

	Problem Solving	Use of Equipment	Scale Drawing	Sketching	Information Processing	Decision Making	Calculator Skills
Units 1–6 NUMBER	●	●		●	●	●	●
Units 7–15 MEASURE	●	●		●	●	●	●
Units 16–25 ALGEBRA	●			●	●	●	
Units 26–34 GEOMETRY/ TRIGONOMETRY	●	●	●	●	●	●	●
Units 35–40 STATISTICS/ PROBABILITY	●	●	●	●	●	●	

CONCEPTS

	Computation	Place Value	+ve/–ve Numbers	Operation Order	Fraction	Money	Time	Measurement	Graphical Representation	Spatial Concept	Statistical Ideas	Area	Volume	Inverse
Units 1–6 NUMBER	●	●	●	●	●		●				●			●
Units 7–15 MEASURE	●				●		●	●		●	●	●	●	
Units 16–25 ALGEBRA	●	●	●	●	●	●			●	●				●
Units 26–34 GEOMETRY/ TRIGONOMETRY	●	●	●	●	●			●	●	●		●	●	●
Units 35–40 STATISTICS/ PROBABILITY	●			●	●	●		●	●	●	●			

NUMBER

Unit 1

The use of a calculator

1.1 Introduction

Modern school mathematics courses leading to GCE O-Level, CSE and GCSE Examinations, are becoming more and more dependent on the use of the electronic calculator. Much of the work covered in this volume will depend quite an amount on you having a calculator and knowing how to use it.

If you are contemplating the purchase of a calculator, then the suitability is of great importance. We are not simply looking for an 'adding machine', but rather an instrument which, in effect, replaces the books of 'tables' which were used until recently.

There is a vast variety of calculators on the market, ranging from basic to extremely sophisticated. For the purposes of mathematics courses up to GCE A-Level standard, a basic scientific calculator is recommended – being relatively inexpensive.

If you are in any doubt concerning calculators, your teacher should be able to advise you. In fact, some schools are able to order suitable calculators for you.

A typical calculator should look something like that shown in Fig. 1.1.

Apart from the main operations of +, −, × and ÷, it should have other important functions on the keyboard including:

$\sqrt{\ }$ (square root), sin, cos, tan, $\sin^{-1}$, $\cos^{-1}$, $\tan^{-1}$, log, ln, $\frac{1}{x}$, y^x, $\sqrt[x]{y}$, and of course a memory

[M+] and [RM]

Since you have had to buy your calculator, it is very important that you treat it with great care and observe the following rules in order that it will remain trouble-free.

1 Do not leave it switched on and always check that it **is** switched off (even the ones that supposedly switch themselves off after 10 minutes or so). Obviously, this will preserve the life of the battery.

2 Do not throw it around or drop it. This could damage the electronic components as well as the outer case.

3 Do not allow it to get wet. Damp in the electronics will ruin it.

4 Do not leave it exposed to sunlight or other heat sources.

Fig. 1.1

5 Treat the calculator gently; a light touch on the keyboard is quite sufficient. It is advisable not to lend your calculator to other people.

Apart from replacing the battery every so often, your calculator should last your school lifetime – provided that you observe the above rules.

Note You may be tempted to purchase a calculator with a solar cell, but remember that the light in a classroom or examination room may not always be sufficient to energize the cell.

Unfortunately the manufacturers of calculators have done very little to standardize the layout of the keyboards on their models and so, whilst the calculators may well perform more or less the same functions, the key positions may vary quite considerably.

In order to overcome this problem it is a good idea to familiarize yourself (with the aid of the instruction book) with your own calculator and discover not only what it will do, but how it does it. Any spare time you may have is well spent experimenting with your machine to discover its capabilities and limitations.

Many of the 2nd functions shown in Fig. 1.1 (2nd F, or INV on some calculators) such as $\sin^{-1}$, $\cos^{-1}$, $\tan^{-1}$, log etc, we shall be using during the course of this Volume and an explanation of how these are used will be given, as and when required.

1.2 Order of operations

As we saw in Volume 1, the order in which the operations of arithmetic are performed is very important indeed. We must follow the same order when using a calculator. As an example, consider

$$5 + 4 \times 3$$

On the calculator, the result would be

$$9 \times 3 = 27$$

However, the ordinary rules of arithmetic would make the answer

$$5 + 12 = 17$$

17 is the correct answer, but obviously we need to tell the calculator to perform the multiplication first (as the rules tell us).

The use of brackets helps considerably, because the rules also say that brackets must be dealt with first of all.

Hence, $5 + (4 \times 3) = 17$

and $(5 + 4) \times 3 = 27$

Note Some calculators are designed to follow arithmetic language automatically. Some have bracket keys. You will need to discover which type of calculator you have.

At this stage it would be a good idea to work through the Activities which follow, to ensure that you are familiar with the basic functions of adding, subtracting, multiplying, dividing and finding square roots and powers of numbers, etc.

It is most important that you always check your working on your calculator either by rough estimate or by repeating the calculation. Remember it is easy to press a key in error, and the calculator is only as accurate as its operator – you!

Activities

Order of operations

Note Some calculators have bracket keys [(] [)] which will help with the following examples. Some follow arithmetical language automatically. If your calculator has no brackets, Question **1** will need thinking about carefully.

1 Find the **two** possible answers for these.

(a) $2 + 4 \times 3$ **(b)** $3 \times 7 - 2$
(c) $7 - 5 \times 3$ **(d)** $8 \div 2 \times 4$
(e) $10 \div 2 \times 4$ **(f)** $9 \div 3 \div 3$

Hint If your calculator has no bracket keys, press the [=] key after the operation which is to be in brackets,
e.g. $2 + 4$ [=] $\times 3$ gives one answer; 4×3 [=] $+ 2$ gives the second answer.

2 Work out the brackets first, then calculate the correct answer.

(a) $(3 + 5) \times 2$ **(b)** $8 + (5 \times 2)$
(c) $5 \times (7 - 3)$ **(d)** $10 - (7 - 3)$
(e) $(18 - 4) \div 7$ **(f)** $16 - (5 \times 2)$

3 Put in the brackets to make these correct.

(a) $7 + 2 \times 3 = 27$ **(b)** $15 - 4 - 2 = 13$
(c) $12 + 9 \div 3 = 7$ **(d)** $8 \times 5 - 2 = 24$
(e) $16 \div 8 - 2 = 0$ **(f)** $24 - 16 \div 2 = 4$

4 Now use your calculator to obtain the correct results of these calculations. You may have to change the order of things and it might help to estimate the answer first.

(a) $4 + (9 \times 7)$ **(b)** $(18 + 7) \times 5$
(c) $17 \times (15 + 15)$ **(d)** $(2.7 + 1.3) \times 10$
(e) $5.6 + (3.8 \times 5)$ **(f)** $55 \div (4 + 7)$
(g) $27 \div (9 \div 3)$ **(h)** $18 + (51 \div 17)$
(i) $99 - (64 \div 4)$ **(j)** $27 - (15 - 5)$

Calculator work

The examples shown in Questions 1–10, following, assume that your calculator has a keyboard with key positions as in Fig. 1.1. Your calculator may have different key positions. For example, on some calculators, the [x^2] and [$\sqrt{\ }$] keys are **not** in the 2nd function. In such cases, you will not, of course, press the [2ndF] (or [INV]) key before the [x^2] or [$\sqrt{\ }$] keys.

There may be other variations in the layout of your keyboard, so look out for these when trying the following questions.

To find 14.2×2.5.

Press in order [1] [4] [·] [2] [×] [2] [·] [5] [=]

The answer is shown on the number display 35.5

Press the clear key [C]

1 Use your calculator to answer these.

(a) $15.9 + 32.5$ **(b)** 17.3×5.9 **(c)** $6.8 - 2.5$
(d) $12.4 \div 6.2$ **(e)** $36.8 + 15$ **(f)** $396 \div 55$

To find $(2.5)^2$.

Press in order [2] [·] [5] [2ndF] [x^2]

The answer is shown on the number display 6.25

Press the clear key [C]

2 Use your calculator to answer these.

(a) $(5.2)^2$ **(b)** 25^2 **(c)** $(6.75)^2$
(d) 245^2 **(e)** $(0.67)^2$ **(f)** 235^2

To find $\sqrt{6.25}$.

Press in order [6] [·] [2] [5] [2ndF] [$\sqrt{\ }$]

The answer is shown on the number display 2.5

Press the clear key [C]

3 Use the calculator to answer these.

(a) $\sqrt{62.41}$ **(b)** $\sqrt{3069.16}$ **(c)** $\sqrt{30.25}$
(d) $\sqrt{1936}$ **(e)** $\sqrt{103\,684}$ **(f)** $\sqrt{6084}$

4 Try these mixed examples.

(a) 6.2^2 **(b)** $\sqrt{26.01}$ **(c)** 12.4^2
(d) $\sqrt{3893.76}$ **(e)** 56×3.2 **(f)** 9.67^2

To find the reciprocal of 2.5 i.e. $\frac{1}{2.5}$.

Press in order $\boxed{2}\boxed{\cdot}\boxed{5}\boxed{\text{2ndF}}\boxed{1/x}$

The answer is shown on the number display 0.4

Press the clear key $\boxed{\text{C}}$

5 Use your calculator to answer these.

(a) $\frac{1}{0.125}$ **(b)** $\frac{1}{155}$ **(c)** $\frac{1}{3.25}$

(d) $\frac{1}{6.25}$ **(e)** $\frac{1}{24.8}$ **(f)** $\frac{1}{0.04}$

To find the sine of an angle, say sin 60°.

Press in order $\boxed{6}\boxed{0}\boxed{\sin}$

The answer is shown on the display 0.8660254

Press the clear key $\boxed{\text{C}}$

6 Use your calculator to answer these.

(a) sin 28° **(b)** tan 68° **(c)** cos 35°

(d) sin 72.8° **(e)** tan 33.9° **(f)** cos 61.2°

To find the angle whose tangent is 0.6420.

Press in order $\boxed{\cdot}\boxed{6}\boxed{4}\boxed{2}\boxed{0}\boxed{\text{2ndF}}\boxed{\tan^{-1}}$

The answer shown on the display is 32.7 (approx)

Press the clear key $\boxed{\text{C}}$

7 Use your calculator to find these angles, to 0.1°.

(a) $\sin^{-1} 0.6820$ **(b)** $\cos^{-1} 0.3420$

(c) $\tan^{-1} 1.8040$ **(d)** $\sin^{-1} 0.9150$

(e) $\cos^{-1} 0.3955$ **(f)** $\tan^{-1} 0{\cdot}4101$

To find the logarithm of a number, say 23.55.

Press in order $\boxed{2}\boxed{3}\boxed{\cdot}\boxed{5}\boxed{5}\boxed{\text{2ndF}}\boxed{\log}$

The answer is shown on the display 1.3719909

Press the clear key $\boxed{\text{C}}$

8 Use your calculator to find the logarithm of these numbers.

(a) 687 **(b)** 25.98 **(c)** 0.045 62

(d) 45 822 (e) 123.34 **(f)** 923 000

To find the number whose logarithm is 1.7403627.

Press in order

$\boxed{1}\boxed{\cdot}\boxed{7}\boxed{4}\boxed{0}\boxed{3}\boxed{6}\boxed{2}\boxed{7}\boxed{\text{2ndF}}\boxed{10^x}$

The answer is shown on the display 55

Press the clear key $\boxed{\text{C}}$

9 Use your calculator to find the numbers whose logarithms are as follows.

(a) 0.2435 **(b)** 3.7824 **(c)** 1.9243

(d) −0.7342 **(e)** −1.4432 **(f)** 2.0367

Note Unit 4.2 explains the basic logarithm theory.

To find the value of any power of a number, say 12^3.

Press in order $\boxed{1}\boxed{2}\boxed{\text{2ndF}}\boxed{y^x}\boxed{3}\boxed{=}$

The answer is shown on the display 1728

Press the clear key $\boxed{\text{C}}$

10 Use your calculator to find the value of,

(a) 15^3 **(b)** 22.1^3 **(c)** 2.25^4 **(d)** 5.1^5

11 Study the method used above to find the power of a number. Now write down the order of keys to find, say $\sqrt[3]{1296}$.

Calculate **(a)** $\sqrt[3]{2197}$ **(b)** $\sqrt[4]{194\,481}$ **(c)** $\sqrt[5]{243}$

Note You may wish to refer to Unit 3.2, Fractional Indices.

Unit 2

Standard form

2.1 The limits of your calculator

Some modern electronic calculators have ten spaces on the display screen, but most have eight spaces. They have to adapt themselves for any calculation that gives an answer above this range.

Example (Assuming your calculator is of the scientific type, and shows eight digits.) Perform $45\,000 \times 25\,000$

The answer on the display screen is given as

1.125 09

The last column shows the number of tens that must multiply the previous figure.

Hence, 1.125 09 actually means

$1.125 \times 10 \times 10 \times 10 \times 10 \times 10 \times 10 \times 10 \times 10 \times 10$

This, of course, is 1 125 000 000 (beyond the limit of the calculator with 8 digits only).

This is a very good method of representing both very large and very small numbers and is known as **standard form**.

2.2 Large numbers in standard form

Example 1 Consider the number 343.

This can be written as 34.3×10

or even as $3.43 \times 10 \times 10$

and so $343 = 3.43 \times 10^2$

3.43×10^2 is known as the **standard form** of the number 343.

Example 2 Consider the number 7250.

This can be written as 7.25×1000

or $7.25 \times 10 \times 10 \times 10$

Hence, 7250 in standard form is 7.25×10^3

A number can be written in standard form by expressing it in the form $a \times 10^n$.

(Where $1 \leqslant a < 10$ and n is a whole number (integer) power of ten.)

Example 3 Put the number 7.3 into standard form.

$7.3 = 7.3 \times 1$

But $10^0 = 1$ (Volume 2, Indices).

Hence, $7.3 = 7.3 \times 10^0$ in standard form.

Example 4 Express 73 400 in standard form.

$73\,400 = 7.34 \times 10 \times 10 \times 10 \times 10$

In standard form, $73\,400 = 7.34 \times 10^4$

We can, of course, reverse the operation by writing in full, a number which is given in standard form, as the following examples show.

Example 1 7.64×10^1

$= 7.64 \times 10$
$= 76.4$

Example 2 2.63×10^0

$= 2.63 \times 1$
$= 2.63$

Example 3 3.84×10^5

$= 3.84 \times 10 \times 10 \times 10 \times 10 \times 10$
$= 384\,000$

2.3 Very small numbers in standard form

So far, we have seen how very large numbers can be expressed in standard form. This can be particularly useful in such scientific areas as Chemistry, Physics, Biology and Astronomy.

However, we must not forget about very small numbers. They too can be expressed in standard form, as shown below.

Example 1 Consider the number 0.085.

It can be written as $0.85 \div 10$

or even as $8.5 \div 10 \div 10$

and so $0.085 = 8.5 \div 10^2$

This is not standard form, however, since it is not in the form $a \times 10^n$.

In order to change this into standard form, we need to recall (from Volume 2, Indices) that dividing by 10^2 is the same as multiplying by $\frac{1}{10^2}$ which we write as 10^{-2}.

Therefore, 0.085 written in standard form will be 8.5×10^{-2}.

Example 2 Express 0.000 036 8 in standard form.

$0.000\,036\,8 = 3.68 \div 10 \div 10 \div 10 \div 10 \div 10$
$= 3.68 \div 10^5$

Hence, in standard form $0.000\,036\,8 = 3.68 \times 10^{-5}$

Again, the operation can be reversed by writing out a number, given in standard form, as the following examples show.

Example 4 3.5×10^{-1}

$= 3.5 \times \frac{1}{10}$ or $3.5 \div 10$
$= 0.35$

Example 5 8.25×10^{-7}

$= 8.25 \times \frac{1}{10} \times \frac{1}{10} \times \frac{1}{10} \times \frac{1}{10} \times \frac{1}{10} \times \frac{1}{10} \times \frac{1}{10}$

or $8.25 \div 10 \div 10 \div 10 \div 10 \div 10 \div 10 \div 10$
$= 0.000\,000\,825$

Activities

Simple examples; the use of standard form

1 Write down the numerical value of these powers of 10.

(a) 10^3 **(f)** 10^{-1}
(b) 10^5 **(g)** 10^0
(c) 10^2 **(h)** 10^{-2}
(d) 10^6 **(i)** 10^{-4}
(e) 10^1 **(j)** 10^4

2 Work out these decimals.

(a) 1.5×10 **(f)** 1.2×100
(b) 2.7×10 **(g)** $2.7 \times 10\,000$
(c) 1.25×10 **(h)** $1.6 \times 1\,000\,000$
(d) 3.2×100 **(i)** 9.9×100
(e) 6.875×1000 **(j)** 7.25×1000

3 Try to combine your results of Questions **1** and **2** to answer these.

(a) $2.4 \times 10^3 = 2.4 \times 1000 = 2400$
(b) $4.4 \times 10^2 =$ $=$
(c) $3.62 \times 10^4 =$ $=$
(d) $5.95 \times 10^6 =$ $=$
(e) $7.03 \times 10^1 =$ $=$
(f) $8.36 \times 10^3 =$ $=$

4 Now try to do these, in just 1 step, e.g. $4.7 \times 10^4 = 47\,000$

(a) $6.87 \times 10^3 =$
(b) $3.689 \times 10^2 =$
(c) $5.04 \times 10^5 =$
(d) $4.58 \times 10^1 =$
(e) $7.08 \times 10^4 =$

5 Work out these decimals.

(a) $\frac{7.5}{100}$ **(b)** $\frac{6.75}{1000}$ **(c)** $\frac{4.57}{10}$

(d) $\frac{4.8}{10\,000}$ **(e)** $\frac{3.98}{1000}$ **(f)** $\frac{6}{100}$

6 Examine this example:

$$3.2 \times 10^{-2} = 3.2 \times \frac{1}{10^2} = 0.032 = 3.2 \div 10^2$$

Now do these in the same way.

(a) $4.95 \times 10^{-3} =$
(b) $9.6 \times 10^{-1} =$
(c) $3.21 \times 10^{-5} =$

7 Each of these is written in standard form. Write them as ordinary numbers.

(a) 2.78×10^3 **(b)** 3.16×10^6
(c) 7.0×10^{-2} **(d)** 5.5×10^{-3}
(e) 3.3×10^1 **(f)** 8.76×10^{-2}

8 Examine this example:

$$31\,500 = 3.15 \times 10\,000 = 3.15 \times 10^4$$

Now do these in the same way.

(a) $2800 =$
(b) $2090 =$
(c) $460\,000 =$
(d) $500 =$
(e) $4\,750\,000 =$

9 Very small numbers are written in standard form like this.

$$0.000\,57 = 5.7 \div 10\,000 = 5.7 \times 10^{-4}$$

Write these in the same way.

(a) $0.0063 =$
(b) $0.071 =$
(c) $0.000\,047\,2 =$

2.4 Multiplication and division, in standard form

We can perform calculations, actually working in standard form. Some typical examples are shown below.

Example 1 $6 \times 10^4 \times 1.3 \times 10^3$
$= 6 \times 1.3 \times 10^4 \times 10^3$
$= 7.8 \times 10^{(4+3)}$ (Volume 2, Laws of Indices)
$= 7.8 \times 10^7$

Example 2 $6.5 \times 10^8 \div (1.3 \times 10^3)$
$= \frac{6.5 \times 10^8}{1.3 \times 10^3} = 5 \times 10^{(8-3)}$ (Index Laws)
$= 5 \times 10^5$

Example 3 $4 \times 10^4 \times 3.8 \times 10^3$
$= 4 \times 3.8 \times 10^{(4+3)}$
$= 15.2 \times 10^7$
(not in standard form since $15.2 = 1.52 \times 10^1$)
$= 1.52 \times 10^1 \times 10^7$
In standard form $= 1.52 \times 10^8$

Example 4 $4 \times 10^{-3} \times 3 \times 10^{-4}$
$= 4 \times 3 \times 10^{-3} \times 10^{-4}$
$= 12 \times 10^{-7} = 1.2 \times 10^1 \times 10^{-7}$
$= 1.2 \times 10^{-6}$

Example 5 $8 \times 10^4 \div (2 \times 10^6)$
$= \frac{8 \times 10^4}{2 \times 10^6} = \frac{4}{10^2}$ or $4 \times \frac{1}{10^2}$
In standard form $= 4 \times 10^{-2}$

Example 6 $1.25 \times 10^{-4} \div (2.5 \times 10^{-7})$
$= \frac{1.25 \times 10^{-4}}{2.5 \times 10^{-7}} = 0.5 \times 10^3$
$= 5 \times 10^{-1} \times 10^3$
$= 5 \times 10^2$

Activities

1 What are the values of these numbers from the calculator?

(a) 2.55 11 **(b)** 4.675 07

(c) 3.3 −09 **(d)** 6.78 −06

2 Write down how a calculator would show these.

(a) 0.000 000 089 5 **(b)** 55 600 000 000

(c) 0.000 000 000 000 682 **(d)** 23 800 000 000 000

3 Perform these calculations on your calculator, but write your answers in standard form.

(a) $154\,000 \times 75\,000$ **(b)** $935\,000 \times 23\,000\,000$

(c) $0.000\,000\,8 \div 64$ **(d)** $0.000\,002\,5 \div 200$

4 Write the answer to each of these in standard form. (Take care!)

(a) $(3 \times 10^2) \times (2.5 \times 10^3)$

(b) $(4.2 \times 10^3) \times (3 \times 10^4)$

(c) $(5.5 \times 10^{-2}) \times (2 \times 10^5)$

(d) $(1.8 \times 10^{-1}) \times (8 \times 10^{-3})$

(e) $(9 \times 10^8) \div (4.5 \times 10^3)$

(f) $(5.5 \times 10^{-3}) \div (8 \times 10^{-2})$

(g) $(1.25 \times 10^7) \div (3.7 \times 10^{-3})$

(h) $(5 \times 10^{-5}) \div (4.5 \times 10^6)$

5 Examine these numbers.

5.2×10^4 5.2×10^8 5.2×10^1 5.2×10^{-1}

Which number best represents,

(a) the age of someone's grandad, in years,

(b) the distance between two planets, in miles,

(c) a good attendance at a soccer match?

2.5 Addition and subtraction, in standard form

It is quite possible to add and subtract two numbers expressed in standard form, provided that both numbers are expressed to the same power of 10.

Example 1 $3 \times 10^2 + 5 \times 10^2$

$= (3 + 5) \times 10^2$

$= 8 \times 10^2$

Example 2 $7.5 \times 10^3 - 3.5 \times 10^3$

$= (7.5 - 3.5) \times 10^3$

$= 4 \times 10^3$

When the powers of 10 are not the same, we must attempt to make them the same before proceeding.

Example 3 $4 \times 10^5 + 3 \times 10^4$

We can overcome the problem either by writing them both in terms of 10^4, or both in terms of 10^5,

i.e. $4 \times 10^5 + 0.3 \times 10^5$ or $40 \times 10^4 + 3 \times 10^4$

$= 4.3 \times 10^5$ $= 43 \times 10^4$

$= 4.3 \times 10^5$

2.6 Comparing large numbers

Standard form can be very useful for comparing very large numbers.

Example Express the following numbers in standard form and arrange them in order of size, from largest to smallest.

(a) 2 380 000 **(b)** 475 000 **(c)** 12 120 000

In standard form, these become,

(a) 2.38×10^6 **(b)** 4.75×10^5 **(c)** 1.212×10^7

↑ smallest ↑ largest

Therefore, the required order is, **(c)**, **(a)**, **(b)**.

2.7 Comparing small numbers

Standard form can also be very useful for comparing very small numbers.

Example Express the following numbers in standard form and arrange them in order of size, from smallest to largest.

(a) 0.000 482 **(b)** 0.001 65 **(c)** 0.000 092 3

In standard form these become

(a) 4.82×10^{-4} **(b)** 1.65×10^{-3} (↑ largest) **(c)** 9.23×10^{-5} (↑ smallest)

Therefore, the required order is, **(c)**, **(a)**, **(b)**.

2.8 Standard form and the calculator

It is possible to put any number into standard form on the calculator quite easily. The following examples outline the method.

Example 1 Put 2.5×10^5 onto the calculator.

Firstly, put 2.5 on the display screen and press [EXP]

The display reads 2.5 00

Then press [5]

The display reads 2.5 05

which is the calculator version of standard form.

Example 2 3.4×10^{-3}

Put 3.4 on the display and press [EXP]

The display reads 3.4 00

Then press [+/−] and [3]

The display reads 3.4 −03

which is the calculator version of standard form.

Note On some calculators, such as that shown in Fig. 1.1, [+/−] is in the 2nd function.

Activities

Further examples, using standard form

1 Calculate the following, giving your answers in standard form.

(a) $(1.5 \times 10^4) + (4.7 \times 10^4)$
(b) $(4.7 \times 10^7) + (6.5 \times 10^7)$
(c) $(5.2 \times 10^{-5}) + (7.3 \times 10^{-5})$
(d) $(8.3 \times 10^5) + (9.2 \times 10^4)$
(e) $(7.6 \times 10^{-3}) + (6.8 \times 10^{-2})$
(f) $(3.6 \times 10^3) - (3.25 \times 10^3)$
(g) $(1.5 \times 10^7) - (8.3 \times 10^6)$
(h) $(4.21 \times 10^{-3}) - (5.36 \times 10^{-4})$

2 If $a = 2.6 \times 10^2$ and $b = 5.7 \times 10^3$, calculate,

(a) ab **(b)** $a + b$ **(c)** $b - a$ **(d)** b^2

3 If $x = 1.2 \times 10^{-2}$ and $y = 2.4 \times 10^{-3}$, calculate,

(a) xy **(b)** $\frac{x}{y}$ **(c)** $x - y$ **(d)** x^2

4 Examine these numbers written in standard form.

2.5×10^2 2.5×10^4 2.5×10^{-2}
2.5×10^8 2.5×10^{-4}

Which of these best describes,

(a) the population of America,
(b) a good week's wages in £s,
(c) the average mileage of a two-year-old car,
(d) the thickness of a £5 note in metres?

5 Answer these in standard form.

(a) Write 1 mm in kilometres.
(b) Write 1 second in hours.
(c) Write 20 kilometres in millimetres.
(d) Write 200 km/hour in metres/second.
(e) Write £1 million in pence.

2.9 Problem solving in standard form

We can solve problems using standard form quite easily, as shown in the following example.

Example The speed of light is given, approximately, as 3×10^5 km per second. Find the approximate distance travelled by light in 24 hours.

Light travels,

3×10^5 km in one second
$= 3 \times 10^5 \times 60$ km, in one minute
$= 3 \times 10^5 \times 60 \times 60$ km, in one hour
$= 3 \times 10^5 \times 60 \times 60 \times 24$ km, in 24 hours
$= 3 \times 10^5 \times 6 \times 10^1 \times 6 \times 10^1 \times 2.4 \times 10^1$ km
$= 3 \times 6 \times 6 \times 2.4 \times 10^5 \times 10 \times 10 \times 10$ km
$= 259.2 \times 10^8$ km
$= 2.592 \times 10^2 \times 10^8$ km
$= 2.592 \times 10^{10}$ km

This, as we may imagine, is a very great distance indeed.

Activities

1 Find the area of a rectangle whose length is 8.5×10^3 metres and whose width is 1.5×10^3 m.

2 A spacecraft travels at 5×10^3 m/s. Find,

(a) its speed in kilometres per hour,

(b) the time, in hours, that it would take to reach the Sun, a distance of 1.5×10^8 km.

3 A metal ball-bearing has a mass of 2.5×10^2 g. Find the total mass of twenty thousand ball-bearings in

(a) grams **(b)** kilograms

4 The areas, in square kilometres, of the countries of the United Kingdom are approximately:

England	1.2×10^{11}
Wales	2.1×10^{10}
Scotland	7.8×10^{10}
N. Ireland	1.3×10^{10}

Calculate, in standard form,

(a) the total area of the UK,

(b) the ratio of the area of N. Ireland to the area of England,

(c) the ratio of the area of England to the area of Scotland.

5 The speed of light is approximately 3×10^8 m/s. The distance from the Earth to the Sun is 1.5×10^{11} m.

(a) What is the speed of light, in kilometres per hour?

(b) What is the distance from the Earth to the Sun, in km?

(c) How long, in hours, does it take light to make this journey?

Unit 3

Powers/indices

3.1 Laws of Indices

In Volume 2, we discovered the summary of the Laws of Indices, as in Table 3.1.

(a) $a^m \times a^n = a^{m+n}$

(b) $a^m \div a^n = a^{m-n}$

(c) $a^0 = 1$

(d) $(a^m)^n = a^{mn}$

(e) $a^{-m} = \dfrac{1}{a^m}$

Table 3.1

It is now necessary to progress a stage further by considering fractional indices. (Up to now we have only considered integer (+ve and −ve) indices.)

3.2 Fractional indices

Suppose we consider the following examples.

Example 1 $5^{\frac{1}{2}} \times 5^{\frac{1}{2}}$

$= 5^{\frac{1}{2}+\frac{1}{2}} = 5^1 = 5$ (Table 3.1, Law **(a)**)

But we also know that $\sqrt{5} \times \sqrt{5} = 5$

Hence, $5^{\frac{1}{2}} = \sqrt{5}$

Example 2 Similarly, $3^{\frac{1}{4}} \times 3^{\frac{1}{4}} \times 3^{\frac{1}{4}} \times 3^{\frac{1}{4}}$

$= 3^{\frac{1}{4}+\frac{1}{4}+\frac{1}{4}+\frac{1}{4}} = 3^1 = 3$

We know that $\sqrt[4]{3} \times \sqrt[4]{3} \times \sqrt[4]{3} \times \sqrt[4]{3} = 3$

Hence, $3^{\frac{1}{4}} = \sqrt[4]{3}$

In a similar way, we can show that,

$9^{\frac{1}{2}} = \sqrt{9} = 3$

$8^{\frac{1}{3}} = \sqrt[3]{8} = 2$ etc.

In general terms $a^{\frac{1}{m}} = \sqrt[m]{a}$

i.e. the mth root of a.

Note m cannot be zero, i.e. $m \neq 0$

Now consider $(9^3)^{\frac{1}{2}}$ (Table 3.1, Law **(d)**)

This will become $9^{\frac{3}{2}}$ or $\sqrt{9^3}$

In general terms $a^{\frac{n}{m}} = \sqrt[m]{a^n}$

(Again, $m \neq 0$)

Hence, $9^{\frac{3}{2}} = \sqrt{9^3} = 3^3 = 27$

or $\sqrt{729} = 27$

It is easier, generally, to find the root (m) first, and then deal with the power (n).

Example $32^{\frac{3}{5}} = \sqrt[5]{32^3} = 2^3 = 8$

Finally, we should now be in a position to deal with

$a^{-\frac{n}{m}}$ which $= \dfrac{1}{a^{\frac{n}{m}}}$

Example $4^{-\frac{5}{2}} = \dfrac{1}{\sqrt{4^5}} = \dfrac{1}{2^5} = \dfrac{1}{32}$

Activities

Examples of indices

1 Simplify the following.

(a) $25^{\frac{1}{2}}$
(b) $16^{\frac{1}{4}}$
(c) $27^{\frac{1}{3}}$
(d) $8^{\frac{2}{3}}$
(e) $625^{\frac{3}{4}}$
(f) 7^{-2}
(g) 5^{-3}
(h) $32^{-\frac{1}{5}}$
(i) 7^0
(j) 10^{-4}
(k) $49^{\frac{3}{2}}$
(l) $(\frac{3}{4})^0$
(m) $(25^{\frac{1}{2}})^3$
(n) 2×2^{-4}
(o) $3^{\frac{1}{2}} \times 3^{-\frac{1}{2}}$
(p) $2^3 \div 2^4$
(q) $5^{\frac{2}{3}} \times 5^{\frac{1}{3}}$
(r) 4×4^{-5}
(s) $5^3 \times 5^{-3}$
(t) $2^3 \div 2^{-3}$
(u) $(10^2)^3$
(v) $125^{-\frac{2}{3}}$

2 Simplify the following.

(a) $3a^2 \times 2a^3$
(b) $2a^2b^3 \times 5ab^2$
(c) $c^2 \times c^3 \times c$
(d) $x^7 \div x^4$
(e) $x^{12} \div x^4$
(f) $e^3 \times e^{-2}$
(g) $x^5 \div x^{-3}$
(h) $g^3 \times g^{\frac{1}{2}}$
(i) $a^{\frac{1}{2}} \times a^{\frac{1}{3}}$
(j) $a^{\frac{3}{4}} \times a^{\frac{1}{2}}$
(k) $a^{\frac{3}{4}} \div a^{\frac{1}{2}}$
(l) $(8x)^{\frac{2}{3}}$
(m) $(5x)^{-2}$
(n) $(27x)^{-\frac{2}{3}}$
(o) $x^{\frac{1}{4}} \div x^{-\frac{1}{4}}$
(p) $a^{\frac{1}{4}} \times a^{-\frac{1}{4}}$
(q) $24x^{-3} \div 4x^{-2}$
(r) $(5x^{\frac{2}{3}})^3$
(s) $(a^{-2})^3$
(t) $p^{\frac{3}{4}} \times p^{\frac{1}{2}} \times p^{\frac{1}{4}}$
(u) $p^{\frac{2}{3}} \times p^{\frac{1}{3}} \div p^{-\frac{1}{3}}$
(v) $x^{-\frac{3}{4}} \div x^{-\frac{1}{2}}$

3 Take extra care with these more difficult questions.

(a) $2^2 \times 8^{\frac{1}{3}} \times 16^{\frac{3}{4}}$ **(b)** $2^{\frac{1}{3}} \times 6^{\frac{2}{3}} \times 3^{\frac{1}{3}}$ **(c)** $\left(\dfrac{x^2}{10}\right)^3$

Note *In the Units which follow, it will be assumed that you know how to use your own calculator. Simple instructions will be given in the form, 'Key ☐'. Sometimes, these will be directly possible, sometimes they may involve pressing* 2ndF *and sometimes you may have to consult the operating manual for your own calculator to find out how to carry out the instruction.*

Guidance will be given, in this Volume, but, with so many models of scientific calculators available, it would be impossible to list every possible variation in operating procedure.

Unit 4

Logarithms

John Napier

4.1 Introduction

The electronic calculator has made the use of logarithms virtually redundant as an aid to calculation.

Before calculators, logarithms were used, particularly, to assist in the calculation of problems involving multiplication, division, powers and roots, and also any combination of these operations.

They were invented in the seventeenth century by a Scottish Mathematician, John Napier, as a way of easing the enormous labour of calculation.

Calculations were performed with the aid of a set of logarithmic tables. They did have limitations though, because the common tables were only corrected to four significant figures. The calculator has a degree of accuracy of 8 significant figures (sometimes 10).

4.2 Basic logarithm theory

We should know something of the theory of logarithms. We shall consider only base 10 logarithms, although there are others, and we shall use our scientific calculators – rather than tables.

Remember,

$$1000 = 10^3 \qquad 100 = 10^2 \qquad 10 = 10^1$$

$$1 = 10^0 \qquad 0.1 = 10^{-1} \qquad 0.01 = 10^{-2} \text{ etc}$$

The basic principle is very simple, because the **logarithm** of any number is simply **the number expressed as a power of 10**.

Hence, $\log_{10} 1000 = 3 \qquad \log_{10} 100 = 2$
$\log_{10} 10 = 1$ etc

Check these on your calculator.

Note On your calculator, the [logx] key may be shown as [log]

Example 1 Put 1000 on the display and key [logx]

The display will then show 3.

Example 2 Put 0.01 on the display and key [logx]

The display will then show −2.

What about the logs of other numbers? Let us consider the log of 2.

Since 2 lies between 1 and 10, then $\log_{10} 2$ lies between 0 and 1.

To find the exact value, put 2 on the display and key [logx]

The display will then show 0.30103
Hence, $\log_{10} 2 = 0.30103$

Another way of representing this would be,

$2 = 10^{0.30103}$ which is, in fact,

$$10^0 \times 10^{0.30103} = 10^{0.30103}$$

In general terms,

If $x = 10^y$ then $y = \log_{10} x$

Another interesting feature of logarithms can be illustrated as follows.

$\log_{10} 2 = 0.30103$, since
$2 = 10^{0 + 0.30103} = 10^{0.30103}$

$\log_{10} 20 = 1.30103$, since
$20 = 10^{1 + 0.30103} = 10^{1.30103}$

$\log_{10} 200 = 2.30103$, since
$200 = 10^{2 + 0.30103} = 10^{2.30103}$

The logarithm of any number is made up of the decimal part, which is called the **mantissa** and the integer before the decimal point, which is called the **characteristic**.

In the case of a log of a number less than 1, the characteristic will be negative.

$\log_{10} 0.2 = -0.69897$, since $0.2 = 10^{-1 + 0.30103}$
$= 10^{-0.69897}$

4.3 Multiplying and dividing with logs

Consider $\log_{10}4$. Put 4 on the display and key $\boxed{\log x}$

The display will then show 0.6020599,

i.e. $\log_{10}4 = 0.6020599$, or $4 = 10^{0.6020599}$

Using the Law of Indices, we can perform the operation of 2×4.

$$2 \times 4 = 10^{0.30103} \times 10^{0.6020599}$$
$$= 10^{0.30103 + 0.6020599}$$
$$= 10^{0.9030899}$$

To evaluate this, put 0.9030899 on the display and key $\boxed{10^x}$

The display will then show 7.9999984 which, allowing for the slight inaccuracy of the logs, is obviously 8.

So, in general terms,

$$\log_{10}(a \times b) = \log_{10}(a) + \log_{10}(b)$$

Suppose we now look at two specific examples of multiplication.

Example 1 Find 0.0071×26.2 by using logs.

$$\log_{10}(0.0071 \times 26.2) = \log_{10}(0.0071) + \log_{10}(26.2)$$

where $\log_{10}(0.0071) = -3 + 0.8512583$
$= -2.1487417$ (as shown on the display)

$\log_{10}(0.0071 \times 26.2) = -2.1487417 + 1.4183013$
$= -0.7304404$ (on display)

Then key $\boxed{10^x}$ and the answer appears on display as 0.1860199.

Check We can check our answer, by simply performing the multiplication on the calculator, i.e. $0.0071 \times 26.2 = 0.18602$. This shows the answer, above, to be correct, allowing for log error (which is very slight).

Example 2 Find $253 \times 38.3 \times 2.9$ by using logs.

$\log_{10}(253 \times 38.3 \times 2.9)$
$= \log_{10}(253) + \log_{10}(38.3) + \log_{10}(2.9)$
$= 2.4031205 + 1.5831988 + 0.4623979$
$= 4.4487173$ (on display)

Then key $\boxed{10^x}$ and the answer appears as 28100.71

Check By ordinary use of calculator,
$253 \times 38.3 \times 2.9 = 28100.71$

Now, in a similar manner, we can also see that $a \div b$ can be handled by considering,

$$\log_{10}(a \div b) = \log_{10}(a) - \log_{10}(b)$$

Example 3 Find $6 \div 3$ by using logs.

$\log_{10}(6 \div 3) = \log_{10}(6) - \log_{10}(3)$
$= 0.7781512 - 0.4771212$
$= 0.30103$ (on display)

Key $\boxed{10^x}$ giving 2 as the answer on the display.

Example 4 Find $4570 \div 1.73$ by using logs.

$\log_{10}(4570 \div 1.73) = \log_{10}(4570) - \log_{10}(1.73)$
$= 3.6599162 - 0.2380461$
$= 3.4218701$ (on display)

Key $\boxed{10^x}$ giving an answer of 2641.6185

Check $4570 \div 1.73$ by direct calculation on the calculator gives 2641.6185.

Example 5 Evaluate $417 \div 0.25$ by using logs.

$\log_{10}(417 \div 0.25) = \log_{10}(417) - \log_{10}(0.25)$
$= 2.6201361 - (-0.60206)$
$= 3.2221961$

($\log_{10}(0.25) = -1.39794 = -1 + 0.39794$ shown on the calculator as -0.60206)

Key $\boxed{10^x}$ giving an answer of 1668.0002

Check By calculator, gives an answer of 1668.

Note It is most important that you are familiar with the workings of your calculator, because careful use of the calculator's Memory will help you to solve this type of problem much more easily.

4.4 Calculating powers and roots by logs

Since we know a^3 to be $a \times a \times a$

then, $\log_{10}a^3 = \log_{10}a + \log_{10}a + \log_{10}a$
$= 3\log_{10}a$

Similarly $\sqrt[3]{a} = a^{\frac{1}{3}}$

then $\log_{10}a^{\frac{1}{3}} = \frac{1}{3}\log_{10}a$ or $\dfrac{\log_{10}a}{3}$

Example 1 by using logs, find $(3.42)^5$

$\log_{10}(3.42)^5 = 5\log_{10}3.42$
$= 5 \times 0.5340261$
$= 2.6701305$ (on display)

Key $\boxed{10^x}$ giving the answer as 467.8757

Check On the calculator, 3.42^5 gives 467.876.

Example 2 Use logs to find $\sqrt[4]{685}$

$\log_{10}(685)^{\frac{1}{4}} = \frac{1}{4}\log_{10}685$
$= \frac{1}{4} \times 2.8356906$
$= 0.7089226$

Key $\boxed{10^x}$ giving the answer as 5.115907

Check $(685)^{\frac{1}{4}} = 5.11591$.

Summary

	1	$\log_{10}5$	$= 0.69897$
hence,		$\log_{10}50$	$= 1.69897$ etc
	2	$\log_{10}(a \times b)$	$= \log_{10}(a) + \log_{10}(b)$
	3	$\log_{10}(a \div b)$	$= \log_{10}(a) - \log_{10}(b)$
	4	$\log_{10}(a)^x$	$= x\log_{10}(a)$
	5	$\log_{10}(a)^{\frac{1}{x}}$	$= \dfrac{1}{x}\log_{10}(a)$

Table 4.1

Activities

Logarithm work

1 Without the use of a calculator, write down,
(a) $\log_{10}100$ **(b)** $\log_{10}1\,000\,000$ **(c)** $\log_{10}10^5$

(d) $\log_{10}0.01$ (e) $\log_{10}0.000\ 01$ (f) $\log_{10}10^{-6}$

2 Use a calculator to find these.

(a) $\log_{10}5$ (b) $\log_{10}50$ (c) $\log_{10}5000$

(d) $\log_{10}0.5$ (e) $\log_{10}0.05$ (f) $\log_{10}0.0005$

3 Given that $\log_{10}8 = 0.9031$, write down,

(a) $\log_{10}80$ (b) $\log_{10}800$ (c) $\log_{10}80\ 000$

(d) $\log_{10}0.8$ (e) $\log_{10}0.08$ (f) $\log_{10}0.008$

4 Examine this example.

Where $\log_{10}4 = 0.6021$, then we can say
$4 = 10^{0.6021}$

Work out each of these log numbers, then rewrite the statement as a power of 10.

(a) $\log_{10}75$ (b) $\log_{10}400$ (c) $\log_{10}2.5$

5 Examine this example.

$4 \times 3 = 10^{\boxed{0.6021}} \times 10^{\boxed{0.4771}} = 10^{\boxed{1.0792}} = 12$

Use the logarithms on your calculator to answer these, as in the example:

(a) $5 \times 6 = 10^{\boxed{}} \times 10^{\boxed{}} = 10^{\boxed{}} =$

(b) $7 \times 9 = 10^{\boxed{}} \times 10^{\boxed{}} = 10^{\boxed{}} =$

(c) $2 \times 8 = 10^{\boxed{}} \times 10^{\boxed{}} = 10^{\boxed{}} =$

(d) $3.3 \times 6.2 = 10^{\boxed{}} \times 10^{\boxed{}} = 10^{\boxed{}} =$

(e) $4.7 \times 8.2 = 10^{\boxed{}} \times 10^{\boxed{}} = 10^{\boxed{}} =$

6 Write these as a single logarithm.

(a) $\log_{10}2 + \log_{10}6 =$
(b) $\log_{10}3 + \log_{10}5 =$
(c) $\log_{10}4 + \log_{10}7 =$
(d) $\log_{10}8 + \log_{10}2.5 =$
(e) $\log_{10}15 + \log_{10}5 =$

7 Given that $\log_{10}2 = 0.3010$ and $\log_{10}3 = 0.4771$, find the following.

(a) $\log_{10}6$ (b) $\log_{10}4$ (c) $\log_{10}9$

(d) $\log_{10}12$ (e) $\log_{10}18$ (f) $\log_{10}8$

8 Given that $\log_{10}2 = 0.3010$, $\log_{10}5 = 0.6990$ and $\log_{10}3 = 0.4771$, find these.

(a) $\log_{10}10$ (b) $\log_{10}15$ (c) $\log_{10}30$

(d) $\log_{10}25$ (e) $\log_{10}50$ (f) $\log_{10}45$

9 Given that $\log_{10}5 = 0.6990$, $\log_{10}7 = 0.8451$ and $\log_{10}11 = 1.0414$, then find,

(a) $\log_{10}35$ (b) $\log_{10}55$ (c) $\log_{10}77$

(d) $\log_{10}49$ (e) $\log_{10}121$ (f) $\log_{10}125$

10 Use logarithms to calculate the following.

(a) 0.0038×568.2 (b) 6.244×595.1
(c) $0.036\ 54 \times 2.469$ (d) 2.344×9867
(e) $2.3 \times 56.78 \times 927.4$
(f) $0.0573 \times 0.1768 \times 456.4$

Now check to see if you get the same answers on your calculator without converting to log numbers.

11 Write each of these as a single logarithm.

(a) $\log_{10}16 - \log_{10}2 =$
(b) $\log_{10}28 - \log_{10}7 =$
(c) $\log_{10}42 - \log_{10}7 =$
(d) $\log_{10}48 - \log_{10}12 =$
(e) $\log_{10}57 - \log_{10}19 =$

12 Given that $\log_{10}16 = 1.2041$ and $\log_{10}2 = 0.3010$, then find without calculators,

(a) $\log_{10}8$ (b) $\log_{10}4$

13 Given that $\log_{10}36 = 1.5563$ and $\log_{10}3 = 0.4771$, find these without using calculators.

(a) $\log_{10}12$ (b) $\log_{10}4$

14 Use logarithms to calculate the following.

(a) $3172 \div 6.25$ (b) $458.2 \div 5.94$
(c) $2360 \div 78.23$ (d) $5592 \div 452.1$

Now check to see if you get the same answers on your calculator without converting to log numbers.

15 Simplify the following.

(a) $\log_{10}4 + \log_{10}25$ (b) $\log_{10}25 - \log_{10}5$

(c) $\log_{10}12 + \log_{10}5$ (d) $\log_{10}20 - \log_{10}2$

(e) $\log_{10}20 + \log_{10}50$ (f) $\log_{10}120 - \log_{10}12$

16 Simplify, without powers, the following.

(a) $\log_{10}a^3$ (b) $\log_{10}m^2$

(c) $\log_{10}5^4$ (d) $\log_{10}2^5$

(e) $\log_{10}h^{\frac{1}{2}}$ (f) $\log_{10}9^{\frac{1}{3}}$

(g) $\log_{10}f^{\frac{2}{3}}$ (h) $\log_{10}4^{\frac{3}{4}}$

17 By using logarithms, find the value of these.

(a) $(7.844)^3$ (b) $(44.03)^3$

(c) $(3.52)^5$ (d) $(1.228)^4$

(e) $(467.9)^{\frac{1}{2}}$ (f) $(39.85)^{\frac{1}{3}}$

(g) $(37.07)^{\frac{2}{3}}$ (h) $(1538)^{\frac{3}{4}}$

18 Given that $\log_{10}4 = 0.6021$, calculate these without using tables.

(a) $\log_{10}2$ (b) $\log_{10}16$ (c) $\log_{10}64$

(d) $\log_{10}8$ (e) $\log_{10}32$

19 Given $\log_{10}5 = 0.6990$, then work these out without the use of a calculator.

(a) $\log_{10}25$ (b) $\log_{10}125$ (c) $\log_{10}625$

20 Say whether the following statements are true or false.

(a) $\log_{10}1000 = 3\log_{10}10$

(b) $\log_{10}5 = \frac{1}{3}\log_{10}125$

(c) $\log_{10}2 + \log_{10}5 = \log_{10}7$

(d) $\dfrac{\log_{10}27}{\log_{10}3} = \log_{10}9$

(e) $\dfrac{\log_{10}a^3}{\log_{10}a} = \log_{10}a^2$

Unit 5

Square roots

5.1 Theory of square roots

Whilst it is very easy to press a button on a calculator in order to find the square root of a number, it is worth while looking into the theory behind square roots.

For instance, suppose we consider $\sqrt{16}$, $\sqrt{160}$, $\sqrt{1600}$, $\sqrt{16\,000}$

Now,
$$\sqrt{16} = 4$$
$$\sqrt{160} = 12.649 \text{ (to 3 decimal places)}$$
$$\sqrt{1600} = 40$$
$$\sqrt{16\,000} = 126.49$$

We can see an obvious pattern developing, in fact we may even predict, for example, $\sqrt{1.6}$ and $\sqrt{160\,000}$
$$\sqrt{1.6} = 1.2649$$
$$\sqrt{160\,000} = 400$$

A check on the calculator proves these results to be true. Further predictions could even include
$$\sqrt{0.16} = 0.4$$
and $\sqrt{0.016} = 0.126\,49$ etc

On closer examination, we can easily find the link.
$$\sqrt{16} = 4$$
$$\sqrt{1600} = \sqrt{16 \times 100} \text{ which may be rewritten } \sqrt{16} \times \sqrt{100} = 4 \times 10 = 40$$

Also,
$$\sqrt{0.16} = \sqrt{16 \div 100} = \sqrt{16} \div \sqrt{100} = 4 \div 10 = 0.4$$

And,
$$\sqrt{160} = 12.649 \text{ (to 3 decimal places)}$$
$$\sqrt{16\,000} = \sqrt{160 \times 100} = \sqrt{160} \times \sqrt{100} = 12.649 \times 10 = 126.49$$

Suppose now, we attempt to find

(a) $\sqrt{1\,600\,000}$ **(b)** $\sqrt{0.0016}$

(a) $\sqrt{1\,600\,000}$
$= \sqrt{16\,000} \times \sqrt{100}$
$= \sqrt{160} \times \sqrt{100} \times \sqrt{100}$
$= 12.649 \times 10 \times 10$
$= 1264.9$

(b) $\sqrt{0.0016}$
$= \sqrt{0.16} \div \sqrt{100}$
$= \sqrt{16} \div \sqrt{100} \div \sqrt{100}$
$= 4 \div 10 \div 10$
$= 0.04$

and so on.

Example Given $\sqrt{2.8} = 1.673$ (to 3 dec pl) and $\sqrt{28} = 5.292$ (to 3 dec pl)
Find, **(a)** $\sqrt{280}$ and **(b)** $\sqrt{0.0028}$

(a) $\sqrt{280} = \sqrt{2.8} \times \sqrt{100} = 1.673 \times 10 = 16.73$

(b) $\sqrt{0.0028} = \sqrt{28} \div \sqrt{100} \div \sqrt{100} = 5.292 \div 10 \div 10 = 0.05292$

Activities

Examples of square roots

1 Write down the square roots in the following, using a calculator if necessary.

(a) $\sqrt{16}$ **(b)** $\sqrt{36}$ **(c)** $\sqrt{100}$ **(d)** $\sqrt{9}$
(e) $\sqrt{1}$ **(f)** $\sqrt{25}$ **(g)** $\sqrt{144}$ **(h)** $\sqrt{81}$
(i) $\sqrt{8.1}$ **(j)** $\sqrt{0.64}$ **(k)** $\sqrt{400}$ **(l)** $\sqrt{2500}$
(m) $\sqrt{0.04}$ **(n)** $\sqrt{250\,000}$ **(o)** $\sqrt{0.01}$ **(p)** $\sqrt{10\,000}$

2 Use your answers to Question **1** to find the following square roots.

(a) $\sqrt{0.09}$ **(b)** $\sqrt{0.16}$ **(c)** $\sqrt{64\,000}$
(d) $\sqrt{0.000\,036}$ **(e)** $\sqrt{9\,000\,000}$ **(f)** $\sqrt{0.0009}$

3 Given, $\sqrt{25} = 5$ and $\sqrt{250} = 15.811$, find
(a) $\sqrt{2500}$ **(b)** $\sqrt{25\,000}$ **(c)** $\sqrt{0.0025}$
(d) $\sqrt{0.025}$

4 Given, $\sqrt{10} = 3.162$ and $\sqrt{100} = 10$, find
(a) $\sqrt{0.1}$ **(b)** $\sqrt{0.001}$ **(c)** $\sqrt{1000}$
(d) $\sqrt{1\,000\,000}$

5 Given, $\sqrt{144} = 12$ and $\sqrt{14.4} = 3.795$, find
(a) $\sqrt{1.44}$ **(b)** $\sqrt{0.144}$ **(c)** $\sqrt{1440}$
(d) $\sqrt{14\,400}$ **(e)** $\sqrt{0.000\,144}$ **(f)** $\sqrt{1\,440\,000}$

6 Example
$$\sqrt{250\,000} = \sqrt{25 \times 100 \times 100} = 5 \times 10 \times 10 = 500$$

Now complete,

(a) $\sqrt{81\,000\,000} =$
$=$ $=$

(b) $\sqrt{490\,000} =$
$=$ $=$

(c) $\sqrt{9\,000\,000} =$
$=$ $=$

5.2 Square roots and standard form

In many circumstances it is quite easy to find the square root of a number by expressing the number in standard form.

Example 1 Find the square root of 90 000.

$90\,000 = 9 \times 10^4$ in standard form

Hence, $\sqrt{9 \times 10^4} = \sqrt{9} \times \sqrt{10^4}$
$= 3 \times 10^2$
$= 3 \times 100$
$= 300$

Example 2 Find the square root of 8.1×10^5.

By changing the standard form 8.1×10^5 into 81×10^4 we can now find the square root.

$\sqrt{81 \times 10^4} = \sqrt{81} \times \sqrt{10^4}$
$= 9 \times 10^2$
$= 9 \times 100$
$= 900$

Example 3 Find the square root of 2.5×10^{-3}

$2.5 \times 10^{-3} = 25 \times 10^{-4}$

Hence, $25 \times 10^{-4} = \sqrt{25} \times \sqrt{10^{-4}}$
$= 5 \times 10^{-2}$
$= \frac{5}{100}$
$= 0.05$

Activities

1 Find the square roots of these powers of ten.

(a) $\sqrt{10^2}$ **(b)** $\sqrt{10^4}$ **(c)** $\sqrt{10^6}$
(d) $\sqrt{10^8}$ **(e)** $\sqrt{10^{10}}$ **(f)** $\sqrt{10^{-2}}$
(g) $\sqrt{10^{-4}}$ **(h)** $\sqrt{10^{-6}}$ **(i)** $\sqrt{10^{-8}}$

2 Find the square roots of the following, by first writing them in standard form.

(a) 250 000 **(b)** 81 000 000 **(c)** 22 500
(d) 1 440 000 **(e)** 1 000 000 **(f)** 1 210 000

3 Find the square root of the following numbers. Remember to adjust the number first.

(a) 3.6×10^5 **(b)** 4.9×10^3 **(c)** 0.4×10^5
(d) 1.69×10^4 **(e)** 8.1×10^3 **(f)** 1.6×10^7

4 Find the square roots of these small numbers.

(a) 1.6×10^{-5} **(b)** 3.6×10^{-3} **(c)** 4.9×10^{-5}
(d) 6.4×10^{-3} **(e)** 8.1×10^{-7} **(f)** 1.21×10^{-6}

5 Find an approximate square root of each of the following numbers (correct to one significant figure).

(a) 5.12×10^3 **(b)** 8×10^{-5} **(c)** 8×10^{-4}
(d) 1.5×10^6 **(e)** 2.2×10^{-4} **(f)** 4.25×10^4

Unit 6

Modulo arithmetic

6.1 Modulo 12

So far, in our study of number, we have only considered infinite number systems. In other words however large a number considered, we could always write down a larger number.

It is now time to consider a finite number system. Such a system is best described by using a 12-hour clock.

If, for example, it is now 9 o'clock and we are due to meet someone in 5 hours time, we shall be meeting them at 2 o'clock. This is because we only use the remainder, after dividing the sum of 9 and 5 by 12, i.e.

$(9 + 5) \div 12$ has a remainder of 2.

This process is known as **addition in modulo 12**, which we write as mod 12.

When we divide any positive number by 12, the only possible remainders are $\{0, 1, 2, 3, 4, 5, 6, 7, 8, 9, 10, 11\}$ and so mod 12 is a finite number system. Thus, any positive integer can be converted to any modulo number.

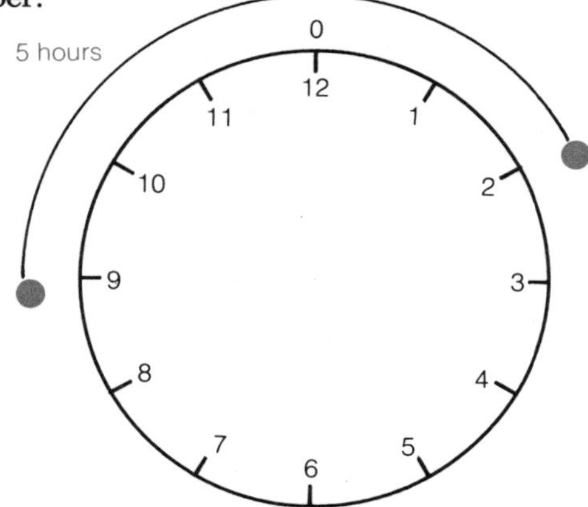

Fig. 6.1

As we see from Fig. 6.1,

$14 \equiv 2 \pmod{12}$
(this means, 14 is equivalent to 2 in mod 12)

Other examples in mod 12 include the following,

$18 \equiv 6 \pmod{12}$
$36 \equiv 0 \pmod{12}$
$64 \equiv 4 \pmod{12}$

6.2 Modulo 6

Suppose we now consider the mod 6 system. Possible remainders are 0, 1, 2, 3, 4, 5. In other words, upon reaching 6, we are again at the starting point, which we call 0.

mod 6

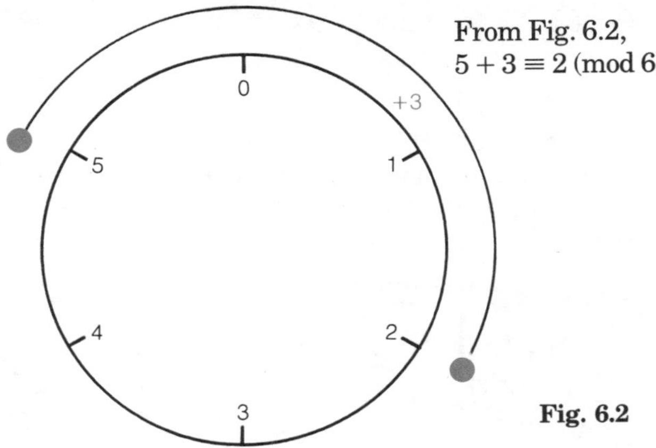

From Fig. 6.2, $5 + 3 \equiv 2 \pmod 6$

Fig. 6.2

6.3 Calculating in modulo arithmetic

The best way of showing results in modulo arithmetic is to construct tables for the operation concerned.

For addition in mod 6, the table will look as in Table 6.1.

+	0	1	2	3	4	5
0	0	1	2	3	4	5
1	1	2	3	4	5	0
2	2	3	4	5	0	1
3	3	4	5	0	1	2
4	4	5	0	1	2	3
5	5	0	1	2	3	4

Table 6.1

For subtraction in mod 6, the table will look as in Table 6.2.

−	0	1	2	3	4	5
0	0	5	4	3	2	1
1	1	0	5	4	3	2
2	2	1	0	5	4	3
3	3	2	1	0	5	4
4	4	3	2	1	0	5
5	5	4	3	2	1	0

Table 6.2

For multiplication in mod 6, the table will look as in Table 6.3.

×	0	1	2	3	4	5
0	0	0	0	0	0	0
1	0	1	2	3	4	5
2	0	2	4	0	2	4
3	0	3	0	3	0	3
4	0	4	2	0	4	2
5	0	5	4	3	2	1

Table 6.3

We can now look at some typical calculations in modulo arithmetic.

Work out the following.

Example 1 $4 + 5 \pmod 8$.
$4 + 5 = 9 \equiv 1 \pmod 8$

Example 2 $4 \times 5 \pmod 7$.
$4 \times 5 = 20 \equiv 6 \pmod 7$

Example 3 $3 - 5 \pmod 6$. (See Table 6.2)
$3 - 5 \equiv 4 \pmod 6$

Example 4 $3^3 \pmod 5$.
$3^3 = 27 \equiv 2 \pmod 5$

Example 5 $4^2 \pmod 8$.
$4^2 = 16 \equiv 0 \pmod 8$

Example 6 $(5 + 6) \times 3 \pmod 9$
$= 11 \times 3 = 33 \equiv 6 \pmod 9$

Activities

1 Consider the clock face, in Fig. 6.3, representing mod 5.

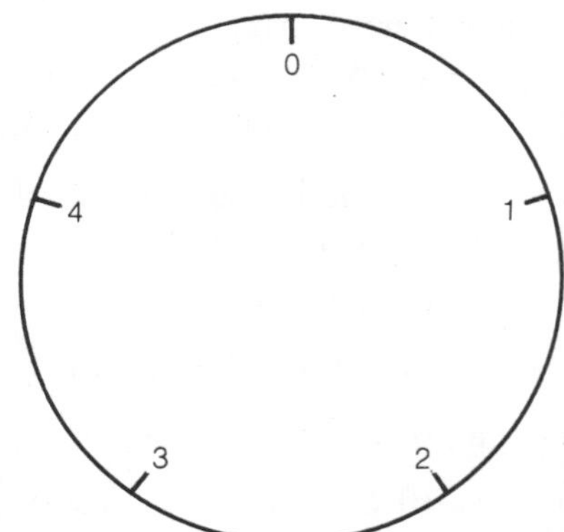

Fig. 6.3

Fill in the missing numbers in the boxes below.

(a) $7 \equiv \square \pmod 5$ **(b)** $9 \equiv \square \pmod 5$
(c) $12 \equiv \square \pmod 5$ **(d)** $15 \equiv \square \pmod 5$
(e) $4 + 2 \equiv \square \pmod 5$ **(f)** $\square + 3 \equiv 1 \pmod 5$

2 Consider the clock face, in Fig. 6.4, representing mod 8.

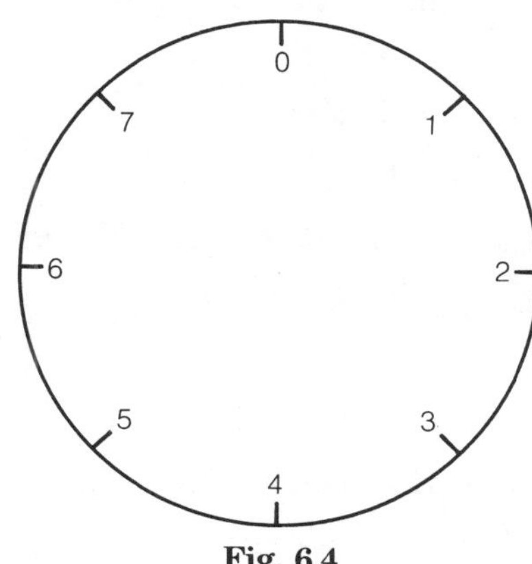

Fig. 6.4

Fill in the missing numbers in the boxes below.

(a) $11 \equiv \square \pmod 8$ **(b)** $14 \equiv \square \pmod 8$
(c) $22 \equiv \square \pmod 8$ **(d)** $25 \equiv \square \pmod 8$
(e) $4+5 \equiv \square \pmod 8$ **(f)** $7+6 \equiv \square \pmod 8$

3 Consider the clock face, in Fig. 6.5, representing mod 12.

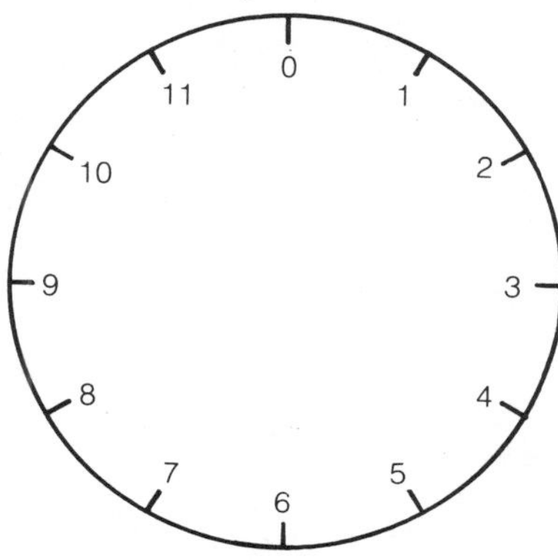

Fig. 6.5

Fill in the missing numbers in the boxes below.

(a) $17 \equiv \square \pmod{12}$ **(b)** $21 \equiv \square \pmod{12}$
(c) $32 \equiv \square \pmod{12}$ **(d)** $43 \equiv \square \pmod{12}$
(e) $9+6 \equiv \square \pmod{12}$ **(f)** $10+10 \equiv \square \pmod{12}$

For Questions **4–7**, copy and complete the modulo arithmetic tables and answer the questions about them.

4 mod 4

+	0	1	2	3
0	0	1	2	3
1	1	2	3	0
2	2	3	0	1
3	3	0		

Table 6.4

(a) $2+3 \pmod 4$
(b) $3+1 \pmod 4$
(c) $2+2+3 \pmod 4$

5 mod 5

×	0	1	2	3	4
0	0	0	0	0	0
1	0	1	2	3	4
2	0	2	4	1	3
3	0	3	1		
4					

Table 6.5

(a) $2 \times 3 \pmod 5$
(b) $2 \times 4 \pmod 5$
(c) $3 \times 4 \pmod 5$

6 mod 6

×	0	1	2	3	4	5
0	0	0	0			
1	0	1	2			
2	0	2	4	0		
3	0	3	0	3		
4	0	4	2	0		
5	0	5	4	3		

Table 6.6

(a) $2 \times 4 \pmod 6$
(b) $3 \times 5 \pmod 6$
(c) $4 \times 4 \pmod 6$
(d) $5 \times 2 \pmod 6$
(e) $5 \times 4 \pmod 6$

7 mod 5

−	0	1	2	3	4
0	0	4	3	2	1
1	1	0	4	3	2
2	2	1			
3					
4					

Table 6.7

(a) $2-4 \pmod 5$
(b) $3-4 \pmod 5$
(c) $2-3 \pmod 5$
(d) $1-4 \pmod 5$

8 Make up a table for multiplication in mod 4. Use your results to write down,

(a) 1×3 **(b)** 2×2 **(c)** 3^2 **(d)** 2×3

9 Make up a table of multiplication in mod 8. Use your results to write down,

(a) 2×7 **(b)** 3×5 **(c)** 6^2 **(d)** 4×6

10 Make up a table of addition in mod 7. Use your results to write down,

(a) $2+4$ **(b)** $3+5$ **(c)** $6+4$ **(d)** $2+6$

11 Make up a table of subtraction in mod 6. Use your results to write down,

(a) $5-3$ **(b)** $2-5$ **(c)** $1-5$ **(d)** $0-2$

12 Working in mod 5, find the missing number in each box.

(a) $2 \times \square \equiv 4$ **(b)** $3 \times \square \equiv 4$
(c) $2 \times \square \equiv 1$ **(d)** $4 + \square \equiv 3$

13 Find in mod 8,

(a) $(5+3)+7$ **(b)** $5+(3+7)$
(c) $(6+7)\times 4$ **(d)** $6+(7\times 4)$

14 Find in mod 6,

(a) $(2+5)+3$ **(b)** $2+(5+3)$
(c) $(2+5)\times 3$ **(d)** $2+(5\times 3)$

15 Find the missing number to make each of these statements true.

(a) $2+\square+4 \equiv 3$ in mod 7
(b) $2\times\square\times 4 \equiv 3$ in mod 5
(c) $7+5+\square \equiv 3$ in mod 9

6.4 Solving equations in modulo arithmetic

We can solve simple equations in modulo arithmetic, as shown below.

Find x for each of the following (x may have more than one value).

Example 1 $x+2 \equiv 1 \pmod 5$
$\Rightarrow x = 4$, since $4+2 \equiv 1 \pmod 5$

Example 2 $2x \equiv 3 \pmod 7$
$\Rightarrow x = 5$, since $2 \times 5 = 10 \equiv 3 \pmod 7$

Example 3 $x^2 \equiv 1 \pmod 5$
$x = 1$ or $x = 4$
since $1^2 = 1 \pmod 5$ and $4^2 = 16 \equiv 1 \pmod 5$

Activities

1 Find in mod 7 the solution of the following

(a) $x+5=2$ **(b)** $x+3=0$
(c) $x\times 3=5$ **(d)** $x^2=2$
(e) $2x+3=4$ **(f)** $2x+4=3$

2 Find in mod 5, the solution of the following.

(a) $x+3=1$ **(b)** $x+4=0$
(c) $x\times 3=1$ **(d)** $x^2=4$
(e) $3x+1=3$ **(f)** $2x+3=1$

3 Find in mod 6, the solution(s) of these.

(a) $y+5=3$ **(b)** $y-4=5$
(c) $5y=3$ **(d)** $y^2=3$
(e) $2y+3=1$ **(f)** $3y=0$

4 Solve the following, given each modulo arithmetic.

(a) $3x+4 \equiv 7 \pmod 8$
(b) $4x-3 \equiv 6 \pmod 7$
(c) $x^2 \equiv 1 \pmod 6$
(d) $x^2 \equiv 4 \pmod 5$
(e) $4x-3 \equiv 1 \pmod 8$

5 Solve the equation $3^x = 3$, in

(a) mod 6 **(b)** mod 5 **(c)** mod 9

6 Solve the following.

(a) $\frac{x}{3}+7 \equiv 1 \pmod 8$
(b) $\frac{2x}{3}+6 \equiv 2 \pmod 8$
(c) $3x^2-3 \equiv 1 \pmod 8$

MEASURE

Unit 7

Area – revision

In this section we shall be extending the ideas developed in Volumes 1 and 2.

Below, is a brief revision of the topics covered so far.

rectangle
(see Fig. 7.1)

area = length × breadth

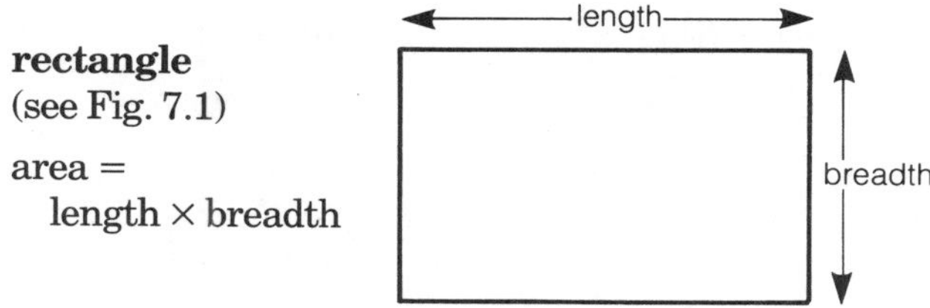

Fig. 7.1

triangle (1)
(see Fig. 7.2)

area = $\frac{1}{2}$ base length × perp. height
$= \frac{1}{2}b \times h$

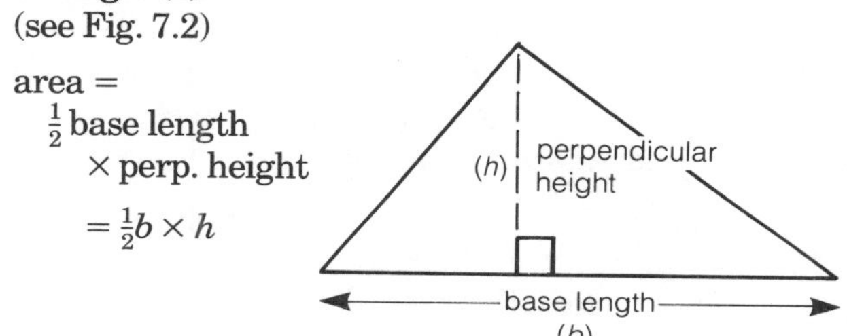

Fig. 7.2

parallelogram (1)
(see Fig. 7.3)

area = base length × perp. height
$= b \times h$

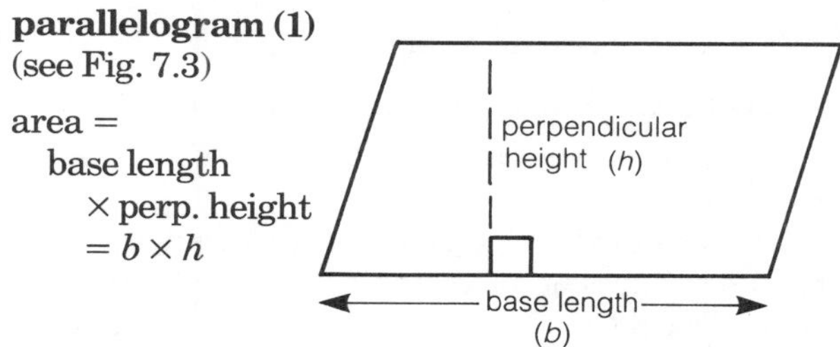

Fig. 7.3

trapezium
(see Fig. 7.4)

area = $\frac{1}{2}$ sum of parallel sides × perp. height
$= \frac{1}{2}(a + b) \times h$

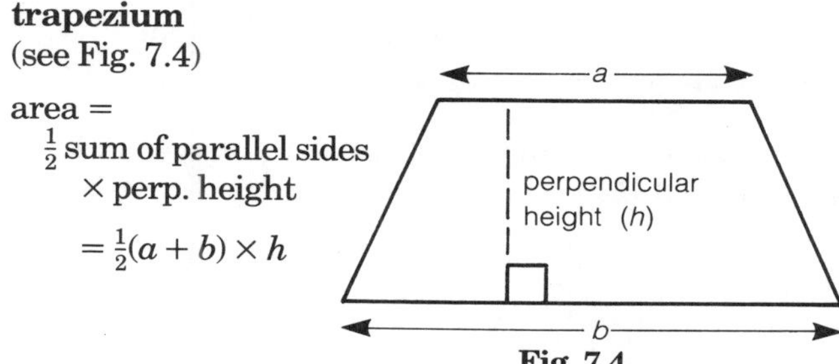

Fig. 7.4

After completing the Activities, we shall be in a position to consider some alternative methods.

Activities

1 Using your knowledge from Volumes 1 and 2, find the areas of the shapes in Figs. 7.5–7.14.

(a)

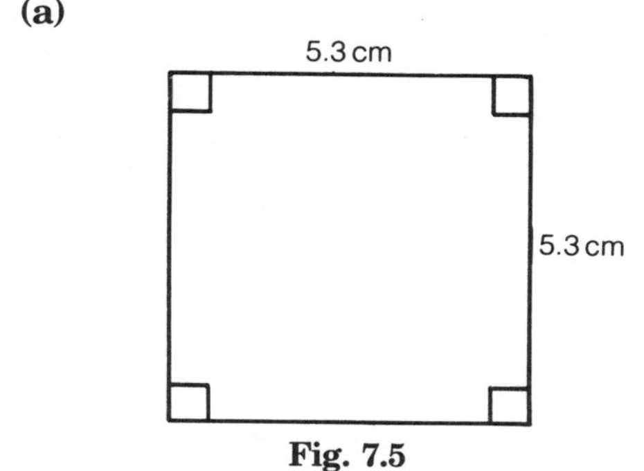

Fig. 7.5

(b)

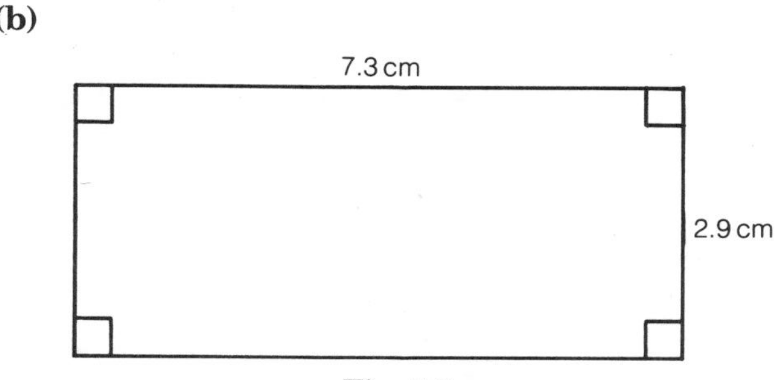

Fig. 7.6

(c)

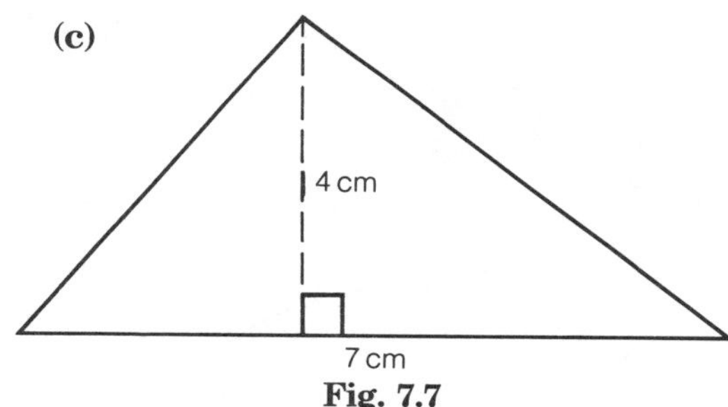

Fig. 7.7

(d)

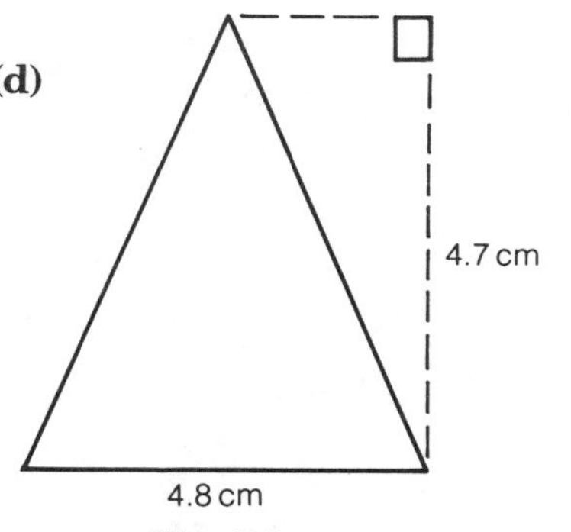

Fig. 7.8

(e)

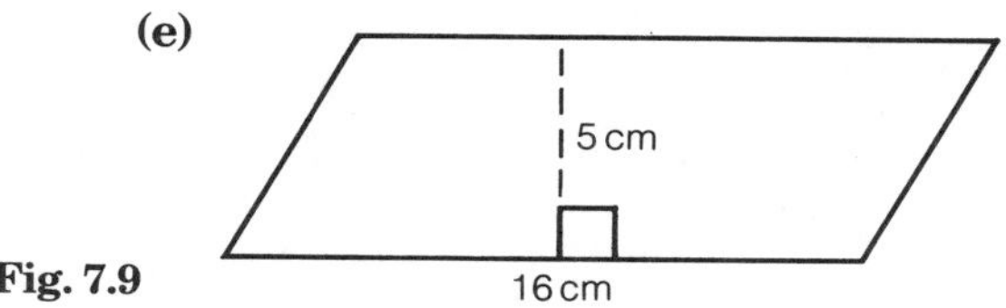

Fig. 7.9

(f)

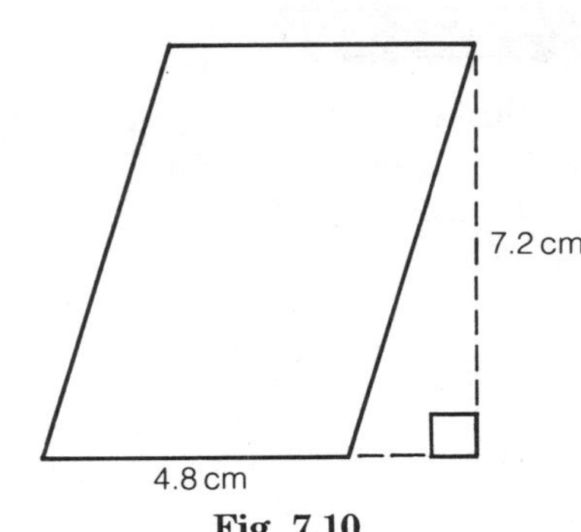

Fig. 7.10

(g)

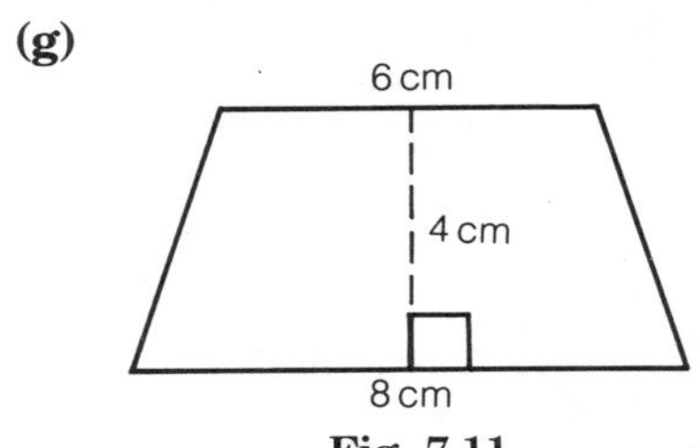

Fig. 7.11

(h)

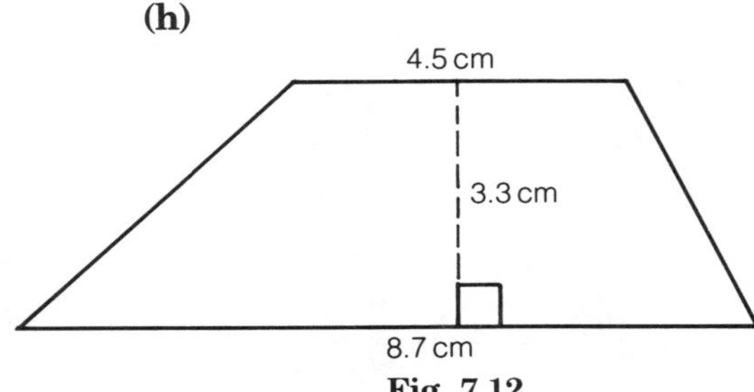

Fig. 7.12

(i)

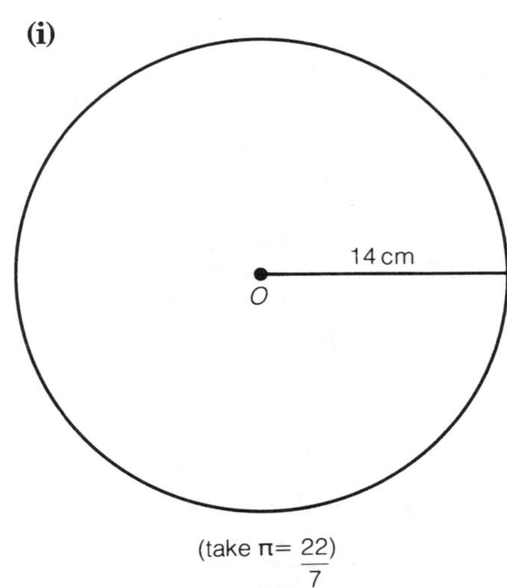

(take $\pi = \frac{22}{7}$)

Fig. 7.13

(j)

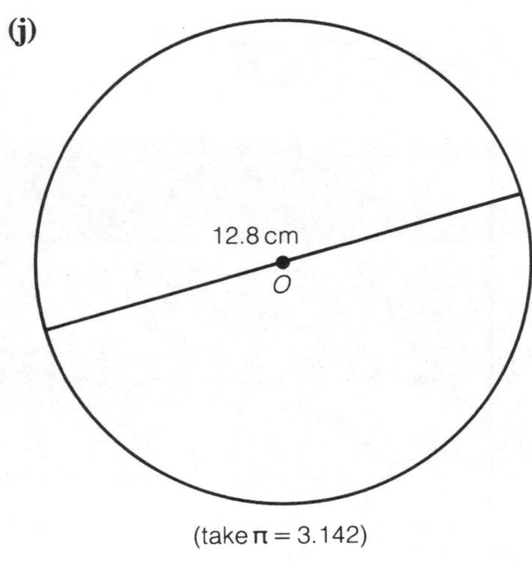

(take $\pi = 3.142$)

Fig. 7.14

2 Calculate the area of a square of side 17.5 cm.

3 A rectangular sheet of card is 15.7 cm long and 8.6 cm wide. Calculate the area.

4 A triangle ABC is such that $\angle B = 90°$, $BA = 5.2$ cm and $BC = 2.8$ cm. Calculate the area of the triangle.

5 Triangle XYZ is such that $\angle Y = 90°$ and the lengths of the sides are 13 cm, 12 cm and 5 cm. Find the length of the perpendicular from Y to the longest side.
Hint Find the area of the triangle and then use the longest side as the base and find the perpendicular height required, knowing the area.

6 Given a parallelogram with side lengths of 8.4 cm and 12.6 cm and area of 85.68 cm^2, find the perpendicular distance between each pair of the parallel sides.

7 A trapezium has parallel sides of length 16 cm and 12 cm which are 8 cm apart (perpendicular distance). Calculate the area of the trapezium.

8 ABC is a triangle of area 160 cm^2 with $BC = 32$ cm.
(a) Calculate the perpendicular distance of A from BC.
(b) The shorter sides of a rectangle are of length 20 cm and the area of the rectangle is six times that of the triangle ABC. Find the length of the longer side of the rectangle.

9 Calculate the area of a circle of
(a) radius 14 mm **(b)** diameter 47.6 cm
(c) diameter 56 m (take $\pi = \frac{22}{7}$)

10 A 10p coin has an area of 6.15 cm^2. Find its radius (take $\pi = 3.14$).

Unit 8

Area of a triangle (2)

8.1 Introduction

Apart from the base and altitude method as shown in Volume 1 (Area of Triangle) there are two quite common alternative methods for finding the area of a triangle, dependent on the given information.

8.2 The trigonometric method

This method is used when we are given two side lengths of a triangle and also the angle, $\theta°$, between those two sides (known as the **included** angle). See Fig. 8.1.

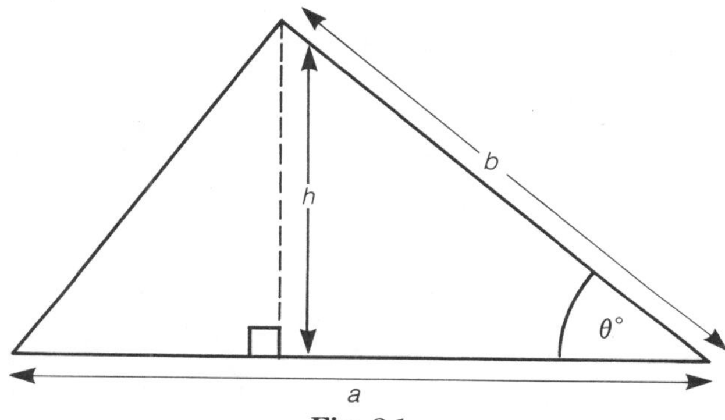

Fig. 8.1

area of triangle $= \frac{1}{2}a \times h$

now, $\frac{h}{b} = \sin\theta°$, $\therefore h = b \times \sin\theta$

So area of triangle $= \frac{1}{2} \times a \times b \times \sin\theta$

$= \frac{1}{2}ab\sin\theta$

Note $\sin\theta°$ is one of the trigonometric ratios which we shall study in more detail later in this Volume.

By using our scientific calculator, the sine of any angle may be found by entering the angle onto the display and then keying [sin].

Example Use your calculator to find the values of
(a) sin 30° **(b)** sin 50°

(a) Enter 30 onto the display, and key [sin].

The result on the display is 0.5.
Hence, sin 30° = 0.5.

(b) Enter 50 onto the display, and key [sin].

The result on the display is 0.7660444.
Hence, sin 50° = 0.7660444.

Suppose we now attempt an example of finding the area of a triangle.

Example 1 Find the area of the triangle shown in Fig. 8.2.

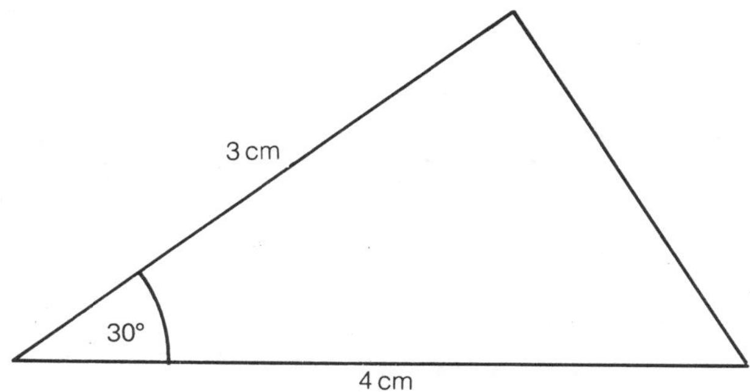

Fig. 8.2

We are given two side lengths and the **included** angle, so we use

area $= \frac{1}{2}ab\sin\theta°$

$\therefore$ area $= \frac{1}{2} \times 3 \times 4 \times \sin 30°\ \text{cm}^2$

$= \frac{12 \times \sin 30°}{2}\ \text{cm}^2$

$= 6 \times \sin 30°\ \text{cm}^2$

We know from **(a)** above, that $\sin 30° = 0.5$

$\therefore$ area of triangle $= 6 \times 0.5 = 3\ \text{cm}^2$

Example 2 Find the area of a triangle having two of its sides of length 5.3 cm and 7.2 cm, having an included angle of 28.3°. (See Fig. 8.3.)

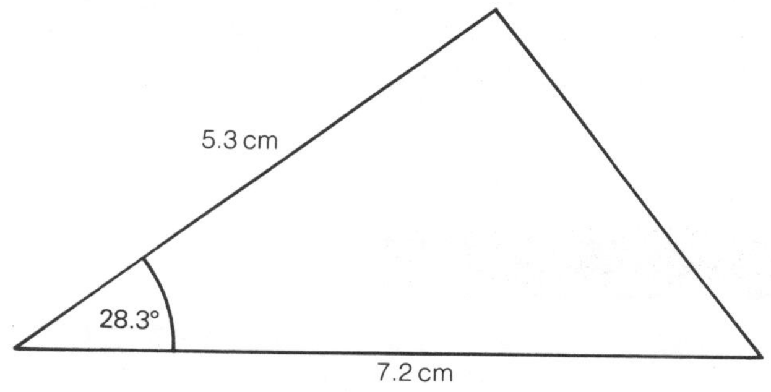

Fig. 8.3

Again we shall use area $= \frac{1}{2}ab\sin\theta°$

$\therefore$ area $= \frac{1}{2} \times 7.2 \times 5.3 \times \sin 28.3°$

Use your calculator as follows.

Enter 28.3 and key [sin] (display shows 0.4740882)

then [×] 7.2 [×] 5.3 [÷] 2 [=] 9.045603

Hence the area of the triangle will be recorded as 9.05 cm² (correct to 2 dec pl).

It is, of course, possible to find one of the side lengths, given another side length, the included angle and the area of the triangle, simply by applying the same formula.

Example Find the length of the side marked x cm in the triangle shown in Fig. 8.4.

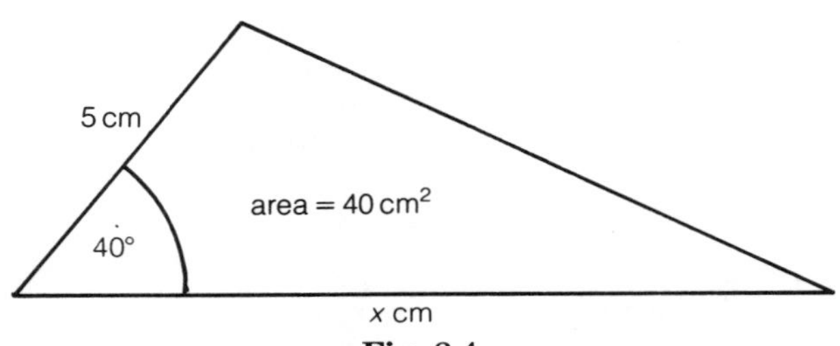

Fig. 8.4

$$\text{area} = \tfrac{1}{2}ab \sin \theta°$$
$$\therefore\ 40 = \tfrac{1}{2} \times 5 \times x \times \sin 40°$$

Multiply through by 2 (to remove the $\frac{1}{2}$)

$$80 = 5 \times x \times \sin 40°$$

Divide through by $5 \times \sin 40°$ (to isolate x)

$$\text{Then, } \frac{80}{5 \times \sin 40°} = x$$

When using your calculator to work out this result, probably the easiest way is to proceed as follows.

Enter 80 and key [÷], then enter 5 and key [÷], then enter 40 and key [sin] and then key [=].

This produces an answer of 24.89 cm, which is the required side length.

Note We have to press the **divide** button twice for the denominator in order for the calculator to cope with the problem.

An alternative method would be firstly to use the memory for the denominator and then divide the numerator by the recalled memory (see your calculator instruction booklet).

Activities

1 Find the areas of the triangles in Figs. 8.5–8.14.

(a)

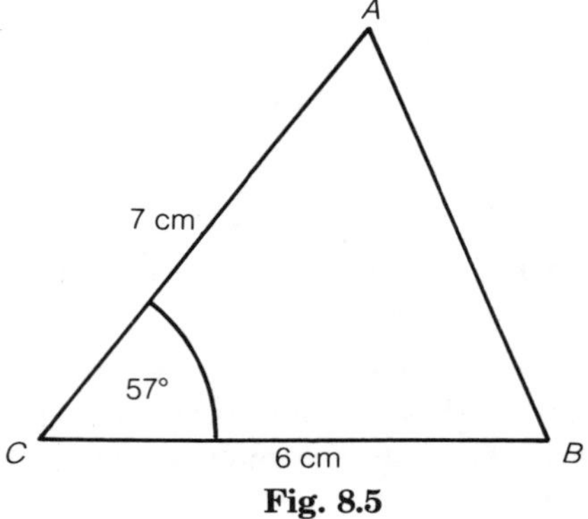

Fig. 8.5

(b)

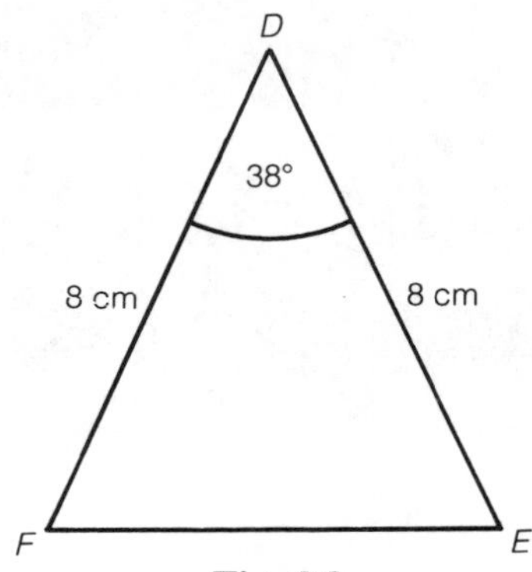

Fig. 8.6

(c)

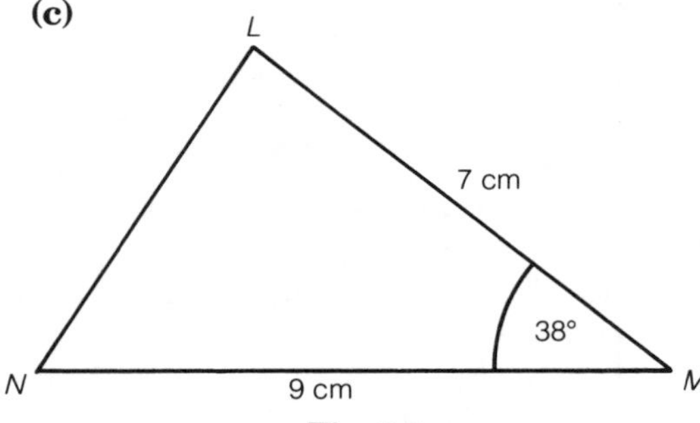

Fig. 8.7

(d)

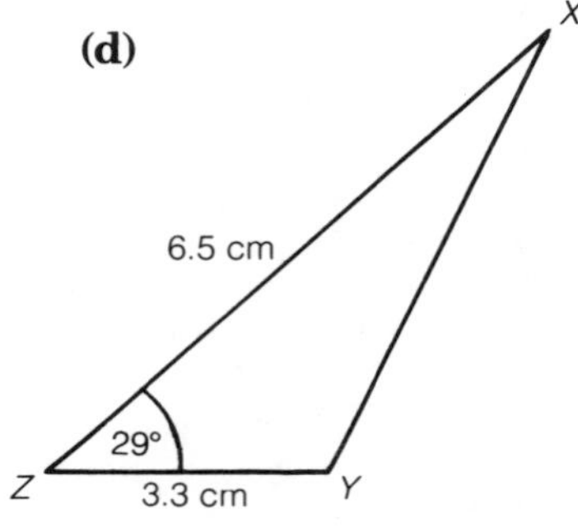

Fig. 8.8

(e)

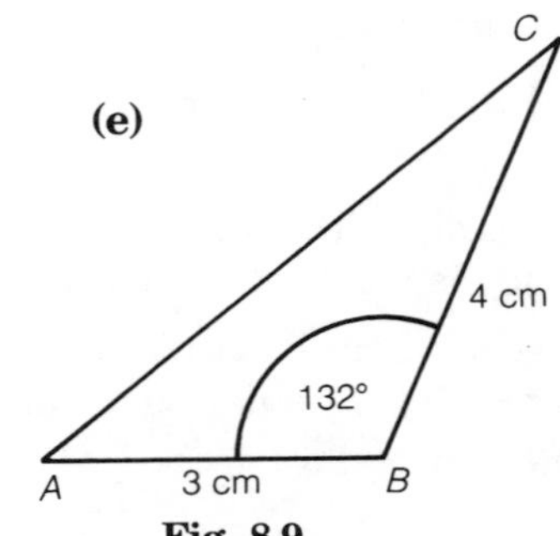

Fig. 8.9

(f)

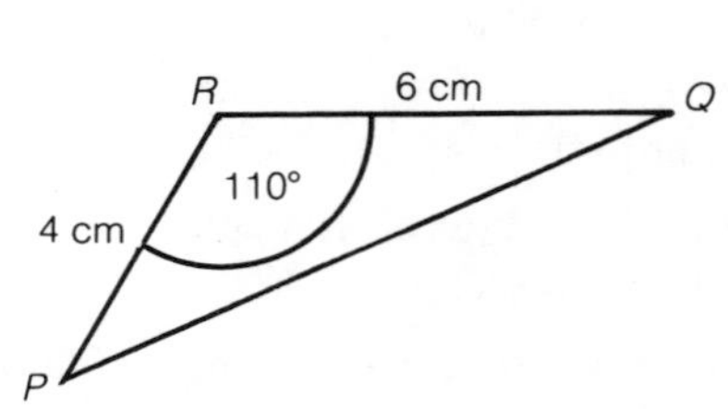

Fig. 8.10

(g)

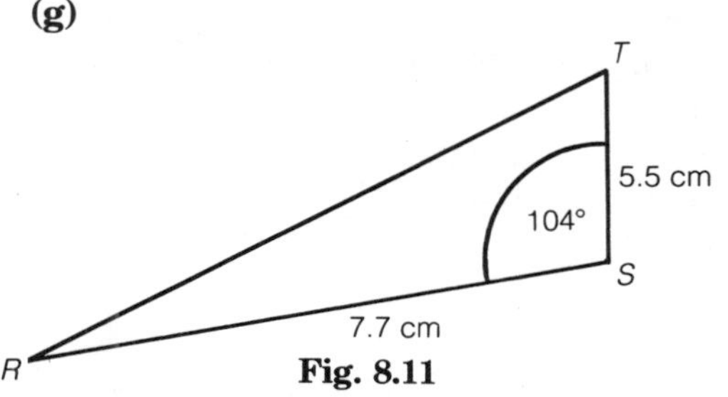

Fig. 8.11

(h)

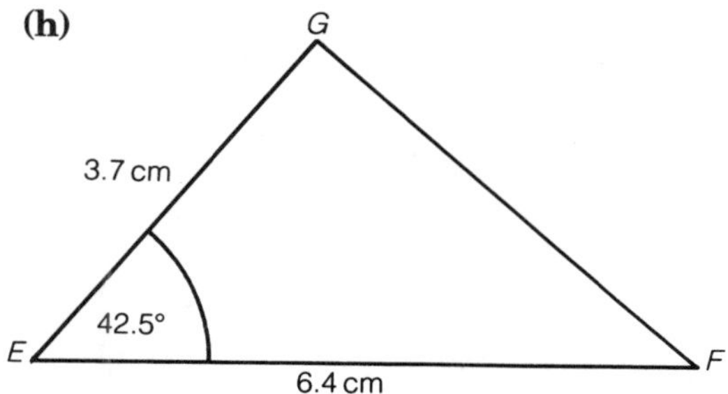

Fig. 8.12

(i)

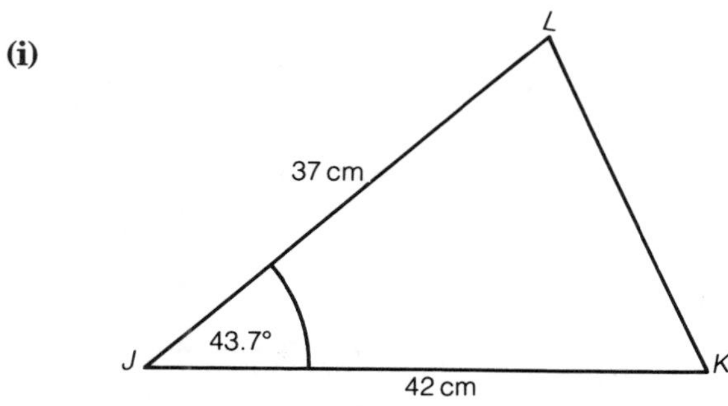

Fig. 8.13

(j)

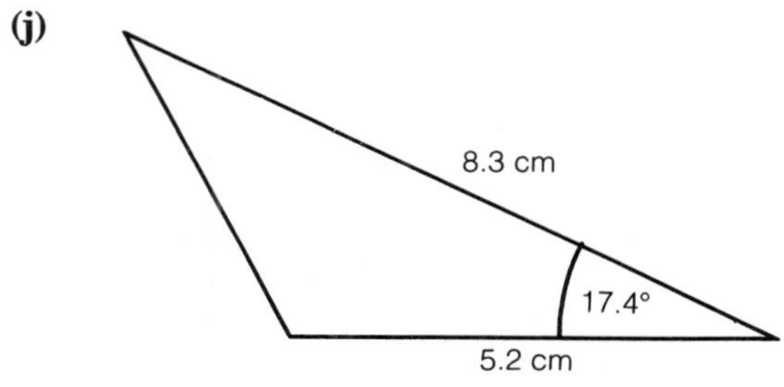

Fig. 8.14

8.3 Hero's method

Hero was another of the Ancient Mathematicians. He discovered a relationship between the area of a triangle and its three side lengths, a, b and c units. He found that the

area of a triangle $= \sqrt{s(s-a)(s-b)(s-c)}$

where $s = \frac{1}{2}(a+b+c)$

i.e. $s =$ half the sum of the side lengths

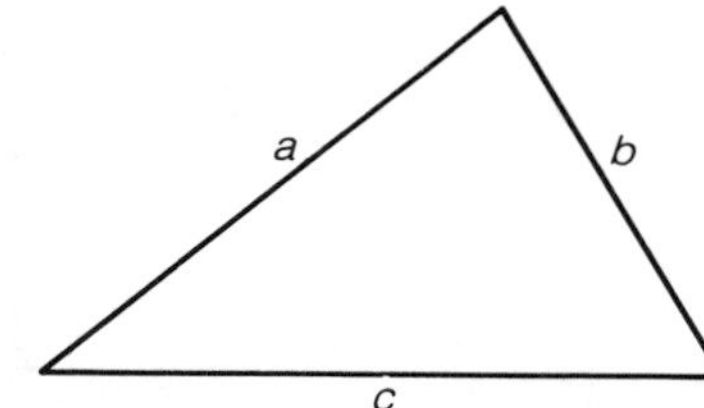

Fig. 8.15

B.

Example 1 Find the area of a triangle with side lengths of 7 cm, 8 cm and 9 cm.

See Fig. 8.16.

Firstly, we need to find s

$s = \frac{1}{2}(a+b+c)$

$\therefore s = \frac{1}{2}(9+8+7)$

$s = \frac{1}{2}(24) = 12$ cm

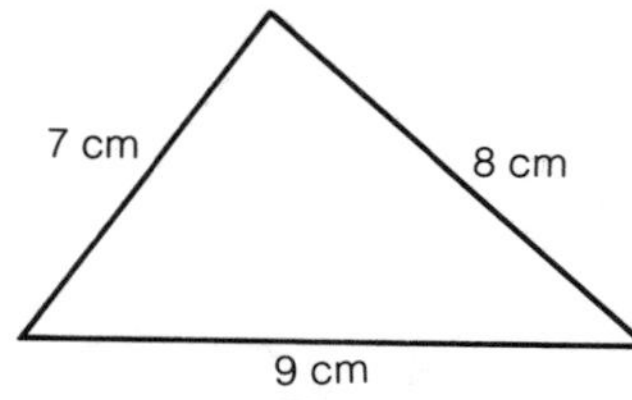

Fig. 8.16

The area, $A = \sqrt{s(s-a)(s-b)(s-c)}$

Hence, $A = \sqrt{12(12-9)(12-8)(12-7)}$

Work out each bracket first,

i.e. $A = \sqrt{12 \times 3 \times 4 \times 5}$

$A = \sqrt{720} = 26.83$

Hence, the area of the triangle is 26.83 cm^2.

Note A problem of this type, with far less convenient numbers than in Example **1**, proves to be relatively straightforward when you use your calculator.

Example 2 Find the area of a triangle with side lengths of 4.85 cm, 7.62 cm and 9.33 cm.

See Fig. 8.17.

$s = \frac{1}{2}(a+b+c)$

$s = \frac{1}{2}(9.33+7.62+4.85)$

$s = \frac{1}{2}(21.80) = 10.9$ cm

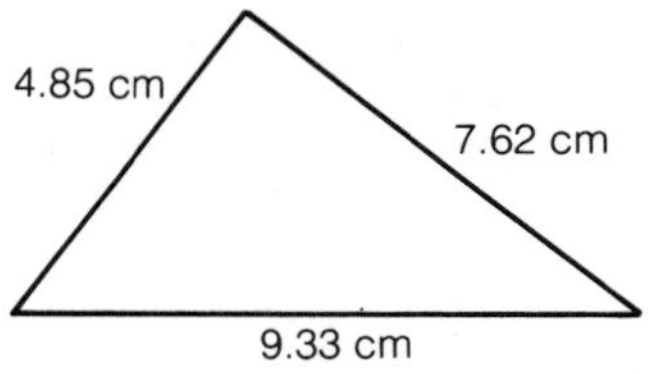

4.85 cm
7.62 cm
9.33 cm

Fig. 8.17

area $= \sqrt{s(s-a)(s-b)(s-c)}$

$= \sqrt{10.9(10.9-9.33)(10.9-7.62)(10.9-4.85)}$

$= \sqrt{10.9 \times 1.57 \times 2.28 \times 5.05}$

$= 14.04$ cm^2 (by calculator, and correct to 2 dec pl)

Note This type of problem would be very involved indeed, if not aided by the calculator.

Activities

1 Find the areas of the triangles in Figs. 8.18–8.23.

(a)

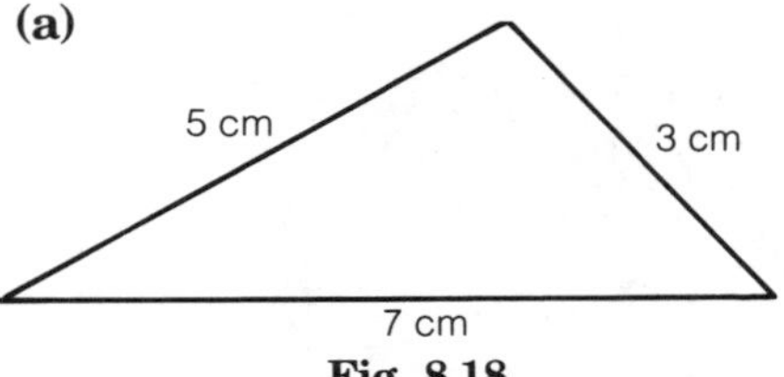

Fig. 8.18

(b)

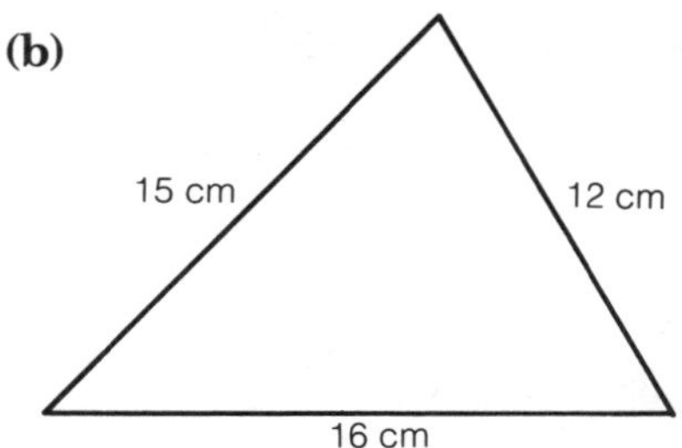

Fig. 8.19

(c)

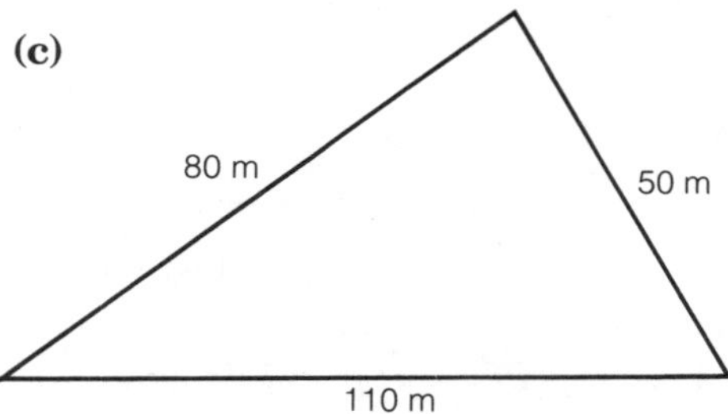

Fig. 8.20

(d)

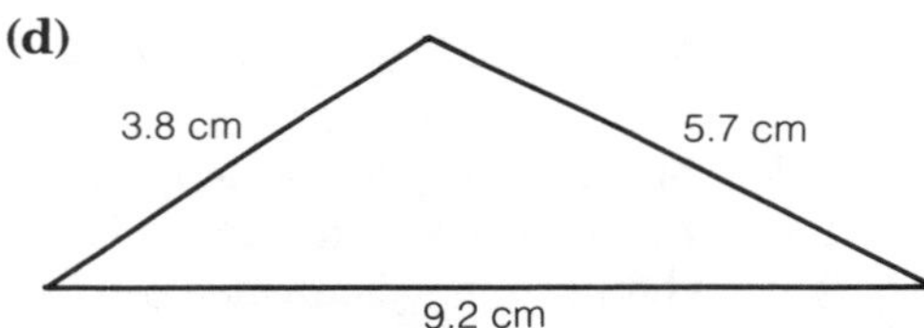

Fig. 8.21

(e)

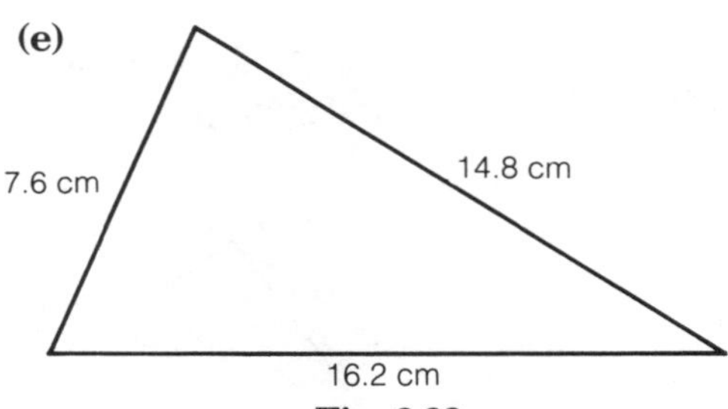

Fig. 8.22

(f)

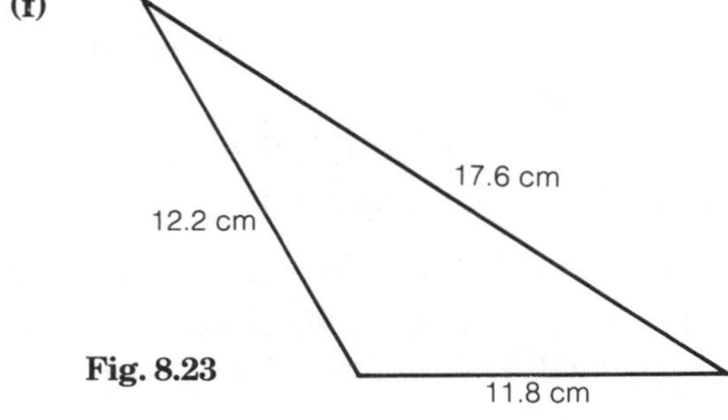

Fig. 8.23

2 Find the areas of the triangles in Figs. 8.24–8.29, using the appropriate method for the information given.

(a)

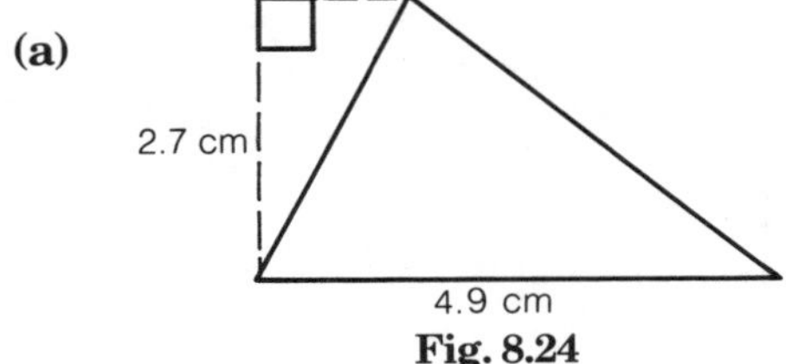

Fig. 8.24

(b)

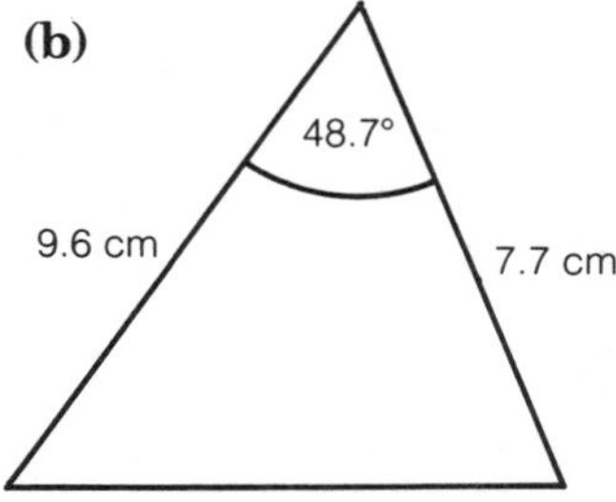

Fig. 8.25

(c)

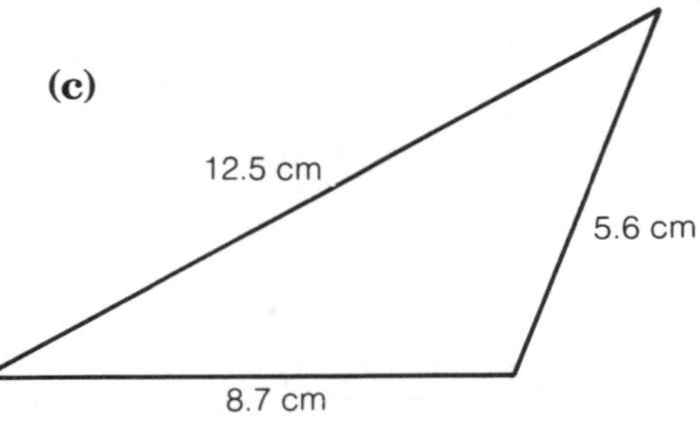

Fig. 8.26

(d)

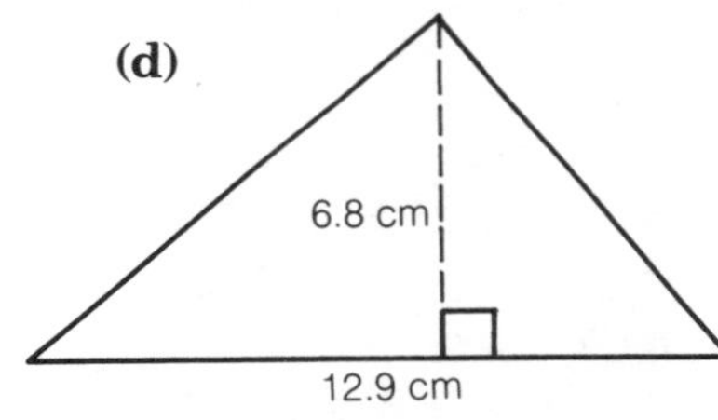

Fig. 8.27

(e)

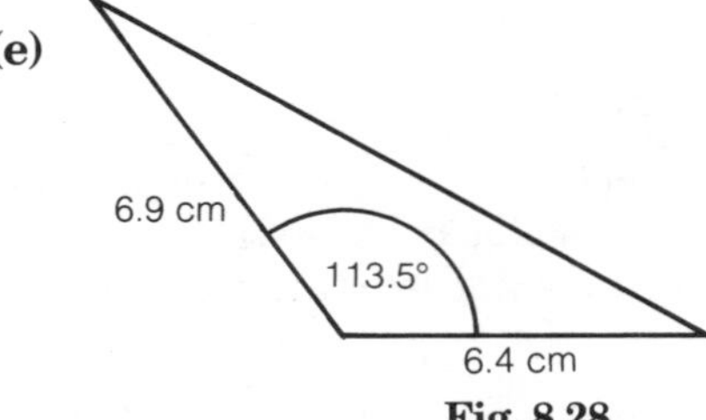

Fig. 8.28

(f)

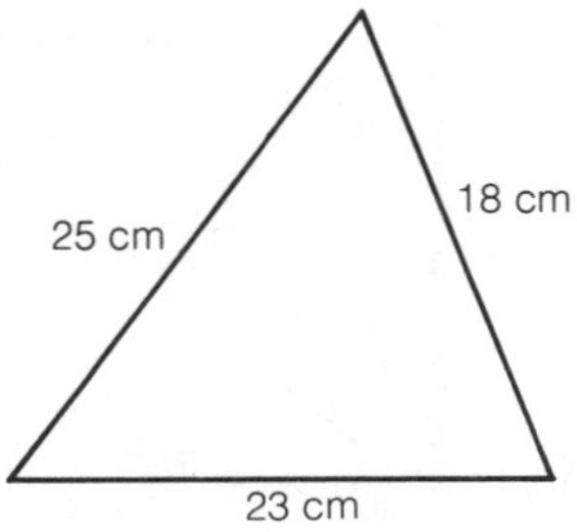

25 cm
18 cm
23 cm

Fig. 8.29

Unit 9

Area of a parallelogram (2)

We saw in Volume 1 that the area of a parallelogram was given as the base length × perpendicular height i.e. $A = b \times h$.

An alternative method, based on the same principle as for the triangle (trigonometric method), can be applied.

Since the area of a triangle may be expressed in terms of two side lengths and an included angle, then it is reasonable to assume that the area of a parallelogram may also be expressed in this manner – bearing in mind that a parallelogram is effectively made up of two triangles, equal in area – see Fig. 9.1.

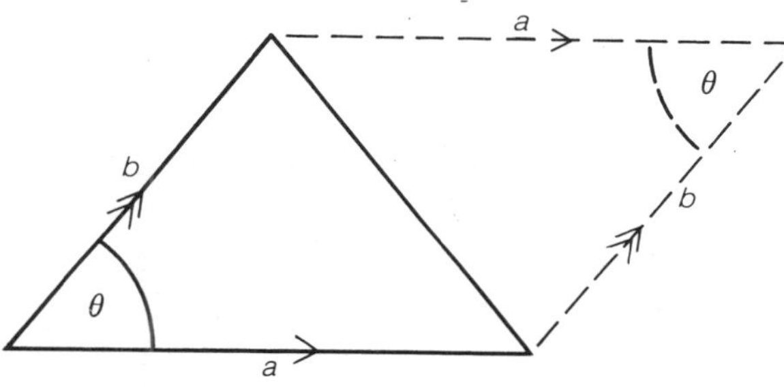

Fig. 9.1

Thus, we can say that the area of a parallelogram is twice $(\frac{1}{2} \times a \times b \times \sin\theta)$.

Hence, area of a parallelogram $= a \times b \times \sin\theta$
$= ab \sin\theta$

Example 1 Find the area of the parallelogram shown in Fig. 9.2.

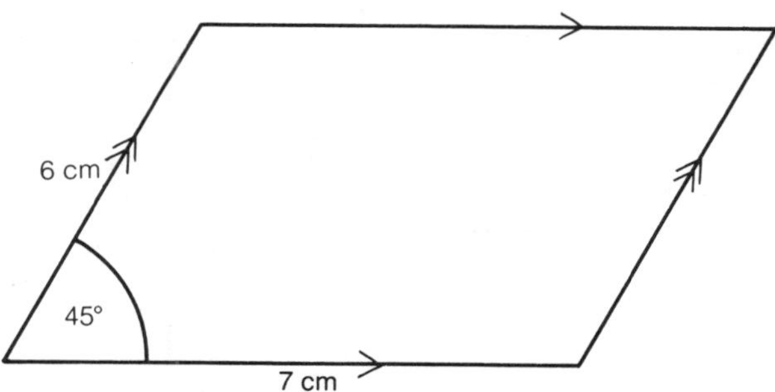

Fig. 9.2

$$\begin{aligned} \text{area} &= ab\sin\theta \\ &= 7 \times 6 \times \sin 45° \\ &= 42 \times \sin 45° \end{aligned}$$

Using the calculator as before to achieve the result, the area is found to be 29.7 cm^2.

Once again, given the area of the parallelogram and one of its side lengths, together with the included angle, it is possible to find the missing side length.

Example 2 Find the length of the side y cm in Fig. 9.3.

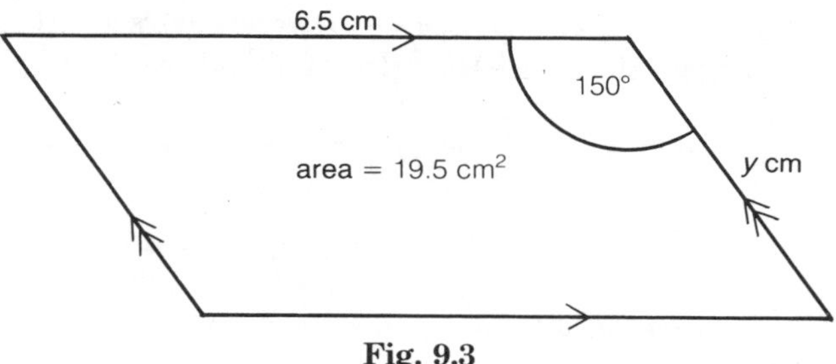

Fig. 9.3

$$\text{area} = ab\sin\theta$$

Hence, $19.5 = 6.5 \times y \times \sin 150°$

Rearranging to isolate y, gives

$$\frac{19.5}{6.5 \times \sin 150°} = y$$

Using the calculator (remember to divide by both 6.5 and sin 150° as described previously) produces $y = 6$ cm, which is the missing side length.

It is interesting to note that, since adjacent angles of a parallelogram are supplementary, i.e. add to 180°, we could consider the problems above using either angle.

Example 3 See Fig. 9.4.

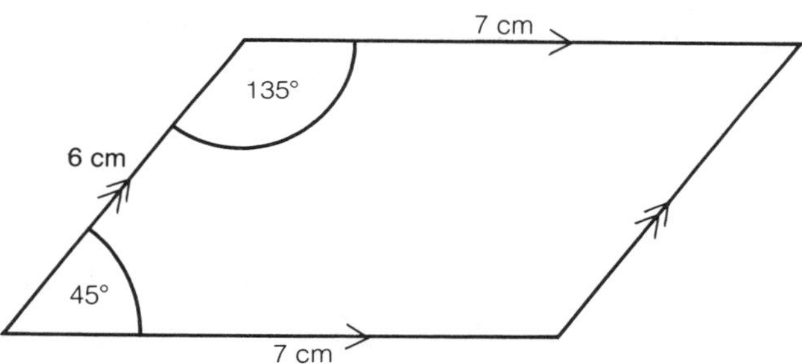

Fig. 9.4

$$\begin{aligned} \text{area} &= ab\sin\theta \\ &= 6 \times 7 \times \sin 135° \\ &= 29.7 \text{ cm}^2 \end{aligned}$$

Example 4 See Fig. 9.5.

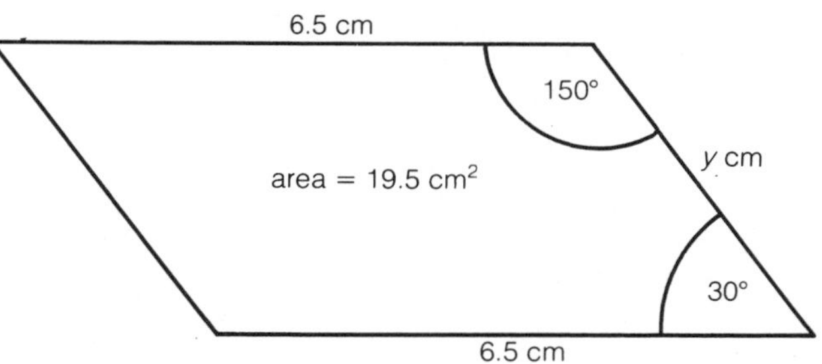

Fig. 9.5

$$\text{area} = ab\sin\theta$$

$$19.5 = 6.5 \times y \times \sin 30°$$

$$y = \frac{19.5}{6.5 \times \sin 30°} = 6 \text{ cm}$$

Note that,
in Examples 1 and 3, sin 45° = sin 135°
in Examples 2 and 4, sin 150° = sin 30°

In general terms, $\sin\theta = \sin(180 - \theta)$

This is explained more fully in the section, Geometry/Trigonometry, later in the Volume.

Fortunately, we do not have to concern ourselves too much about this, since the calculator deals with it for us.

Prove it for yourself by using the calculator to find sin 45° and sin 135°. Are they both the same?

Note For areas of triangles and parallelograms, we must ensure that we apply the correct formulae for the data given. Always consider carefully the information provided, before proceeding.

Activities

Areas of parallelograms

1 Find the areas of the parallelograms, in Fig. 9.6–9.9, using trigonometric method.

(a)

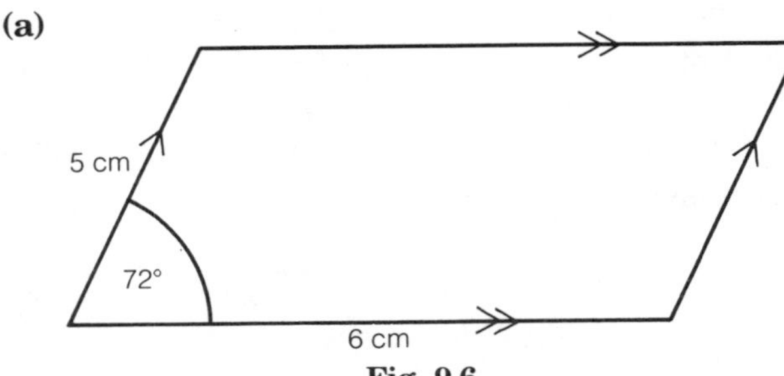

Fig. 9.6

(b)

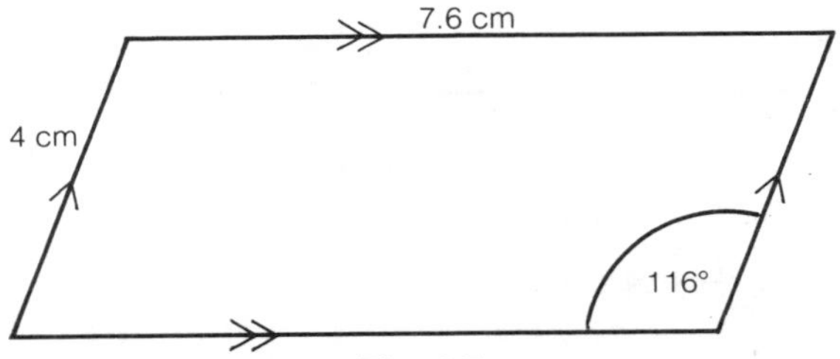

7.6 cm
4 cm
116°

Fig. 9.7

(c)

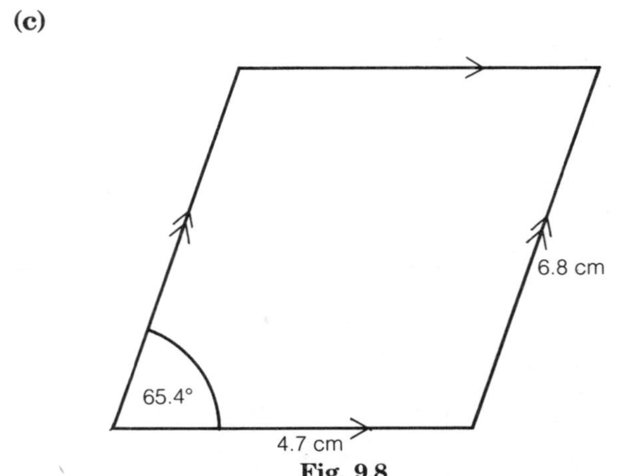

Fig. 9.8

(d)

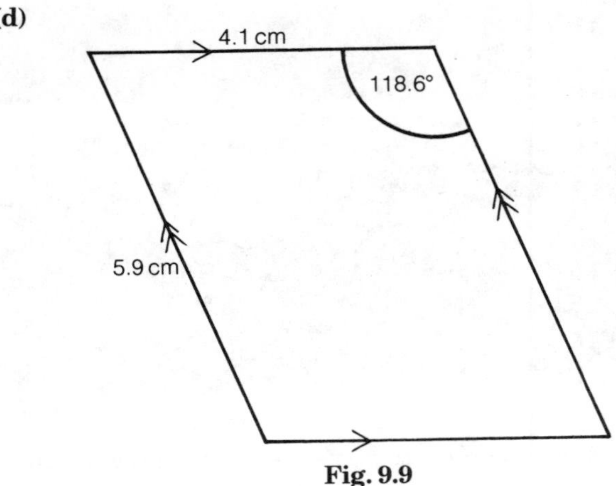

Fig. 9.9

2 Find the areas of the parallelograms in Figs. 9.10–9.13, using the appropriate method.

(a)

7.3 cm
4.7 cm

Fig. 9.10

(b)

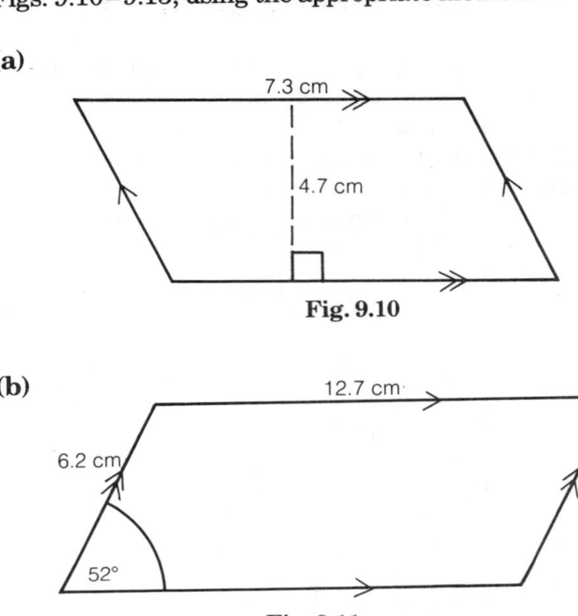

Fig. 9.11

(c)

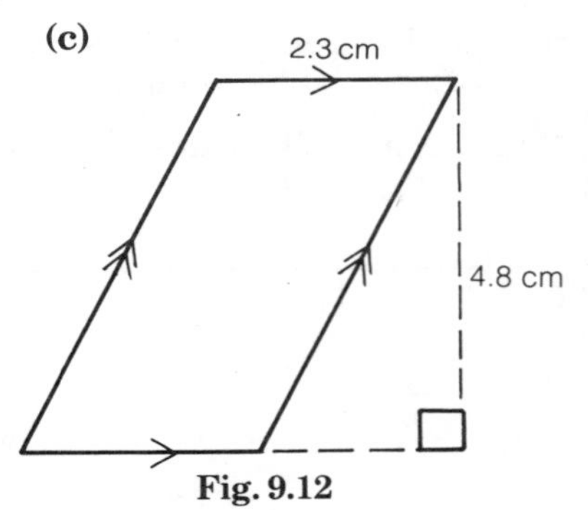

Fig. 9.12

(d)

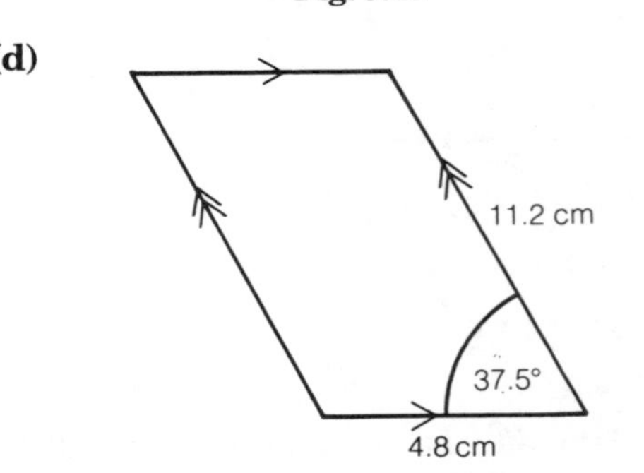

Fig. 9.13

Areas of triangles and parallelograms

In Questions **1–6** (Figs. 9.14–9.19), find the value of the side length marked x cm, in each case.

1

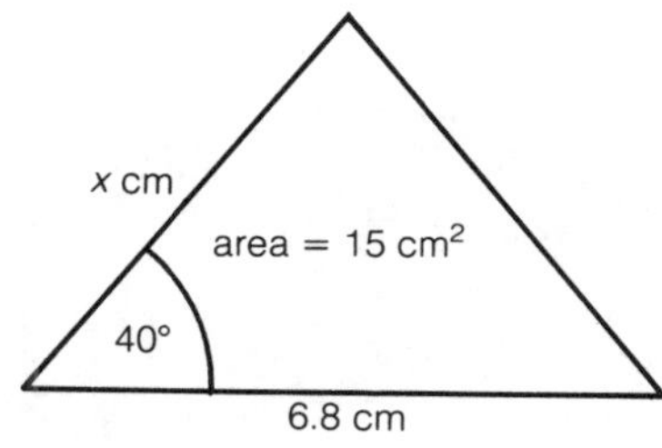

Fig. 9.14

2

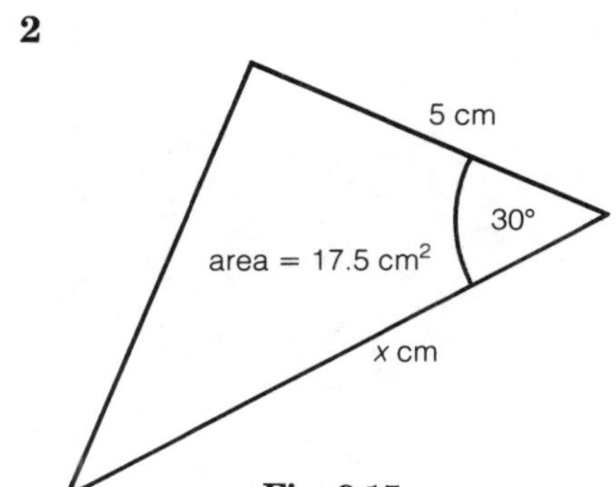

Fig. 9.15

3

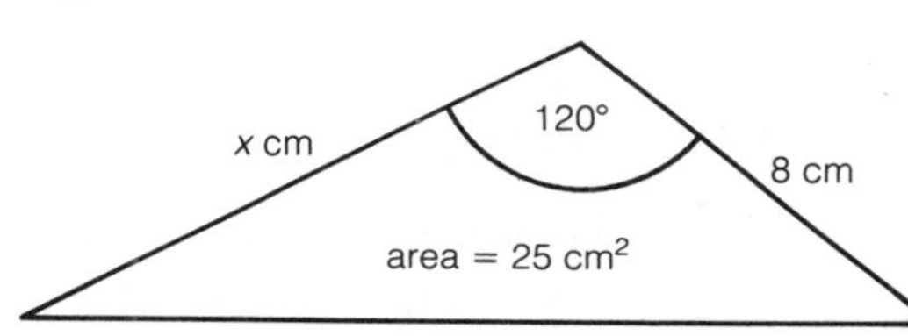

Fig. 9.16

4

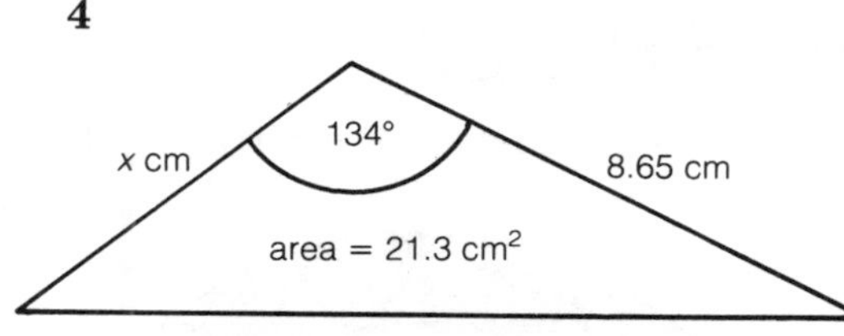

Fig. 9.17

5

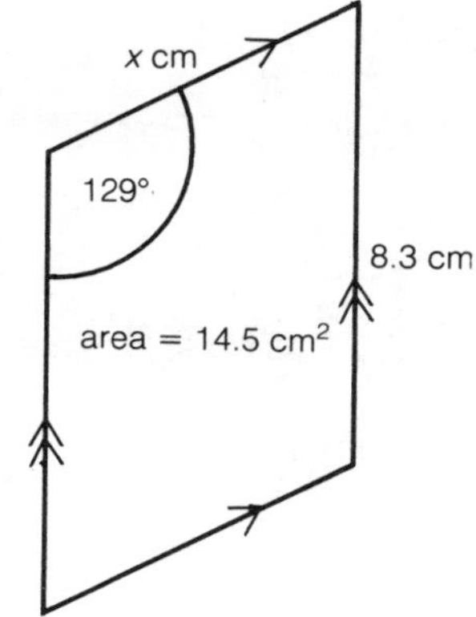

Fig. 9.18

6

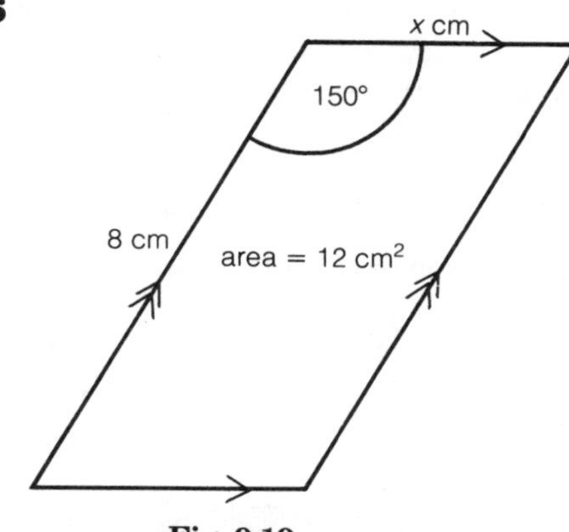

Fig. 9.19

7 Find the area of a triangle ABC, if $AB = 6$ cm, $BC = 7$ cm and $A\widehat{B}C = 34°$.

8 Find the area of a triangle PQR, if $PR = 5.5$ cm, $QR = 6.6$ cm and $P\widehat{R}Q = 128°$.

9 Find the area of a triangle XYZ, with $XY = 6.8$ cm, $XZ = 4.3$ cm and $Y\widehat{X}Z = 63.4°$.

10 Find the area of a triangle with side lengths of 4 cm, 5 cm and 7 cm.

11 Find the area of a triangular field with side lengths of 110 m, 80 m and 140 m.

12 Find the area of a parallelogram $ABCD$ in which $AD = 7$ cm, $DC = 9$ cm and $A\widehat{D}C = 58°$.

13 The area of a parallelogram $ABCD$ is 43 cm^2, $AB = 7$ cm, $BC = 9$ cm. Calculate both the acute angle and the obtuse angle between the two sides.

Unit 10

Circular area

10.1 Introduction

In Volume 2, we were introduced to the area and circumference of a circle. We are now in a position to develop these facts, to enable us to find the areas of rings or washers, arc lengths and sector areas.

10.2 Areas of rings or washers

The area of the shaded part of the circle (called the annulus or ring) can be found by subtracting the area of the inner circle from the area of the outer circle.

Remember, the area of a circle $= \pi r^2$ (where π is a constant value, and r is the radius of the circle).

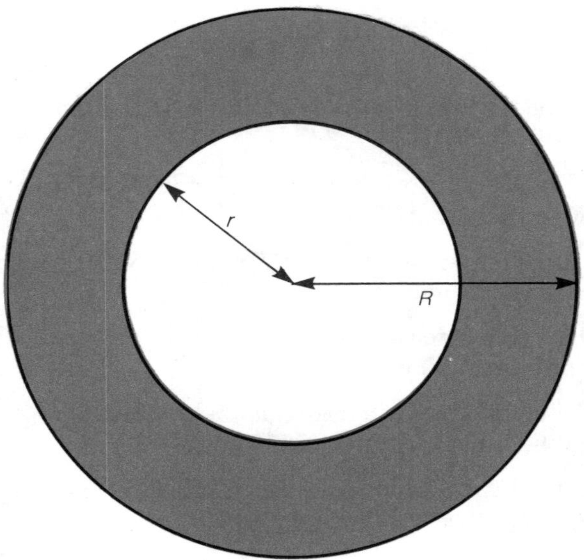

Fig. 10.1

Suppose the radius of the outer circle is R and the radius of the inner circle is r, as shown in Fig. 10.1, then area of ring

= area of outer circle − area of inner circle

Hence, area of ring $= \pi R^2 - \pi r^2$
which we can simplify by factorization (taking out a common factor of π) to give

$$\text{area} = \pi(R^2 - r^2)$$

Example Find the area of a flat washer of outside diameter 4.8 cm and inside diameter 2.2 cm.
(take $\pi = \frac{22}{7}$)

See Fig. 10.2.

Since the diameters of the two circles are given, the first task is to find the respective radii.

This we do by halving the diameters, and hence the radii are 2.4 cm and 1.1 cm, respectively.

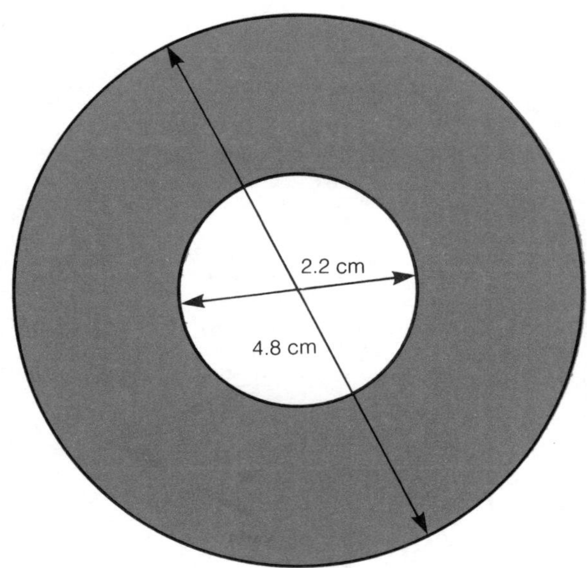

Fig. 10.2

$$\text{area of ring (shaded)} = \pi(R^2 - r^2)$$
$$= \tfrac{22}{7}(2.4^2 - 1.1^2)$$
$$\text{use your calculator} = \tfrac{22}{7}(5.76 - 1.21)$$
$$= \tfrac{22}{7} \times 4.55 = 14.3 \text{ cm}^2$$

Hence, area of washer (shaded part) = 14.3 cm^2

Note It is also possible to find $(2.4^2 - 1.1^2)$ simply by using the 'difference of two squares' principle, as shown in the Algebra section of this Volume.

Activities

1 Find the area of the shaded part in Fig. 10.3 (take $\pi = \frac{22}{7}$)

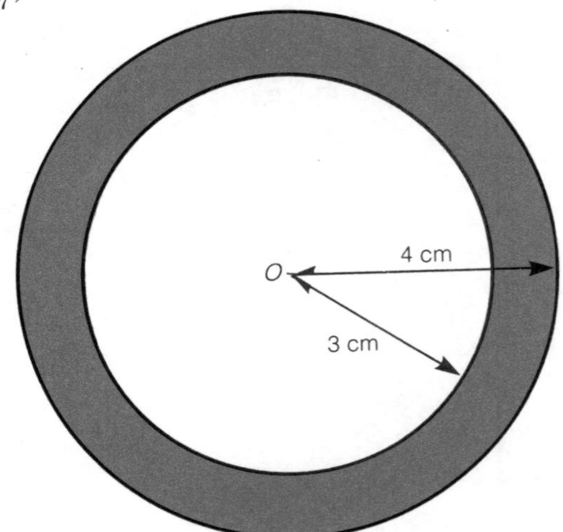

Fig. 10.3

2 Calculate the shaded part in Fig. 10.4 (take $\pi = \frac{22}{7}$)

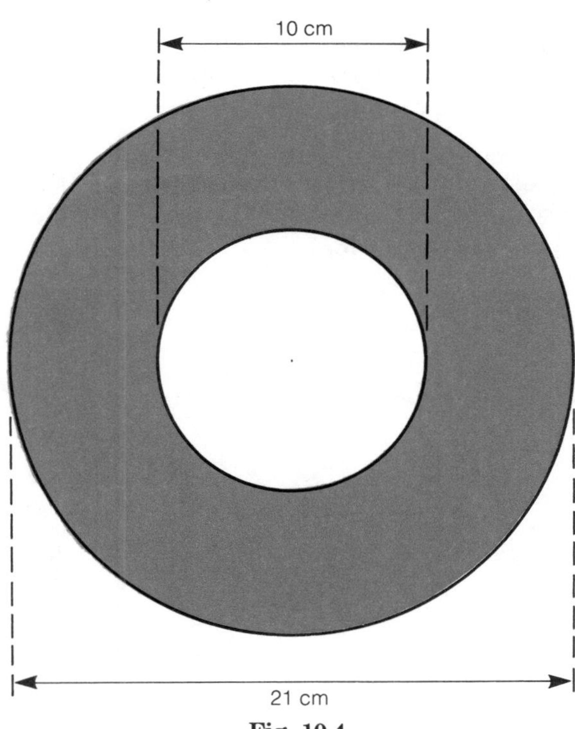

Fig. 10.4

3 Calculate the area of the shaded part in Fig. 10.5 (take $\pi = 3.142$).

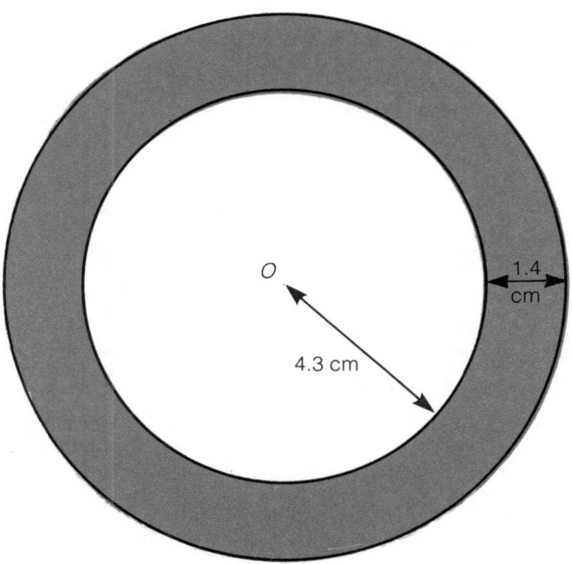

Fig. 10.5

4 A roundabout on a main road is of diameter 140 m and is surrounded by a road 20 m wide all the way round. Taking $\pi = 3.14$, find

(a) the area of the roundabout (centre)
(b) the area of the roadway

5 A metal washer has an outside radius of 5.5 mm and an inside radius of 2.3 mm. Find the area of the metal. Take $\pi = \frac{22}{7}$

6 Fig. 10.6 shows a target. Find, taking $\pi = 3.14$,

(a) the area of the centre (bull's eye, '10')
(b) the area of the '5' ring
(c) the area of the '2' ring
(d) the area of the '1' ring

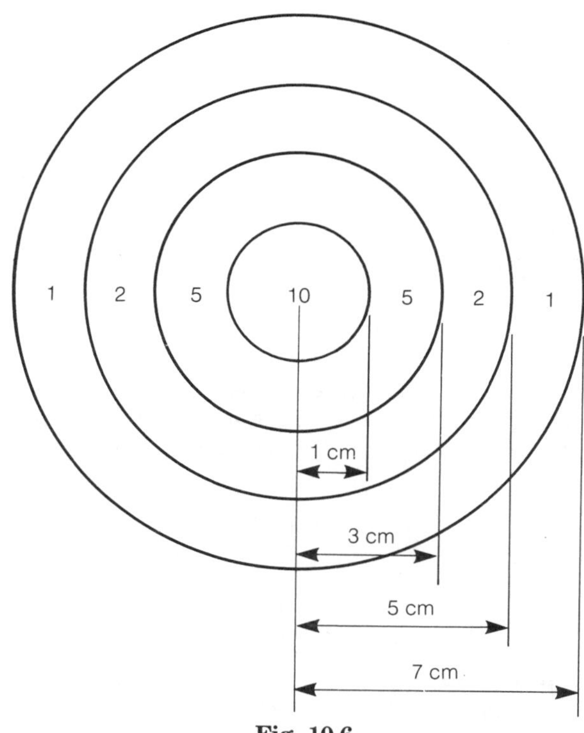

Fig. 10.6

7 Find the area of glass required to fit over the clock face in Fig. 10.7 (i.e. within the surround area). Take $\pi = \frac{22}{7}$

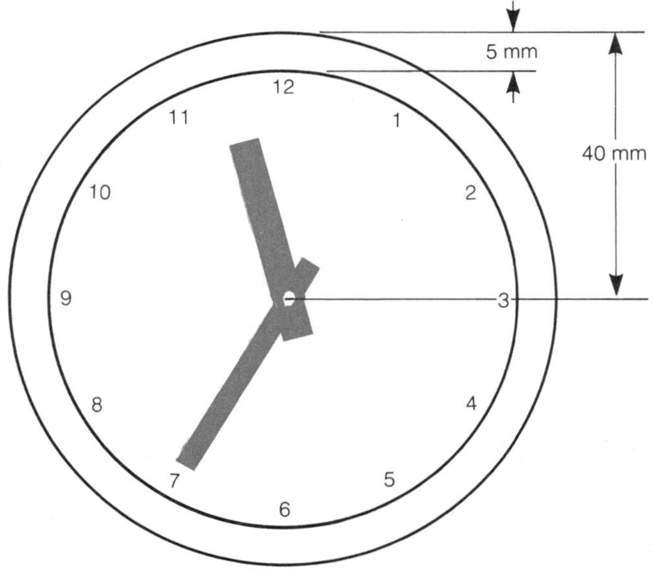

Fig. 10.7

10.3 Arc lengths and sector angles

Arc length is the distance from A to B, around the circumference of a circle, as shown in Fig. 10.8.

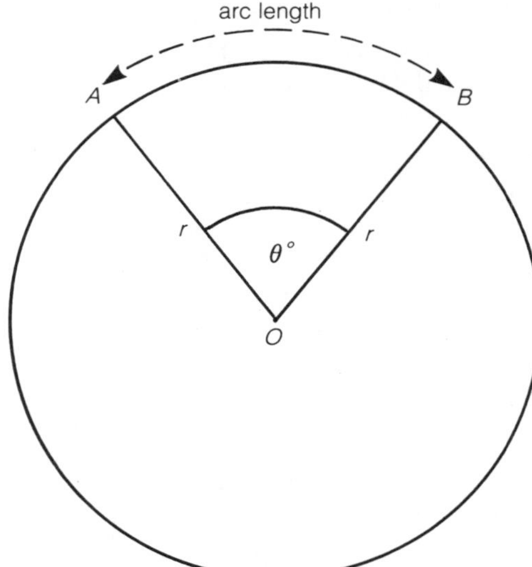

Fig. 10.8

If the angle subtended at the centre O of the circle is $\theta°$, then it is quite logical to assume that the ratio of the arc length to the whole circumference of the circle will be

$$\frac{\theta°}{360°}$$

Hence, arc length $AB = \frac{\theta°}{360°} \times 2\pi r$

(where $2\pi r$ = circumference of the circle)

Example 1 Find the length of the arc AB in the circle shown in Fig. 10.9. Take $\pi = \frac{22}{7}$

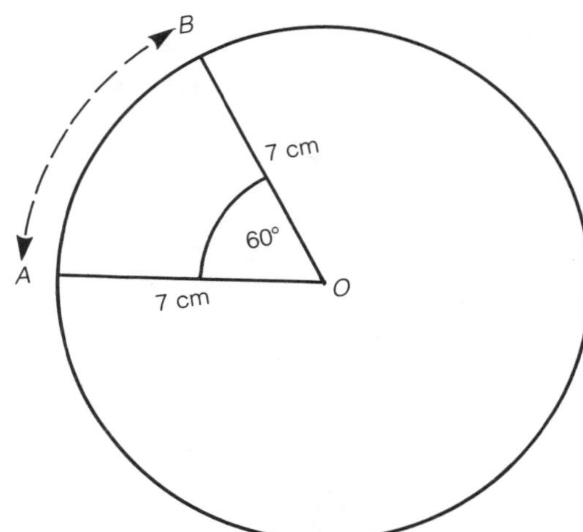

Fig. 10.9

Circumference of circle $= 2\pi r$

$$= 2 \times \tfrac{22}{7} \times 7 = 44 \text{ cm}$$

length of arc $AB = \frac{\theta°}{360°} \times 2\pi r$

In this case, arc length AB

$$= \frac{60°}{360°} \times 44 \text{ cm}$$
$$= \tfrac{1}{6} \times 44$$
$$= 7\tfrac{1}{3} \text{ (or 7.33) cm}$$

Hence, the arc length AB is $7\frac{1}{3}$ cm.

It is, of course, possible to find the angle subtended at the centre by an arc of given length, provided the radius of the circle is also given.

Example 2 Find the angle, α, subtended at the centre of a circle, radius 3.5 cm, by an arc AB of 5 cm length. Take $\pi = \frac{22}{7}$

Firstly draw a diagram, putting on all the given information (see Fig. 10.10). The slice of the circle, AOB, with angle $\alpha°$ at the centre, is a **sector** of the circle. α is the **sector angle**.

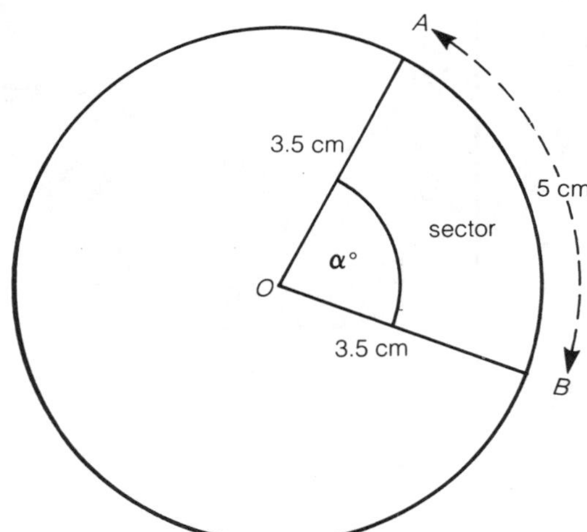

Fig. 10.10

Circumference of circle $= 2\pi r$

$$= 2 \times \tfrac{22}{7} \times 3.5 \text{ cm}$$
$$= 22 \text{ cm}$$

So, $\frac{\alpha°}{360°} = \frac{5}{22}$

Cross-multiply, $22\alpha = 5 \times 360$

$$\alpha = \frac{5 \times 360}{22} = 81.8°$$

Hence, the sector angle, the angle subtended at the centre of the circle by the arc, is 81.8°.

Activities

1 Express each angle, in its simplest form, as a fraction of 360°.

(a) 24° **(f)** 144°
(b) 30° **(g)** 135°
(c) 36° **(h)** 210°
(d) 40° **(i)** 270°
(e) 108° **(j)** 300°

2 Find the length of the arc in each of the following in Table 10.1.

	circumference of circle	sector angle
(a)	180 cm	60°
(b)	200 mm	45°
(c)	400 cm	72°
(d)	16 cm	225°
(e)	60 mm	150°

Table 10.1

3 Find the length of the arc in each of the following in Table 10.2. Take $\pi = 3.14$.

	radius	sector angle
(a)	3 cm	90°
(b)	6 cm	60°
(c)	12 mm	45°
(d)	2.5 cm	180°
(e)	12.5 cm	144°

Table 10.2

4 Find the sector angle for each of the following in Table 10.3.

	arc length	circumference
(a)	9 cm	45 cm
(b)	25 mm	30 mm
(c)	21 cm	36 cm
(d)	16 mm	40 mm
(e)	20 cm	48 cm

Table 10.3

5 Find the sector angle for each of the following.

(a) arc length 11 cm, radius 14 cm (take $\pi = \frac{22}{7}$)

(b) arc length 18.84 mm, radius 9 mm (take $\pi = 3.14$)

10.4 Longitude, and distances between places

Finding the distance between two points on the same line (circle) of longitude on the Earth's surface, is really a practical application of finding the length of an arc.

Lines of **longitude** are imaginary vertical lines, from the North Pole to the South Pole, drawn on maps of the surface of the Earth. They are known as Meridians and indicate whether a place is to the East or to the West of the Greenwich Meridian, which is 0° Longitude.

Lines of **latitude** are imaginary horizontal lines drawn on maps on the Earth's surface. The Equator is 0° Latitude.

By using these lines of longitude and latitude, we can pin-point exact positions on the Earth's surface (in a similar manner to using co-ordinates).

Note Latitude is always given first.

We can find the distance between places on the same circle of longitude.

Example The position of Tokyo is given as Latitude 36°N, Longitude 139°E (36°N, 139°E).
The position of Adelaide is given as (34°S, 139°E).
The distance between Tokyo and Adelaide can be determined by finding the arc length of the line of longitude which subtends an angle of 70° at the Earth's centre (see Fig. 10.11).

Given that the radius of the Earth is 6300 km and $\pi = 3.142$,

$$\text{arc length} = \frac{70°}{360°} \times 2\pi r$$
$$= \frac{70}{360} \times 2 \times 3.142 \times 6300$$
$$= 7698 \text{ km}$$

Hence the approximate distance between Tokyo and Adelaide is 7698 km.

Note The answer will be approximate only, because we have assumed that the Earth is a sphere (i.e. that its radius is a constant).

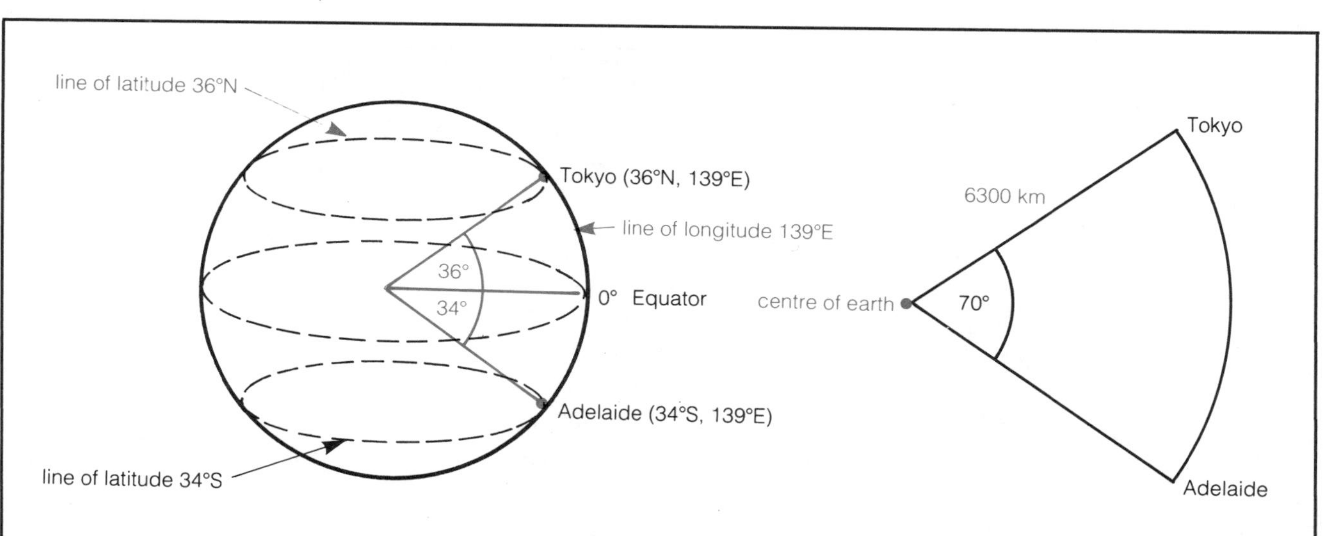

Fig. 10.11

Activities

1 Find the distance, to the nearest km, between each pair of cities in Table 10.4, lying on the same circle of longitude. Take $\pi = 3.142$ and the radius of the Earth to be 6300 km.

	City	Position
(a)	Moscow	(55°N, 37°E)
	Nairobi	(1°S, 37°E)
(b)	Boston	(42°N, 71°W)
	Santiago	(33°S, 71°W)
(c)	Budapest	(47°N, 19°E)
	Cape Town	(33°S, 19°E)
(d)	Leningrad	(60°N, 29°E)
	Johannesburg	(24°S, 29°E)
(e)	Buffalo	(42°N, 78°W)
	Lima	(12°S, 78°W)

Table 10.4

2 Find the distance, to the nearest km, between each pair of cities, in Table 10.5, lying on the same circle of longitude. Take $\pi = 3.142$ and the radius of the Earth to be 6300 km.

Note You will see below that, in each pair, the cities are in the same hemisphere. In order to find the angle subtended at the centre of the Earth, you must firstly **subtract** the latitudes, rather than adding them as we did in Question **1**.

	City	Position
(a)	Winnipeg	(49°N, 98°W)
	Mexico City	(19°N, 98°W)
(b)	Oslo	(60°N, 11°E)
	Bologna	(45°N, 11°E)
(c)	Prague	(50°N, 14°E)
	Naples	(41°N, 14°E)
(d)	London	(51°N, 0°)
	Accra	(6°N, 0°)
(e)	Durban	(30°S, 31°E)
	Salisbury	(18°S, 31°E)

Table 10.5

10.5 Sector area

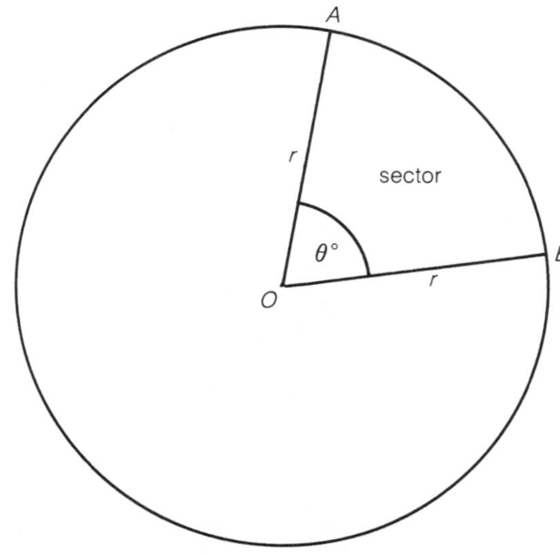

Fig. 10.12

Fig. 10.12 shows a sector of a circle. As was the case with arc length, we again use the ratio of the part compared with the whole. This time, however, we use area rather than circumference.

Hence, a sector area will be $\frac{\theta°}{360°}$ of πr^2

(πr^2 being the total area of the circle)

Example Find the area of a sector of a circle of radius 7 cm, subtending an angle of 72° at the centre of the circle. Take $\pi = 3.142$.

Draw a diagram, as in Fig. 10.13, putting in all the relevant information.

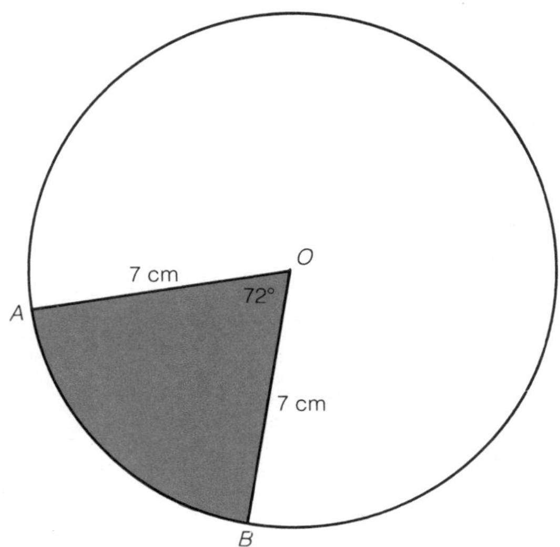

Fig. 10.13

area of circle $= \pi r^2$
$= 3.142 \times 7 \times 7 = 154 \text{ cm}^2$

The angle subtended at the centre is 72°, so area of sector is $\frac{72}{360}$ of the area of the whole circle.

Hence, area of sector $AOB = \frac{72}{360} \times 154 = 30.8 \text{ cm}^2$

Activities

Sector area problems

1 Find the sector areas of the following, in Table 10.6.

	area of circle	sector angle
(a)	112 cm^2	45°
(b)	135 mm^2	40°
(c)	60 cm^2	210°
(d)	32 cm^2	135°
(e)	45 mm^2	240°

Table 10.6

2 Find the sector angle of each of the following, in Table 10.7.

area of sector	area of circle
(a) 15 cm^2	50 cm^2
(b) 3 mm^2	45 mm^2
(c) 49 mm^2	84 mm^2
(d) 14 mm^2	168 mm^2
(e) 40 cm^2	96 cm^2

Table 10.7

3 Find the areas of the sectors of the following, in Table 10.8. Take $\pi = \frac{22}{7}$

radius of circle	sector angle
(a) 70 mm	72°
(b) 21 cm	40°
(c) 7 cm	180°
(d) 14 cm	90°
(e) 21 cm	60°

Table 10.8

4 Find the area of the sector of each of the following, in Table 10.9. Take $\pi = 3.142$

radius of circle	sector angle
(a) 2 mm	135°
(b) 2 cm	270°
(c) 3 cm	40°
(d) 6 cm	60°
(e) 2 mm	45°

Table 10.9

5 Find the area of a sector of a circle of radius 7 cm if the sector angle is 36°. Take $\pi = \frac{22}{7}$

Arc length and sector area problems

1 Find **(a)** the arc length AB and **(b)** the sector area AOB in Fig. 10.14. Take $\pi = 3.142$

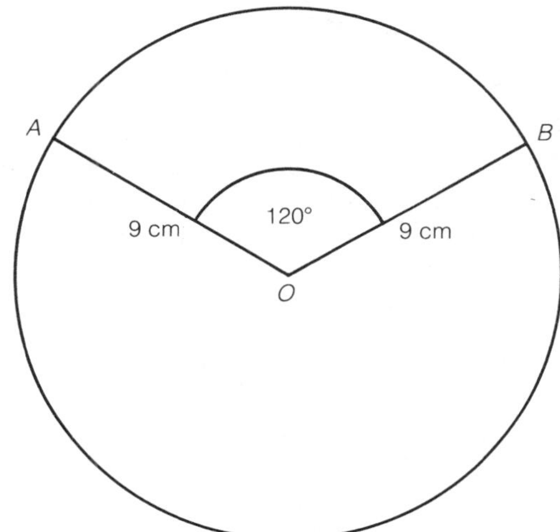

Fig. 10.14

2 In Fig. 10.15, the radius of the steering wheel is 30 cm. Take $\pi = 3.142$. Find,

(a) arc length AB **(c)** sector area AOB
(b) arc length AC **(d)** sector area AOC

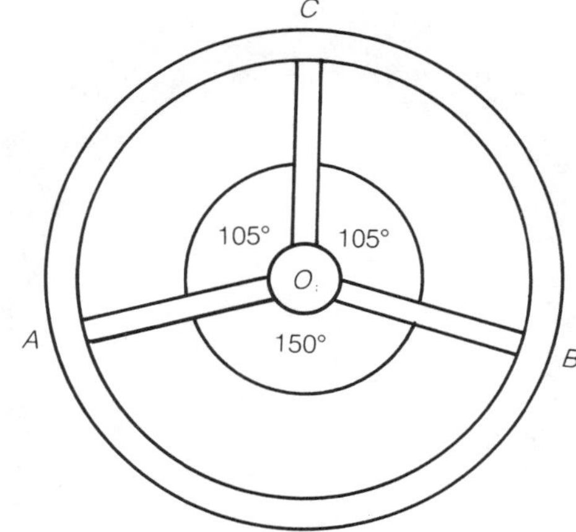

Fig. 10.15

3 In Fig. 10.16, calculate the angle $\theta°$, subtended at the centre by the arc XY. Take $\pi = \frac{22}{7}$

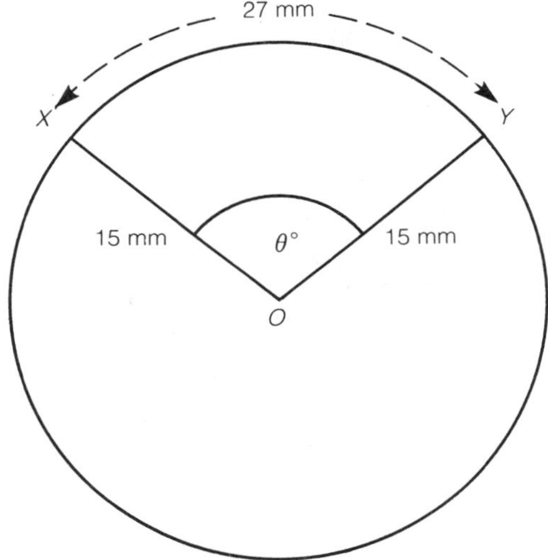

Fig. 10.16

4 How far will the tip of the long hand of a clock, of radius 11 cm, travel in 37 minutes? Take $\pi = 3.142$

5 What is the sector angle subtended by an arc of length 21 cm, in a circle of radius 14 cm? Take $\pi = \frac{22}{7}$

6 Taking π as 3.142, calculate the area of the shaded part in Fig. 10.17.

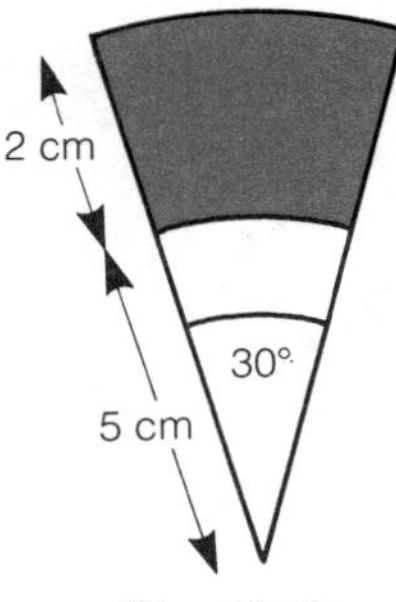

Fig. 10.17

7 Taking π as 3.142, calculate the area of the shaded part in Fig. 10.18.

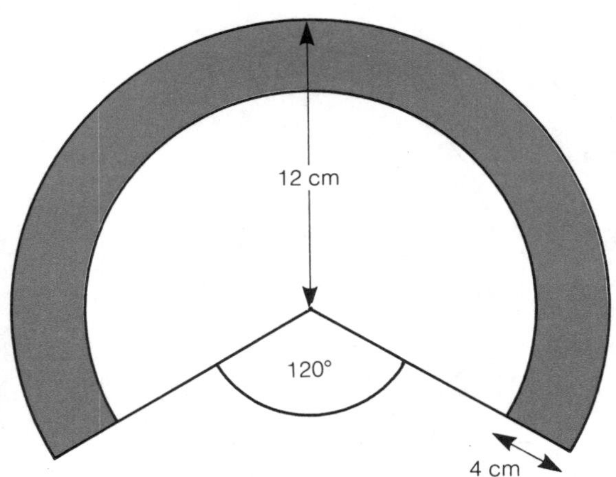

Fig. 10.18

8 Calculate the radius of the sector in Fig. 10.19, taking π as $\frac{22}{7}$

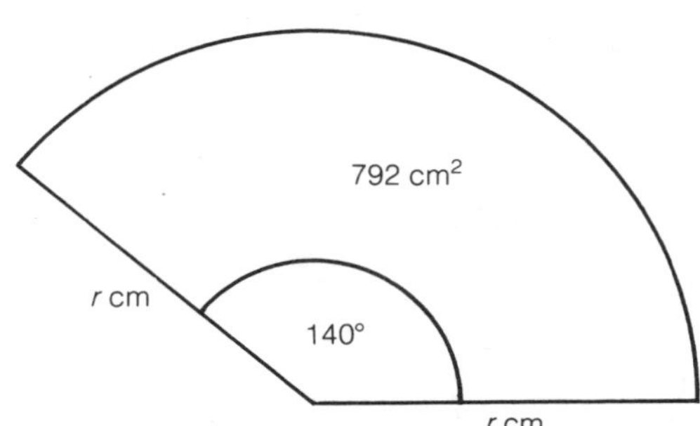

Fig. 10.19

Unit 11

The cylinder

11.1 Volume of a cylinder

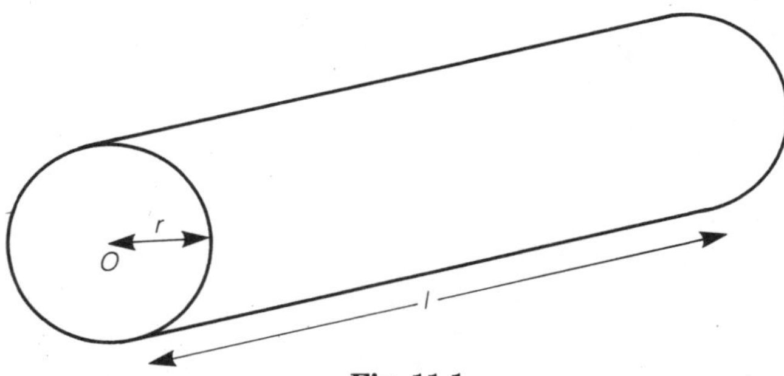

Fig. 11.1

As we saw in Volume 2, the volume of any solid with uniform cross-section throughout its length is simply the end area multiplied by its length.

The cylinder certainly has uniform cross-section, see Fig. 11.1, and so

$$\begin{aligned}\text{volume of cylinder} &= \text{end area} \times \text{length}\\ &= \pi r^2 \times l\\ &= \pi r^2 l\end{aligned}$$

When the cylinder is standing vertically, l becomes its height, h, and its volume is written as $\pi r^2 h$.

Example A cylindrical bar is 8.5 cm long with a cross-sectional diameter of 3.5 cm. Find the volume of the bar. Take $\pi = 3.142$.

Firstly, draw a diagram of the bar including the dimensions given, as in Fig. 11.2.

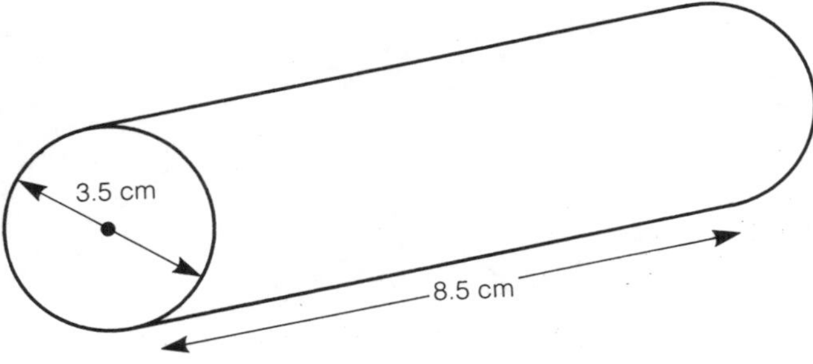

Fig. 11.2

Remember, diameter = 3.5 cm
hence radius = 1.75 cm

$$\begin{aligned}\text{volume of cylinder} &= \text{end area} \times \text{length}\\ &= \pi r^2 \times l\\ &= 3.142 \times 1.75 \times 1.75 \times 8.5\\ &= 81.8 \text{ cm}^3\end{aligned}$$

Hence, the volume of the cylindrical bar is 81.8 cm^3.

11.2 Surface area of a cylinder

The area of the curved surface of a cylinder can best be seen by imagining a cut along the dotted line AB, opening the shape out and flattening it into a rectangular shape, as shown in Fig. 11.3.

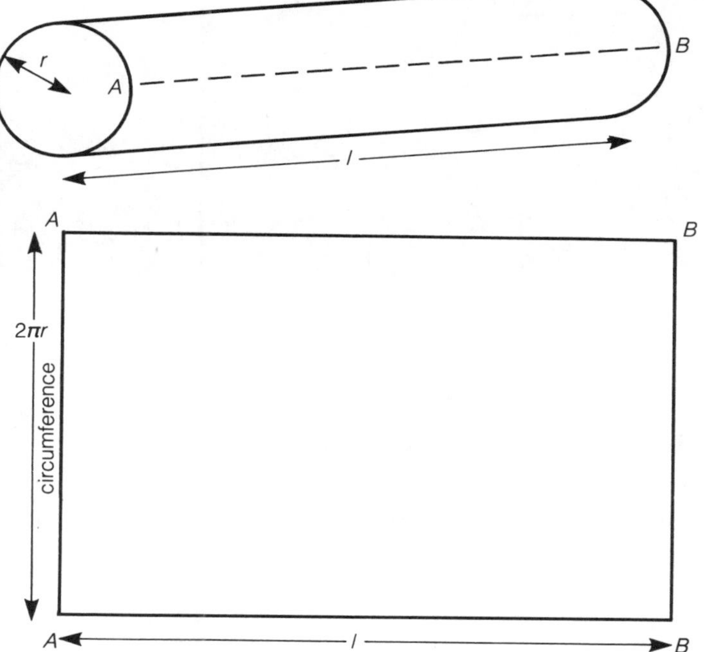

Fig. 11.3

Since the area of the surface is rectangular, the area of the rectangle is length × breadth and hence, the curved surface area of the cylinder

$$= 2\pi r \times l = 2\pi rl \text{ units}^2$$

If the cylinder has a base but no top, see Fig. 11.4, then its total surface area is the curved surface area (as above) plus one end area,

$$= 2\pi rl + \pi r^2$$

This may be factorized as $\pi r(2l + r)$

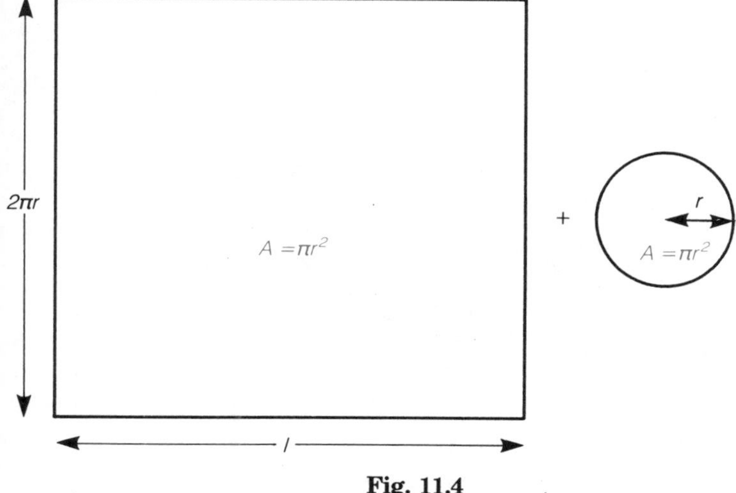

Fig. 11.4

If the cylinder has both a base and a top, see Fig. 11.5, then the total surface area is the curved surface area plus two end areas,

$$=2\pi rl + 2\pi r^2$$

This may be factorized as $2\pi r(l + r)$

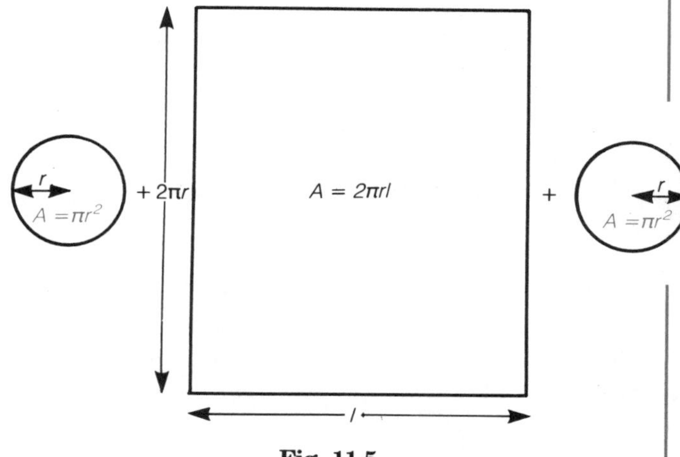

Fig. 11.5

Example Find the total surface area of a cylindrical can, 14 cm diameter and 20 cm deep, having a base but no lid. Also, find its capacity (volume). Take $\pi = \frac{22}{7}$

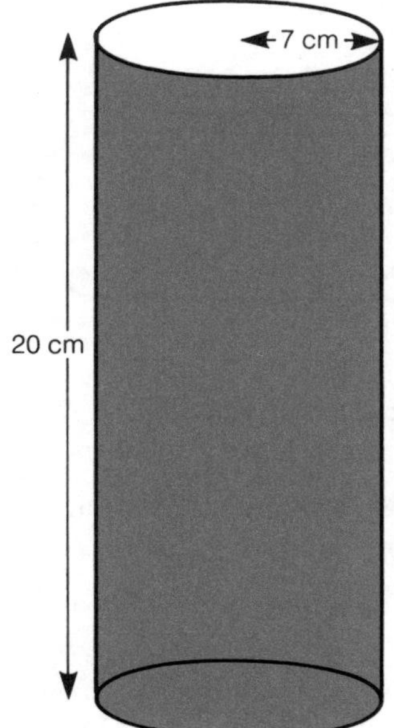

Fig. 11.6

See Fig. 11.6.

diameter = 14 cm

so, radius = 7 cm

Total surface area = curved surface area + area of one end

$$= 2\pi rl + \pi r^2$$
$$= \pi r(2l + r)$$
$$= 3.142 \times 7(2 \times 20 + 7)$$
$$= 3.142 \times 7 \times 47$$
$$= 1033.7 \text{ cm}^2$$

Hence, the total surface area of the can is approximately 1034 cm^2

volume of the can = end area × length

$$= \pi r^2 \times h$$
$$= 3.142 \times 7 \times 7 \times 20 \text{ cm}^3$$
$$= 3080 \text{ cm}^3$$

Hence, the capacity of the can is 3.08 litres.

Activities

Volumes and surface areas of cylinders

1 Find **(a)** the volume
(b) the curved surface area
of the cylinder shown in Fig. 11.7. Take $\pi = \frac{22}{7}$

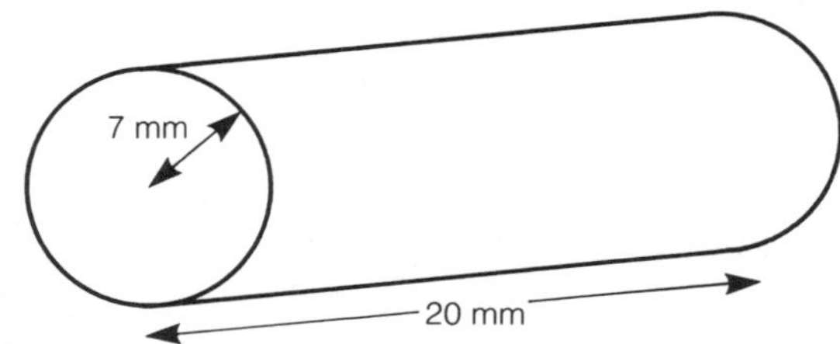

Fig. 11.7

2 Find the volume and the total surface area of the cylinder shown in Fig. 11.8. It is closed at one end. Take $\pi = 3.14$.

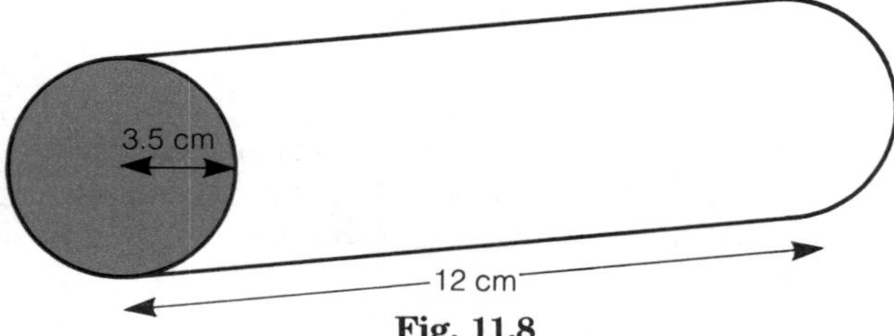

Fig. 11.8

3 Find the volume and the total surface area of the cylinder in Fig. 11.9. It is closed at both ends. Take $\pi = 3.142$.

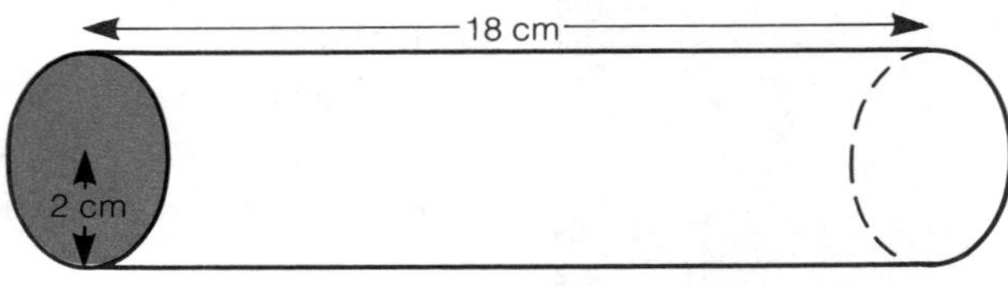

Fig. 11.9

4 A cylindrical coffee tin is 18 cm high and has a diameter of 15 cm. Find its volume. Take $\pi = 3.14$.

5 A cylinder of radius 8 cm has a volume of 2930 cm^3. Find the height of the cylinder. Take $\pi = 3.14$.

6 Find the volume of the semi-circular prism shown in Fig. 11.10. π is taken as $\frac{22}{7}$

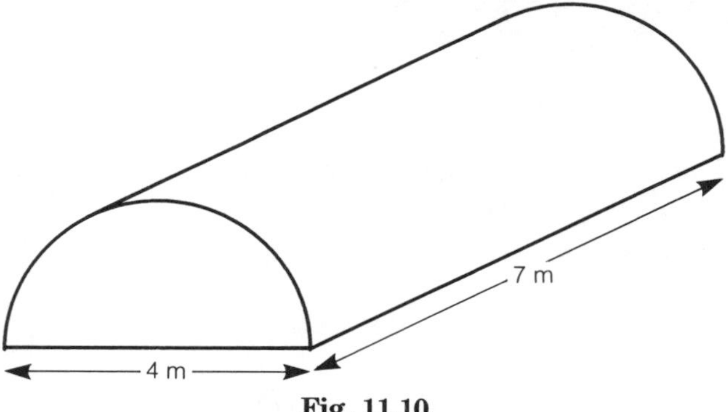

Fig. 11.10

7 Find the total surface area of the prism in Question **6**, assuming it to be solid. Take $\pi = \frac{22}{7}$

Hint Remember to include the base.

8 The diagram in Fig. 11.11 shows the dimensions of a stair rod. Find its volume. Take $\pi = \frac{22}{7}$

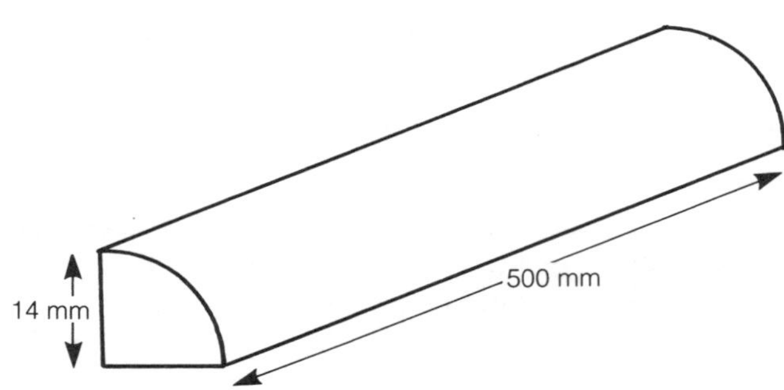

Fig. 11.11

9 Use the dimensions shown in Question **8**, to find the total surface area of the rod. Take $\pi = \frac{22}{7}$

10 Fig. 11.12 illustrates a greenhouse.

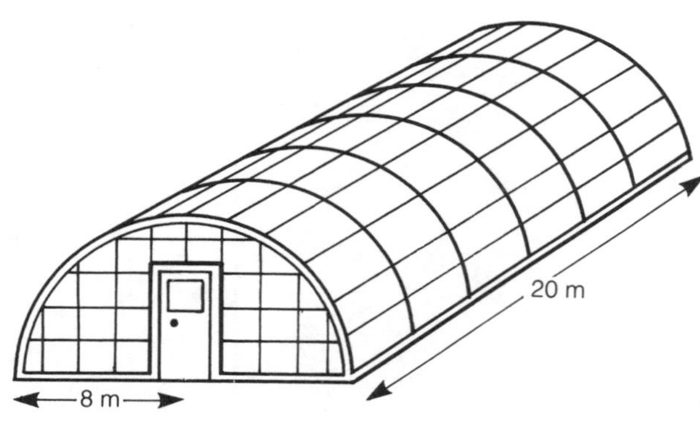

Fig. 11.12

Calculate, taking $\pi = 3.142$,

(a) the volume of the greenhouse

(b) the surface area of the glass (assuming the door to be glass)

Unit 12

Volume, density and mass

Having found the volume of a particular solid shape, we can easily find its **mass** if we know the density of the material from which it is made.

The **density** is simply a measure of the mass of the material per unit of volume of the material. Usually it is given in grams per cubic centimetre (i.e. g/cm^3).

The connection between mass, volume and density is given as

$$\text{mass} = \text{volume} \times \text{density}$$

Consider the Example in Unit 11.1, of the cylindrical bar (refer to Fig. 11.2). Suppose the metal from which the bar is made has a density of 9.5 g/cm^3.

We found that its volume is 81.8 cm^3, so the mass of the bar

$$= 81.8 \times 9.5 \text{ g}$$
$$= 777.1 \text{ g}$$

Activities

1 A wooden block in the shape of a cuboid has dimensions of 1.5 m × 1 m × 60 cm. Calculate the mass of the block if the density of the wood is 0.5 g/cm^3. (Be careful with units of volume.)

2 A solid cylinder of radius 5 cm and height 9 cm, is made of metal of density 8 g/cm^3. Find the mass of the cylinder correct to the nearest 10 g. Take $\pi = 3.14$.

3 What is the mass, in kilograms, of a cylindrical brass bar, 5 m long and 28 mm in diameter, if the density of brass is 8.5 g/cm^3. Take $\pi = \frac{22}{7}$

Hint Change the dimensions to cm, in order to find the volume.

4 A solid concrete cylinder is used as a road bollard. It is 1 m long and 56 cm in diameter. Calculate its volume in m^3 and hence find its mass, if one cubic metre of concrete has a mass of 2050 kg.
Take $\pi = 3.142$.

5 An iron pipe is of rectangular cross-section as shown in Fig. 12.1, the iron being of 2 cm thickness. Find the mass of a 2 m length of the pipe, given that the density of cast iron is 7.2 g/cm^3.

Hint Find the volume of cast iron, by taking the interior volume from the exterior volume.

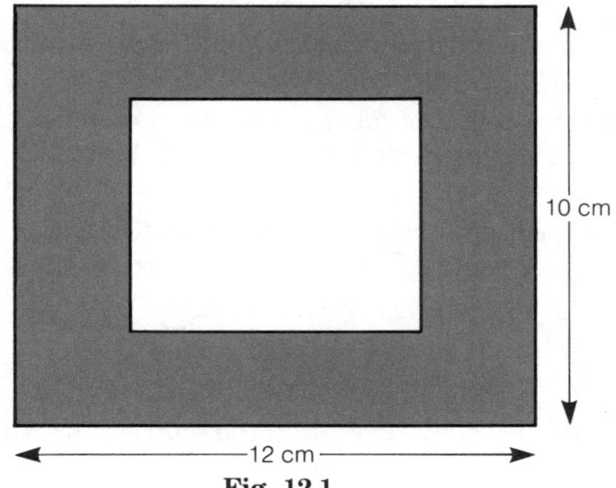

Fig. 12.1

Unit 13

The cone and the pyramid

13.1 Volume of a cone

Fig. 13.1 shows a right-circular cone.

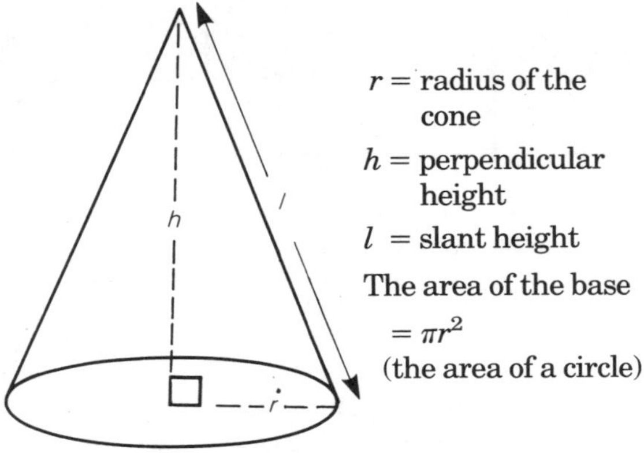

r = radius of the cone

h = perpendicular height

l = slant height

The area of the base
$= \pi r^2$
(the area of a circle)

Fig. 13.1

The volume of the cone is one third of the base area × the perpendicular height.

Hence, volume $= \frac{1}{3}\pi r^2 h$

13.2 Curved surface area of a cone

The curved surface area of a right-circular cone $= \pi rl$

The **slant height**, l, can be calculated, if not given, from the radius of the base and the perpendicular height – using Pythagoras' Theorem (Volume 2, Unit 23.2).

If the cone is solid, then the total surface area will be the curved surface area plus the area of the base.

Hence, total surface area of a cone

$= \pi rl + \pi r^2$

$= \pi r(l + r)$ when factorized.

Example Find the volume and total surface area of a solid right-circular cone of radius 3 cm and vertical height 4 cm. Take $\pi = 3.142$.

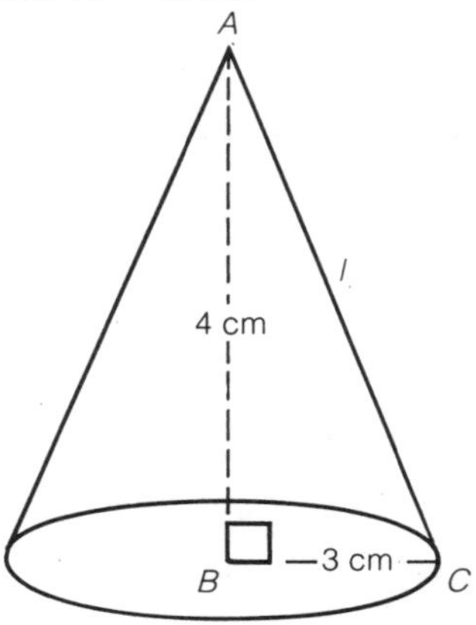

Fig. 13.2

See Fig. 13.2.

volume of cone $= \frac{1}{3}\pi r^2 h$

$= \frac{1}{3} \times 3.142 \times 3 \times 3 \times 4$

$= 37.7\ \text{cm}^3$

surface area of cone = curved surface area + base area

$= \pi rl + \pi r^2$

Since $\triangle ABC$ is a 3-4-5 right-angled triangle (proof by Pythagoras' Theorem),

$l = 5$ cm

Hence, total surface area of cone

$= 3.142 \times 3 \times 5 + 3.142 \times 3 \times 3$

$= 75.41\ \text{cm}^2$

13.3 Volume of a pyramid

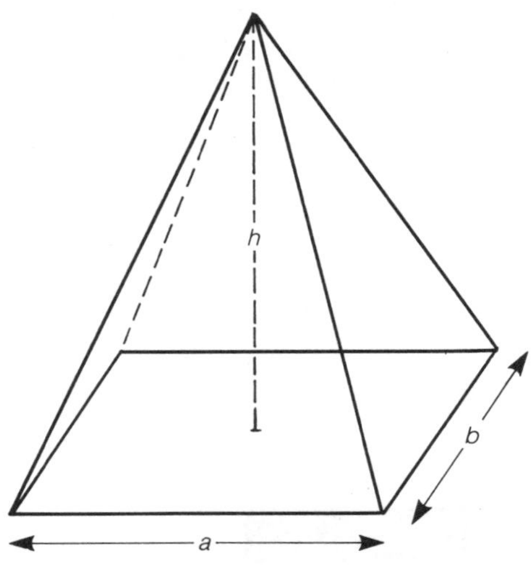

Fig. 13.3

The volume of a pyramid is also one third of the base area × the perpendicular height.

See Fig. 13.3. In this case, for a rectangular-based pyramid,

volume of pyramid $= \frac{1}{3} \times a \times b \times h$

$= \frac{1}{3}abh$

If the base is square, it is even easier to find the volume of the pyramid.

Note If the surface area were required, this could be found by finding the total areas of the triangular faces plus the area of the base.

Activities

Cones and pyramids, volume and surface area

1 Find the volume of a cone of radius 3 cm and perpendicular height 7 cm. Take $\pi = \frac{22}{7}$

2 Find the volume of a cone of radius 20 mm and perpendicular height 60 mm. Take $\pi = 3.142$.

3 Fig. 13.4 shows a solid right-circular cone of radius 5 cm and vertical height 12 cm. Find, taking $\pi = 3.14$,

(a) the slant height, l cm

(b) the curved surface area of the cone

(c) the total surface area of the cone
(d) the volume of the cone

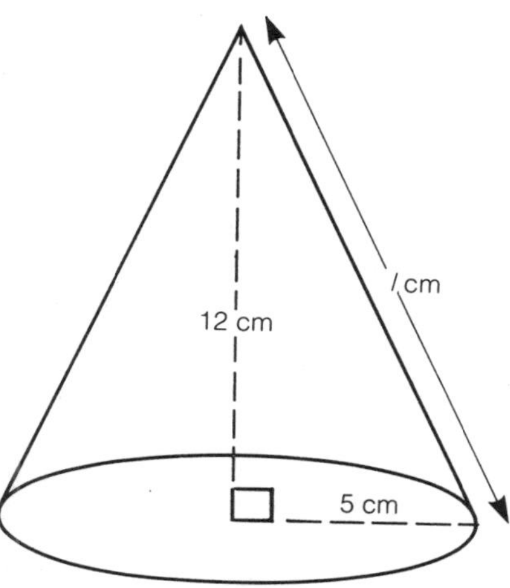

Fig. 13.4

4 A pyramid stands on a base 6 cm square. Find the volume of the pyramid if its perpendicular height is 8.2 cm.

5 A solid pyramid stands on a base 12 cm square. If its perpendicular height is 8 cm, find its volume and its total surface area (including the base).

6 Find the volume of a pyramid standing on a rectangular base measuring 8.5 cm × 6.5 cm, if its perpendicular height is 10.5 cm.

7 Calculate, **(a)** the volume, **(b)** the total surface area, of a solid right-circular cone of base diameter 4 cm and perpendicular height 6 cm. Take $\pi = 3.142$.

Unit 14

The sphere

14.1 Volume of a sphere

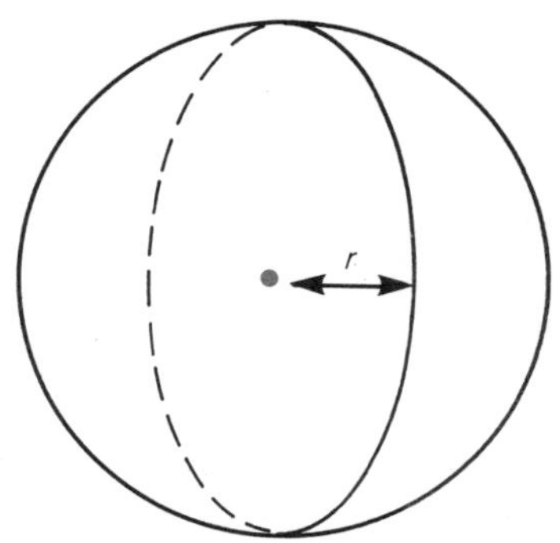

Fig. 14.1

See Fig. 14.1
The volume of a sphere is given as $\frac{4}{3}\pi r^3$

14.2 Surface area of a sphere

The surface area of a sphere is given as $4\pi r^2$.

Example Find the volume and surface area of a sphere of radius 7 cm. Take $\pi = \frac{22}{7}$

$$\text{volume} = \tfrac{4}{3}\pi r^3$$
$$= \tfrac{4}{3} \times \tfrac{22}{7} \times 7 \times 7 \times 7$$
$$= 1437.3 \text{ cm}^3$$

$$\text{surface area} = 4\pi r^2$$
$$= 4 \times \tfrac{22}{7} \times 7 \times 7$$
$$= 616 \text{ cm}^2$$

Activities

Spheres and hemispheres, volume and surface area

1 Taking $\pi = \frac{22}{7}$, find the volume of,
(a) a ball of radius 14 cm
(b) a snowball of radius 10 cm
(c) a scoop of ice-cream of diameter 4 cm
(d) a pompon of diameter 8 cm
(e) a balloon of radius 28 cm

2 Taking $\pi = \frac{22}{7}$, find the surface area of,
(a) a ball of radius 3.5 cm
(b) a balloon of radius 7 cm
(c) a ball of putty of radius 10.5 cm
(d) a squash ball of diameter 4 cm
(e) a cricket ball of diameter 8.75 cm

3 Find the volume and surface area of the sphere shown in Fig. 14.2. Take $\pi = 3.14$.

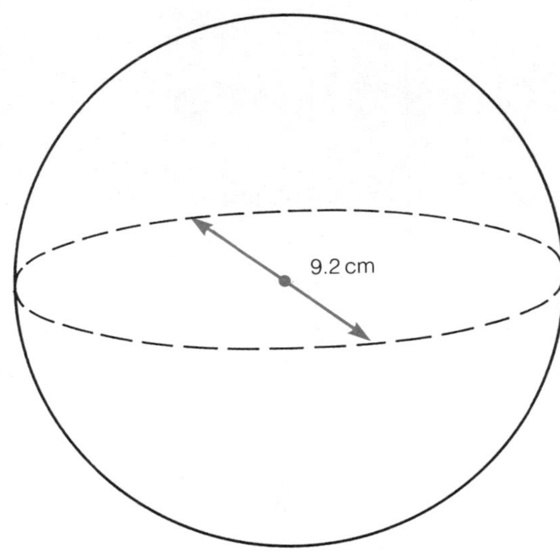

Fig. 14.2

4 Find, **(a)** the volume and **(b)** the surface area of the solid hemisphere shown in Fig. 14.3. Take $\pi = 3.142$.

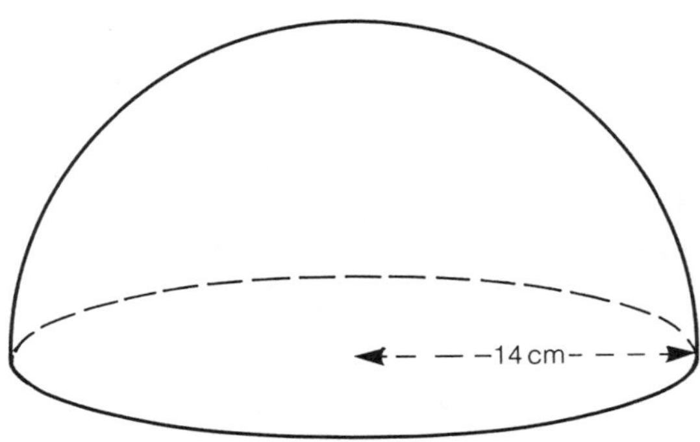

Fig. 14.3

Hint Volume of hemisphere = $\frac{1}{2}$ volume of sphere. Also, remember that this hemisphere has a base.

5 Find the volume of water contained in a full hemispherical bowl of radius 5.5 cm. Take $\pi = 3.14$ and give your answer correct to the nearest cm^3.

Volume and surface area – more examples

1 Calculate the total surface area of the 'non-topple' toy shown in Fig. 14.4. Take $\pi = 3.14$.

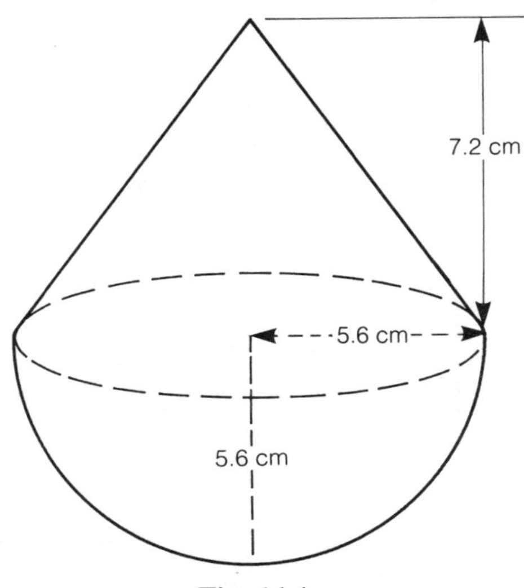

Fig. 14.4

2 What is the total volume of the cylinder with the hemispherical end, as shown in Fig. 14.5? Take $\pi = 3.142$.

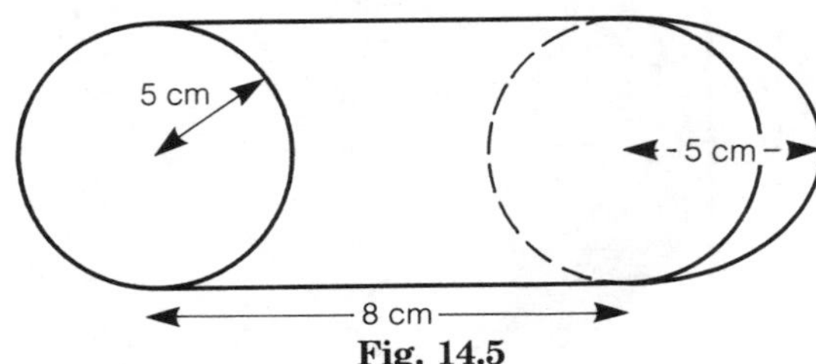

Fig. 14.5

3 Fig. 14.6 shows a cylindrical pipe.

(a) What is the volume of metal in this cylindrical pipe? (Take $\pi = \frac{22}{7}$)

(b) If the metal has a density of 7.8 g/cm^3. What will be the mass of the pipe?

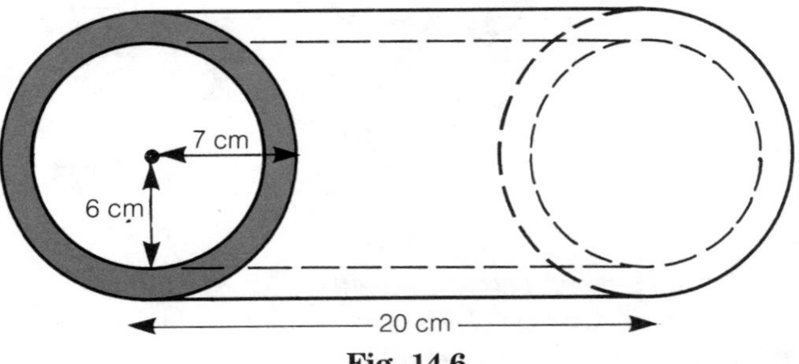

Fig. 14.6

4 Calculate the volume of a lead shot, if its radius is 6.8 cm. Find also its mass, if lead has a density of 12.3 g/cm^3. Take $\pi = 3.14$.

5 A cylinder and a sphere have equal volumes. Given that the radius of each is 30 cm, calculate the length of the cylinder. Take $\pi = 3.142$.

Unit 15

Distance, speed and time

A speed of 100 kilometres per hour (100 km/h) shown on the speedometer of a vehicle would mean that, if the vehicle were to keep up that speed for one hour, it would cover a distance of 100 km. In 30 minutes it would cover 50 km and in 15 minutes it would cover 25 km etc.

However, unless the vehicle were on a motorway throughout its journey, it is unlikely that it would be able to keep to a constant speed.

We can easily find the average speed for a journey, by dividing the total distance travelled by the total time taken.

$$\text{Hence, average speed} = \frac{\text{total distance travelled}}{\text{total time taken}}$$

Note We must make sure that the units are compatible, because speed is usually expressed in km/h or m/s and so we would want to avoid unlikely units of speed such as m/min, or cm/h etc.

Example 1 A lorry driver covers 300 km in 6 hours. What is the average speed for his journey?

$$\text{average speed} = \frac{300\text{ km}}{6\text{ hours}}$$

$$= 50\text{ km/h for the journey}$$

Example 2 A family drives 80 km in $1\frac{1}{2}$ hours and stops for a meal for an hour. It then completes the final 60 km in 1 hour. Find the average speed for the journey.

Total distance travelled $= 80 + 60 = 140$ km

Total time taken for the journey

$$= 1\tfrac{1}{2} + 1 + 1 = 3\tfrac{1}{2}\text{ hours}$$

$$\text{average speed} = \frac{140\text{ km}}{3.5\text{ hours}}$$

$$= 40\text{ km/h for the journey}$$

It is, of course, possible to find the distance travelled, given the speed and the time taken.

Example 3 A walker averaged 6 km/h on a weekend ramble. How far did he travel in $3\frac{1}{2}$ hours?

He walked 6 km in 1 hour, so in $3\frac{1}{2}$ hours he walked

$$6 \times 3\tfrac{1}{2}\text{ km} = 21\text{ km}$$

As we would expect,

distance travelled = average speed × time

$$\text{or, time taken} = \frac{\text{distance travelled}}{\text{average speed}}$$

Activities

1 A car is driven on a motorway at an average speed of 120 km/h. Find how far it will travel in,

(a) $\frac{1}{2}$ hour **(b)** 20 minutes **(c)** 12 minutes
(d) 30 seconds **(e)** $2\frac{1}{4}$ hours

2 A coach travels 360 km in 4 hours. What is its average speed for the journey?

3 Ted the tortoise travels 4 m in 10 minutes. Calculate his average speed in cm/second. (Be very careful with the units.)

4 A car travels 150 km at an average speed of 60 km/h. How long does it take to complete its journey?

5 A train covers the first 100 km of its journey in $1\frac{1}{2}$ hours and then covers the final 160 km in $2\frac{1}{2}$ hours. What will be its average speed for the whole journey?

6 A motorcyclist starts his journey in a large city and takes one hour, at an average speed of 26 km/h, to reach the city boundary. He then continues his journey for a further 2 hours at an average speed of 80 km/h. Calculate,

(a) how far he rode altogether,
(b) the average speed for the whole journey.

7 The members of a family set out in their car for a circular day-tour. They travel for $1\frac{1}{2}$ hours and cover 90 km, and then stop for 1 hour for lunch. They then travel at an average speed of 70 km/h for $2\frac{1}{2}$ hours, and finish back at home. Calculate,

(a) the total distance travelled on the tour,
(b) their average speed from leaving home to arriving back.

8 **(a)** Change a speed of 36 km/h into m/s.
(b) Change a speed of 35 m/s into km/h.

ALGEBRA

Unit 16

Algebraic fractions

16.1 Introduction

$$\frac{y}{2} \qquad \frac{3}{a} \qquad \frac{m}{x}$$

Terms such as these are called algebraic fractions.

The value of such an algebraic fraction is not changed when both the numerator and the denominator are multiplied or divided by the same number.

Example 1 $\frac{y}{2}=\frac{y\times 2}{2\times 2}=\frac{2y}{4}$ (multiply through by 2)

Example 2 $\frac{3}{a}=\frac{3\times a}{a\times a}=\frac{3a}{a^2}$ (multiply through by a)

Example 3 $\frac{4x}{10}=\frac{4x\div 2}{10\div 2}=\frac{2x}{5}$ (divide through by 2)

In fact, calculations with algebraic fractions use the same rules as ordinary fractions.

16.2 Addition and subtraction

To add or to subtract algebraic fractions we find the L.C.M. of the denominators, writing each fraction with this L.C.M., and then simplifying the numerator.

Example 1

$\frac{x}{8}+\frac{3x}{8}=\frac{x+3x}{8}=\frac{4x}{8}=\frac{x}{2}$ (in simplest form)

(L.C.M. is 8)

Example 2

$$\frac{a}{3}+\frac{b}{2}=\frac{2a}{6}+\frac{3b}{6}=\frac{2a+3b}{6}$$

(L.C.M. is 6)

Example 3

$$\frac{3}{y}+\frac{2}{y}=\frac{3+2}{y}=\frac{5}{y}$$

(L.C.M. is y)

Example 4

$$\frac{4c}{7}-\frac{2c}{7}=\frac{4c-2c}{7}=\frac{2c}{7}$$

(L.C.M. is 7)

Example 5

$\frac{5a}{6}-\frac{a}{2}=\frac{5a}{6}-\frac{3a}{6}=\frac{2a}{6}=\frac{a}{3}$ (in simplest form)

(L.C.M. is 6)

Example 6

$$\frac{1}{p}-\frac{1}{4p}=\frac{4}{4p}-\frac{1}{4p}=\frac{3}{4p}$$

(L.C.M. is $4p$)

Example 7

$$\frac{3}{2x}-\frac{4}{3y}=\frac{9y}{6xy}-\frac{8x}{6xy}=\frac{9y-8x}{6xy}$$

(L.C.M. is $6xy$)

Example 8

$$\frac{y+6}{5}+\frac{y-2}{2}=\frac{2(y+6)}{10}+\frac{5(y-2)}{10}$$

$$=\frac{2y+12+5y-10}{10}=\frac{7y+2}{10}$$

(L.C.M. is 10)

Example 9

$$\frac{3p-q}{3}-\frac{2p-q}{5}=\frac{5(3p-q)}{15}-\frac{3(2p-q)}{15}$$

$$=\frac{15p-5q-6p+3q}{15}=\frac{9p-2q}{15}$$

(L.C.M. is 15)

16.3 Multiplication and division

To multiply algebraic fractions, firstly factorize the numerator and the denominator whenever possible, then cancel down and multiply out.

Example 1 $\frac{a}{b}\times\frac{3b^2}{a}=\frac{\cancel{a}^1}{\cancel{b}_1}\times\frac{\cancel{3b^2}^{3b}}{\cancel{a}_1}=3b$

Example 2 $\frac{2a+6b}{5c}\times\frac{15c^2}{a+3b}$

Factorizing and cancelling, then multiplying,

$$=\frac{2\cancel{(a+3b)}^1}{{}_1\cancel{5c}_1}\times\frac{{}^3\cancel{15c^2}^c}{\cancel{a+3b}_1}=6c$$

In order to divide algebraic fractions, we firstly factorize as in multiplication, whenever possible. Multiply by the inverse of the divisor after any possible cancelling.

Example 1 $\frac{3b}{d}\div\frac{6}{d^2}=\frac{{}^1\cancel{3}b}{\cancel{d}_1}\times\frac{\cancel{d^2}^d}{\cancel{6}_2}=\frac{bd}{2}$

Example 2 $\frac{4x+8y}{3}\div\frac{3x+6y}{6}$

Factorizing,

$$=\frac{4(x+2y)}{3}\div\frac{3(x+2y)}{6}$$

Changing to multiplication,

$$=\frac{4\cancel{(x+2y)}^1}{\cancel{3}_1}\times\frac{\cancel{6}^2}{3\cancel{(x+2y)}_1}$$

$$=\frac{8}{3}=2\tfrac{2}{3}$$

As we can see, all the above operations are exactly identical to the equivalent operations with common fractions, and as such, we do not need to learn any new techniques.

Activities

Examples of algebraic fractions

1 Write each of the following in its simplest form.

(a) $\frac{6a}{10}$ (b) $\frac{10b}{12}$ (c) $\frac{6}{8y}$ (d) $\frac{4m}{10n}$

(e) $\frac{8}{20m}$ (f) $\frac{16u}{20v}$ (g) $\frac{10x}{25y}$ (h) $\frac{20}{12q}$

(i) $\frac{20b}{5}$ (j) $\frac{9x}{15y}$

2 Copy and complete the following.

(a) $\frac{x}{4} = \frac{?}{8}$

(b) $\frac{x}{5} = \frac{?}{15}$

(c) $\frac{x}{y} = \frac{?}{3y}$

(d) $\frac{8a}{6} = \frac{?}{3}$

(e) $\frac{5}{x} = \frac{20}{?}$

(f) $\frac{9c}{12} = \frac{?}{4}$

(g) $\frac{9v}{6v} = \frac{?}{2}$

(h) $\frac{2t}{12t} = \frac{?}{6}$

(i) $\frac{10}{16m} = \frac{5}{?}$

(j) $\frac{12e}{16e} = \frac{3}{?}$

3 Simplify the following.

(a) $\frac{3a}{3b}$

(b) $\frac{5u^2}{6uv}$

(c) $\frac{9b^2}{36bc}$

(d) $\frac{16qr}{24r^2}$

(e) $\frac{8p^2}{21p^2q}$

(f) $\frac{6y^2z}{30yz^2}$

(g) $\frac{9x^3}{12xy^2}$

(h) $\frac{30q^2r}{36q^3}$

(i) $\frac{15b^3}{24bc^2}$

(j) $\frac{21yz^2}{36y^3}$

4 Complete the following by filling the gaps with the correct result.

(a) $\frac{a}{b} = \frac{3a}{?} = \frac{a^2}{?} = \frac{am}{?}$

(b) $\frac{m}{n} = \frac{?}{5n} = \frac{?}{nm} = \frac{?}{n^2}$

(c) $\frac{2p}{3q} = \frac{8p}{?} = \frac{2px}{?} = \frac{6p^2}{?}$

5 Write these as simply as possible.

(a) $\frac{a}{2} + \frac{b}{2}$

(b) $\frac{x}{2} - \frac{y}{2}$

(c) $\frac{a}{4} + \frac{b}{2}$

(d) $\frac{3p}{4} - \frac{1}{2}$

(e) $\frac{3x}{2} - \frac{y}{4}$

(f) $\frac{2x}{3} + \frac{3y}{4}$

(g) $\frac{x}{3} + \frac{x}{3}$

(h) $\frac{x}{3} + \frac{2x}{5}$

(i) $\frac{2}{3} \times \frac{a}{b}$

(j) $\frac{4m}{3} \times \frac{2}{n}$

(k) $5 \times \frac{2p}{3}$

(l) $\frac{4m}{3n} \times \frac{2m}{3n}$

(m) $\frac{ab}{cd} \times \frac{ac}{bd}$

(n) $\frac{m^2}{3n^2} \times \frac{8m}{mn}$

(o) $\frac{s}{t} \div \frac{s}{t}$

(p) $\frac{12ab}{5} \div \frac{4a}{15b^2}$

6 Try to simplify these more difficult expressions.

(a) $\frac{2a}{5} + \frac{3a}{4} + \frac{a}{2}$

(b) $\frac{a+4}{3} + \frac{2a-1}{4}$

(c) $\frac{2a+5}{3} + \frac{a}{2}$

(d) $\frac{2x-1}{5} + \frac{x+4}{3}$

(e) $\frac{3a+4}{6} + \frac{2a-5}{9}$

(f) $\frac{4}{a} + \frac{3}{2a}$

(g) $\frac{2a+1}{3} - \frac{a-2}{4}$

(h) $\frac{2a-7}{5} - \frac{a+2}{3}$

(i) $\frac{4a-8b}{30c^2} \times \frac{6c}{a-2b}$

(j) $\frac{15x+5y}{20x^3} \div \frac{3x+y}{32x^2}$

16.4 Solving more difficult algebraic equations

In Volumes 1 and 2, we discovered that the basic technique of solving equations was to isolate unknowns (xs etc) on one side of the equation and all the numbers on the other side.

We are now in a position to consider equations containing algebraic fractions, and the following examples illustrate the method of solution.

Example 1 Solve $\frac{2x}{7} = 4$

Remove denominator of 7 by multiplying both sides by 7, giving

$$\frac{2x \times 7}{7} = 4 \times 7$$

Hence, $2x = 28 \quad \therefore x = 14$

Example 2 Solve $\frac{3x}{5} + 3 = 12$

Subtract 3 from each side, giving

$$\frac{3x}{5} = 9$$

Multiply both sides by 5,

Hence, $3x = 45 \quad \therefore x = 15$

Alternatively, it is possible to solve the problem by multiplying through by 5 first of all, giving

$$3x + 15 = 60$$

and then removing 15 from both sides.

Hence, $3x = 45 \quad \therefore x = 15$, thus producing the same result.

Which method is used, is really a matter of personal preference.

Example 3 Solve $\frac{7m+2}{3} - \frac{9m-2}{5} = 2$

Probably the easiest way to solve this problem is to first multiply through by 15, in order to remove the denominators of 3 and 5, i.e.

$$\frac{\overset{5}{\cancel{15}}(7m+2)}{\underset{1}{\cancel{3}}} - \frac{\overset{3}{\cancel{15}}(9m-2)}{\underset{1}{\cancel{5}}} = 15 \times 2$$

$$5(7m+2) - 3(9m-2) = 30$$

Remove the brackets,

$$35m + 10 - 27m + 6 = 30$$
$$8m + 16 = 30$$
$$8m = 14$$

Hence, $m = \frac{14}{8} = \frac{7}{4}$ $\quad \therefore m = 1\frac{3}{4}$

It is worth mentioning that the equation could have been solved by treating the left-hand side of the equation as a subtraction of fractions, although this would have involved far more work.

Note Each solution may be checked by substitution which, if correct, will produce a balanced equation.

Activities

Algebraic equations

1 Solve these for x.

(a) $\frac{x}{2} = 5$

(b) $\frac{x}{5} = 4$

(c) $\frac{3x}{4} = 6$

(d) $\frac{2x}{5} = 10$

(e) $\frac{5x}{4} = 1$

(f) $\frac{x}{3} + 4 = 7$

(g) $\frac{x}{5} - 3 = 6$

(h) $\frac{x}{3} - 6 = 1$

(i) $\frac{2x}{7} + 3 = 5$

(j) $\frac{5x}{3} - 3 = 4$

2 Solve these harder equations.

(a) $\frac{3x}{4} + \frac{x}{3} = 5$

(b) $\frac{x}{4} = \frac{2}{5} + \frac{x}{2}$

(c) $\frac{4x}{9} - \frac{2}{3} = \frac{x}{2}$

(d) $\frac{x+1}{4} + \frac{x+3}{5} = 1$

(e) $\frac{2x+3}{4} + \frac{x+2}{3} = 2$

(f) $\frac{3x-2}{4} - \frac{x+1}{3} = 5$

(g) $\frac{5x-2}{3} - \frac{2x+3}{2} = 3x - 11$

(h) $5x + \frac{x-3}{4} = \frac{2x+5}{3}$

(i) $2 + \frac{3}{x} = \frac{x-1}{2x}$

(j) $\frac{3x}{4} + x = \frac{7x}{8} + x - 5$

(k) $\frac{3x-2}{3} - \frac{4x+1}{2} = 3$

(l) $\frac{2-5x}{4} - \frac{3-4x}{3} = 1$

Unit 17

Simple algebraic problems

In the equations we have solved so far, it has only been necessary to find the number represented by a letter. The following examples show how the ability to solve an equation can be of use in practical problems. In each case we introduce a letter to represent the number to be found and, from the given information, we attempt to build our own equation written in algebraic shorthand. Having done this, we then solve the equation and finally check the result obtained to make sure that it is sensible.

Example 1 A number is multiplied by 5; 10 is added to the product, giving the result 25. Find the number.

Suppose we let x be the number, then 5 times the number is $5x$.

So, $5x + 10 = 25$

Hence, $5x = 15$ $\quad \therefore x = 3$

Therefore the number is 3.

Check $(5 \times 3) + 10 = 25$

Example 2 A tray has a length 30 cm longer than its width. If its perimeter is 180 cm, find its area.

Let the length of the tray be x cm

$\therefore$ the width of the tray will be $x - 30$ cm

Since its perimeter is 180 cm,

then $x + x - 30 + x + x - 30 = 180$ cm

i.e. $4x - 60 = 180$ cm

$4x = 240$ cm $\quad \therefore x = 60$ cm

Hence the length = 60 cm and the width = 30 cm (This checks because the perimeter is 180 cm.)

Now, area = length × width
= 60 × 30 = 1800 cm^2

Example 3 When I add 55 to a certain number and divide the sum by 3, the result is four times the original number. Find the number.

Let the original number be x.

Adding 55, gives $x + 55$

Dividing the sum by 3, gives $\frac{x+55}{3}$

Hence, $\frac{x+55}{3} = 4x$ (i.e. 4 times the original number)

$\therefore x + 55 = 12x$

$55 = 11x$ $\quad \therefore$ the number is 5

Check $5 + 55 = 60$ and $\frac{60}{3} = 20$ (which is 4 times 5).

Activities

1 Three women go shopping together. Mrs Green spends £x, Mrs Smith spends twice as much as Mrs Green and Mrs Jones spends three times as much. If they spend £210 altogether, what is the value of x?

2 A rectangular field is twice as long as it is wide. If the width is x metres and the perimeter is 420 m, calculate, **(a)** the width of the field **(b)** the area

3 Jim has £x in his pocket. Pete has £6 more. If they have £20 altogether, how much does Jim have?

4 This week you save £y and last week you saved half as much. If you have saved £21 altogether, find the value of y.

5 A shopkeeper buys radios at £x each. He adds on one quarter of this cost price, so that he sells them for £35 each. Find the value of x.

6 Mr Jones buys x carpet tiles for his kitchen. One third of them are green, one half of them are brown and the rest are orange. If he bought 5 orange tiles, how many carpet tiles did he buy altogether?

7 The angles of a triangle are 33°, $x°$ and $\frac{2}{5}x°$.
(a) write the equation for x **(b)** find the value of x

8 A barrel of beer holds x litres. I drink 3 litres myself and use half of what is left at a party. If there are 7 litres left, find how many litres were in the full barrel.

9 Mr Williams has a mass of x kg. His wife has a mass of 8 kg less. His daughter has a mass exactly half the mass of Mr Williams. If the total mass of the family is 442 kg, what is the mass of Mr Williams?

Unit 18

Inequalities

18.1 Solution of inequalities

The methods used for solving linear inequalities are similar to those used to solve linear equations.

Adding or subtracting a number on both sides of an inequality, leaves the inequality sign unchanged. Multiplying and dividing both sides by a **positive** number also leaves the inequality sign unchanged.

Example 1 Solve $a + 3 > 5$

$a + 3 - 3 > 5 - 3$ (subtract 3 from both sides)
gives $a > 2$

Example 2 Solve $n - 6 < -1$

$n - 6 + 6 < -1 + 6$ (add 6 to both sides)
gives $n < 5$

Example 3 Solve $3y \geqslant 9$

gives $y \geqslant 3$ (divide both sides by 3)

Example 4 Solve $\frac{c}{4} \leqslant 2$

gives $c \leqslant 8$ (multiply both sides by 4)

Example 5 Solve $\frac{2x}{5} \leqslant 6$

$\therefore$ $2x \leqslant 30$ (multiply both sides by 5)
Hence, $x \leqslant 15$ (divide both sides by 2)

Example 6 Solve $\frac{m+4}{2} > 6$

$\therefore$ $m + 4 > 12$ (multiply both sides by 2)
Hence, $m > 8$ (subtract 4 from both sides)

Example 7 Solve $5(n - 2) \geqslant 3(n + 4)$

$5n - 10 \geqslant 3n + 12$ (remove brackets)
$2n \geqslant 22$ (subtract $3n$, add 10 on both sides)
Hence, $n \geqslant 11$ (divide both sides by 2)

When, however, we have to multiply or divide by a **negative** number, the inequality sign is **reversed**.

Example 8 Solve $3 - 2a \geqslant 7$

$-2a \geqslant 4$ (subtract 3 from both sides)
Hence, $a \leqslant -2$ (divide both sides by -2)

Note The reversal of the inequality.

Example 9 Solve $4 - \frac{x}{2} \leqslant -2$

$-\frac{x}{2} \leqslant -6$ (subtract 4 from both sides)

Hence, $x \geqslant 12$ (multiply both sides by -2)

Note Again, the reversal of the inequality.

Activities

1 Solve these inequalities for x.

(a) $2x > 6$ **(b)** $3x < 15$ **(c)** $4x \geqslant 20$

(d) $7x \leqslant 21$ **(e)** $3x \geqslant -12$ **(f)** $5x < -25$

(g) $2x + 3 > 13$ **(h)** $4x - 6 < 10$ **(i)** $7x - 8 \geqslant 20$

(j) $3x + 4 \leqslant 31$ **(k)** $2x + 1 \leqslant x - 5$

2 Write down the integers that satisfy x in these.

(a) $2 \leqslant x \leqslant 6$ **(e)** $-1 \leqslant 2x + 1 \leqslant 5$

(b) $-2 < x < 1$ **(f)** $-2 \leqslant 3x - 1 \leqslant 8$

(c) $-8 < x < -5$ **(g)** $1 < 2x - 3 \leqslant 7$

(d) $-2 \leqslant 2x < 7$ **(h)** $5 < 2x - 1 < 10$

3 Simplify these inequalities.

(a) $2x + 3 \geqslant 8$ **(d)** $9x + 2 > 5x + 2$

(b) $3x + 4 \geqslant 6$ **(e)** $2(x - 5) < 11$

(c) $2x - 7 > 4$ **(f)** $8x - 1 < 3x + 4$

4 Solve these for x, but be careful with the signs.

(a) $-2x + 4 > 6$ **(f)** $12 - 5x \geqslant 2$

(b) $-3x - 5 < 3$ **(g)** $9 - 2x > 3$

(c) $4 - x < 7$ **(h)** $8 - 3x \geqslant 14$

(d) $1 - 3x \geqslant 10$ **(i)** $8 - 3x > 2x + 1$

(e) $3 - 2x < -14$ **(j)** $5 + x > -4 - 3x$

5 Write down the integers where the two inequalities overlap.

(a) $2x + 1 \geqslant 5$, $3x + 2 \leqslant 14$

(b) $3x - 1 < 11$, $5x + 1 > -4$

(c) $2 - x < -1$, $2x + 5 \leqslant 17$

(d) $x + 3 \leqslant 1$, $2x + 7 \geqslant 1$

(e) $3x + 1 \leqslant -2$, $2x - 1 \geqslant 8$

18.2 Solution sets for inequalities

Quite often inequalities are given in set form, and the solution is required in set form.

Example 1 Find the solution set for

$\{x : 2x \leqslant 10\}$

We read this as the set of values of x such that $2x \leqslant 10$.

Hence, we treat the inequality as before,

$2x \leqslant 10$

$\therefore x \leqslant 5$ (divide both sides by 2)

The solution is then put back into set form as follows,

$\{x : x \leqslant 5\}$

i.e. the set of values of x, such that $x \leqslant 5$

Example 2 Find the solution set for

$\{a : 5 > a + 2\}$

$5 > a + 2$

$\therefore 3 > a$ (subtracting 2 from both sides)

This, we would rewrite as

$a < 3$

Hence, the solution set would be $\{a : a < 3\}$

Example 3 Find the solution set for

$\{p : 3(p + 2) > p + 4\}$

$3(p + 2) > p + 4$

$3p + 6 > p + 4$ (expand brackets)

$2p > -2$ (subract p and 6 from both sides)

$p > -1$ (both sides divided by 2)

Hence, the solution set is $\{p : p > -1\}$

Example 4 Find the solution set for

$\{t : \frac{2}{9}t \leqslant -4\}$

Note that, $\frac{2}{9}t = \frac{2t}{9}$ hence, $\frac{2t}{9} \leqslant -4$

$\therefore$ $2t \leqslant -36$ (multiply both sides by 9)

and $t \leqslant -18$ (dividing both sides by 2)

Hence, solution set is $\{t : t \leqslant -18\}$

All the above solution sets are infinite, (i.e. they have an unlimited number of solutions). We can have finite solution sets, if upper and lower limits are given.

Example 5 Find the solution set (integers) for

$\{x : -3 < x \leqslant 5\}$

In this case, the solution set will be

$\{-2, -1, 0, 1, 2, 3, 4, 5\}$

which is of course a finite set.

Activities

1 Find the solution set for each of these inequalities.

(a) $\{x : 2x + 1 > 5\}$ **(f)** $\{x : 3x - 5 > 1\}$

(b) $\{x : 3x + 5 < 14\}$ **(g)** $\{x : 4x - 17 \geqslant 7\}$

(c) $\{x : 4 + 7x \geqslant 39\}$ **(h)** $\{x : 8x - 4 \geqslant 5x + 8\}$

(d) $\{x : 5x - 3 \leqslant 17\}$ **(i)** $\{x : 2x + 13 \leqslant 8 - 3x\}$

(e) $\{x : 3 - 5x < -12\}$ **(j)** $\{x : 5 + 2x > 3 - 2x\}$

2 Find the solution set for these.

(a) $\{x : 3(x - 2) > 32\}$ **(f)** $\{x : \frac{2x}{3} > 8\}$

(b) $\{x : 4(3 + x) \geqslant 16\}$

(c) $\{x : 3(x + 2) > x + 4\}$ **(g)** $\{x : \frac{5x}{7} \geqslant -10\}$

(d) $\{x : 15 \leqslant 2(x - 5)\}$

(e) $\{x : 5(x - 1) \geqslant 2(3 + x)\}$ **(h)** $\{x : \frac{2x}{9} < 18\}$

3 If set A and set B represent the solution sets of two inequalities, then write down $A \cap B$ for these.

(a) $A = \{x : 2x - 5 > 3\}$ $B = \{x : 3x + 2 < 17\}$

(b) $A = \{x : 5x - 3 < 33\}$ $B = \{x : 2x + 1 \geqslant 5\}$

(c) $A = \{x : x + 3 > -2\}$ $B = \{x : 2x - 1 \leqslant 1\}$

(d) $A = \{x : x - 1 > -2\}$ $B = \{x : 3x - 1 \leqslant 8\}$

(e) $A = \{x : \frac{1}{2}x > 3\}$ $B = \{x : \frac{1}{4}x \leqslant 2\}$

(f) $A = \{x : 5x > 20\}$ $B = \{x : 3x < 9\}$

(g) $A = \{x : \frac{3}{4}x > 6\}$ $B = \{x : \frac{2}{3}x \leqslant 8\}$

(h) $A = \{x : 5 - 2x \leqslant 3\}$ $B = \{x : 2 - x > 3\}$

4 Write down the solution sets to $A \cap B$ in Question **3**, above, if $\mathscr{E} = \{\text{Integers}\}$.

Unit 19

Solution of simultaneous equations

There are many values of x and y which will satisfy the equation $x + y = 10$ (i.e. $x = 10, y = 0$; or $x = 9, y = 1$, etc). However, if a second equation is introduced, i.e. $x - y = 4$, then the values of x and y have to satisfy both equations. There will, of course, be only one possible value of each. Pairs of equations like these are called **simultaneous equations**.

If both the x-terms (or the y-terms) in a pair of simultaneous equations are the same, the equations can be solved by a process known as **elimination**.

When the signs of the equal terms are different, the two equations are added to eliminate x (or y).

When the signs of the equal terms are the same, one equation is subtracted from the other to eliminate x (or y).

Example 1 Solve the following for x and y (Note we have numbered the equations, **(1)** and **(2)**.)

$$x + y = 10 \;\dots\dots\dots\; \textbf{(1)}$$
$$x - y = 4 \;\dots\dots\dots\; \textbf{(2)}$$

(1) + **(2)** $2x = 14$ Adding the two equations eliminates y

$$\therefore x = 7$$

We then put this value of x into either Equation **(1)** or Equation **(2)** to find the corresponding value of y.

Hence, in **(1)**, $x + y = 10$

$7 + y = 10$

$\therefore\ y = 3$

So the solution is $x = 7$ and $y = 3$

Alternatively, for the same example, we could have eliminated x by subtracting **(2)** from **(1)**, but we do have to be very careful with the signs involved, i.e.

$$x + y = 10 \;\dots\dots\; \textbf{(1)}$$
$$x - y = 4 \;\dots\dots\; \textbf{(2)}$$

(1) – **(2)** $2y = 6$ Subtracting the two equations eliminates x

(Remember, $y - (-y) = 2y$)

$$\therefore y = 3$$

Substitute this value of y into either **(1)** or **(2)**

Putting $y = 3$ in **(2)**, gives $x - 3 = 4$

$$\therefore x = 7$$

Hence, the solution is $x = 7$ and $y = 3$, as before.

Note The solution of a pair of simultaneous equations always consists of two results.

As a means of checking the correctness of our answers, we should always substitute our values into both equations, to ensure that they do satisfy both.

In examples which do not have equal terms, these have to be created by multiplying all the terms of either one or both of the equations until they are the same, so that the elimination process can start.

Example 2 Solve $x + y = 6 \;\dots\dots\; \textbf{(1)}$

$2x - 3y = 2 \;\dots\dots\; \textbf{(2)}$

Multiply **(1)** by 3; **(2)** remains the same.

$3x + 3y = 18 \;\dots\dots\; \textbf{(1)}$

$2x - 3y = 2 \;\dots\dots\; \textbf{(2)}$

The y terms are now equal. Since the signs are different, we add to eliminate.

(1) + **(2)** gives $5x = 20$

so, $x = 4$

Then, put $x = 4$ in **(1)**, $4 + y = 6$

Hence, $y = 2$

$\therefore$ the solution is $x = 4, y = 2$

Check by putting $x = 4$ and $y = 2$ in **(2)**. This gives the answer 2, so the solution is correct.

Example 3 Solve $5x + 2y = 7 \;\dots\dots\; \textbf{(1)}$

$x + 3y = 4 \;\dots\dots\; \textbf{(2)}$

(1) remains the same; multiply **(2)** by 5.

$5x + 2y = 7 \;\dots\dots\; \textbf{(1)}$

$5x + 15y = 20 \;\dots\dots\; \textbf{(2)}$

The x terms are now equal. Since the signs are the same, we subtract to eliminate.

(1) – **(2)** gives $-13y = -13$

Hence, $y = 1$

Then put $y = 1$ in **(1)** $5x + 2 = 7$

$5x = 5$

So, $x = 1$

$\therefore$ the solution is $x = 1, y = 1$

Check by putting $x = 1$ and $y = 1$ in **(2)**. This gives 4, so the solution is correct.

In some examples, we need to multiply both equations by different numbers in order to equalize the coefficients.

Example 4 Solve $3x + 2y = 14 \;\dots\dots\; \textbf{(1)}$

$13x - 5y = 6 \;\dots\dots\; \textbf{(2)}$

To equalize y coefficients multiply **(1)** by 5 and **(2)** by 2

$15x + 10y = 70 \;\dots\dots\; \textbf{(1)}$

$26x - 10y = 12 \;\dots\dots\; \textbf{(2)}$

(1) + **(2)** gives $41x = 82$

$\therefore\ x = 2$

Then put $x = 2$ in **(1)** $30 + 10y = 70$

$10y = 40$

$y = 4$

$\therefore$ the solution is $x = 2, y = 4$ (and perform the check, as usual)

Example 5 Solve

$$\begin{aligned} 3x + 4y &= 25 \quad \dots\dots (1) \\ 5x + 3y &= 27 \quad \dots\dots (2) \end{aligned}$$

To equalize y coefficients

multiply (1) by 3 $\quad 9x + 12y = 75 \quad \dots\dots (1)$

and (2) by 4 $\quad 20x + 12y = 108 \quad \dots\dots (2)$

(1) – (2) gives $-11x = -33$

$\therefore \quad x = 3$

Then, put $x = 3$ in (1) $\quad 9 + 4y = 25$

$4y = 16$

$y = 4$

$\therefore$ the solution is $x = 3, y = 4$ (which is checked in the usual way).

Activities

1 Eliminate either x or y by adding the pairs of equations, and then solve them.

(a) $x + y = 5$, $x - 1 = 3$
(b) $2x - y = 4$, $x + y = 5$
(c) $5x + y = 13$, $2x - y = 1$
(d) $-2x + 3y = 19$, $2x + y = 1$
(e) $4x + 3y = 23$, $3x - 3y = 12$
(f) $7x + 2y = 8$, $6x - 2y = 5$
(g) $2x - 3y = 6$, $-2x + 5y = -2$
(h) $8x + 6y = 2$, $2x - 6y = 3$

2 Eliminate either the x or y by subtracting the pairs of equations, and then solve them.

(a) $3x + y = 10$, $x + y = 4$
(b) $5x + y = 8$, $3x + y = 6$
(c) $3x + 2y = 16$, $7x + 2y = 24$
(d) $x + 3y = 9$, $-x + 3y = -3$
(e) $x + y = 3$, $x + 4y = 12$
(f) $2x + y = 1$, $2x + 7y = 19$
(g) $7x + y = 3$, $2x + y = -2$
(h) $5x + 2y = 1$, $3x + 2y = 3$

3 Subtract these, but be careful with the signs.

(a) $5x - y = 3$, $3x - y = 1$
(b) $2x - 5y = 8$, $x - 5y = 4$
(c) $9x - 3y = 15$, $5x - 3y = 7$
(d) $2x - y = -1$, $5x - y = 5$

4 First decide whether you should add or subtract, then solve the following.

(a) $7x + 2y = 27$, $3x - 2y = 3$
(b) $2x + 3y = 19$, $2x - y = 7$
(c) $x + 5y = 12$, $2x - 5y = -6$
(d) $10x + 3y = 2$, $7x - 3y = -19$
(e) $4x - 5y = 19$, $x - 5y = 4$
(f) $3x + y = 2$, $5x + y = 3$

5 Multiply one equation in each pair by a number, before adding or subtracting.

(a) $2x + y = 7$, $3x - 2y = 0$
(b) $4x + y = 13$, $3x - 3y = 6$
(c) $2x - y = 8$, $4x + 3y = 16$
(d) $x + 5y = 27$, $3x + 4y = 26$
(e) $3x + 2y = 17$, $5x + 4y = 29$
(f) $x + 3y = 7$, $3x - 5y = -7$
(g) $8x + 3y = 33$, $2x - 5y = -9$
(h) $4x - 3y = 11$, $2x + y = 3$
(i) $3x - 8y = -19$, $2x + 2y = 2$
(j) $5x - 3y = 1$, $4x + 6y = 5$

6 Multiply both equations by a number, before adding or subtracting.

(a) $3x + 2y = 10$, $5x + 3y = 16$
(b) $4x + 2y = 10$, $7x + 3y = 16$
(c) $4x + 3y = 32$, $10x - 2y = 42$
(d) $5x + 3y = 26$, $4x - 5y = -31$
(e) $3x - 8y = 1$, $5x - 12y = 3$
(f) $5x + 3y = 15$, $6x - 4y = 18$
(g) $7x - 2y = 2$, $12x + 5y = 54$
(h) $6x + 2y = 2$, $9x - 6y = -33$
(i) $-2x + 7y = -9$, $3x - 2y = 5$
(j) $11x - 4y = -3$, $9x - 3y = -3$

7 Before you solve the following pairs of equations, you will need to rearrange them.

(a) $2x = y + 1$, $x + 3y = 11$
(b) $2x = 6 - y$, $x = y$
(c) $4x = 4 + 2y$, $x - 16 = -2y$
(d) $3x - 4y - 3 = 0$, $3x = 18 - y$

Unit 20

Quadratic functions

20.1 Factorizing quadratic functions

A quadratic function is one which contains a square as the highest power of the unknown.

Not all quadratics can be factorized, but those that will are usually expressed as a product of two brackets.

In order to factorize the function $x^2 + 5x + 6$, we have to fill in the brackets in the statement,

$$x^2 + 5x + 6 = (\qquad)(\qquad)$$

The first term expression is x^2, and this can only be obtained by putting x first in each bracket, i.e.

$$(x \qquad)(x \qquad)$$

The next term we consider is the last in the expression, i.e. 6. This number is the product of the last two terms in the two brackets, and there is a choice of 3 and 2, -3 and -2, 6 and 1, -6 and -1.

Hence, the possibilities are, with their solutions,

(a) $(x + 3)(x + 2) = x^2 + 5x + 6$ (the given expression)

(b) $(x - 3)(x - 2) = x^2 - 5x + 6$

(c) $(x + 6)(x + 1) = x^2 + 7x + 6$

(d) $(x - 6)(x - 1) = x^2 - 7x + 6$

(See removal of brackets in Volume 2.)

Note In all four cases above, the coefficient of x on the right-hand side, is the sum of the numbers coming last in the two brackets i.e.

$5 = 3 + 2, \ -5 = -3 + -2, \ 7 = 6 + 1, \ -7 = -6 + -1$

Hence, **(c)** and **(d)** can be immediately discarded, and **(a)** is obviously the required result.

Thus, factorizing, $x^2 + 5x + 6 = (x + 3)(x + 2)$
or $(x + 2)(x + 3)$

It does not matter which bracket comes first, since the product is, of course, commutative.

Example 1 Factorize $x^2 + 7x + 10$

The factors of 10 are,

10 and 1, -10 and -1, $\boxed{5 \text{ and } 2}$, -5 and -2

Obviously, the sum of 5 and 2 gives 7 (the middle term coefficient) and so the required factors are,

$$(x + 5)(x + 2)$$

Example 2 Factorize $x^2 - 6x + 5$

The factors of 5 are, 5 and 1, $\boxed{-5 \text{ and } -1}$

$-5 + -1 = -6$ (middle term coefficient)

Hence, $x^2 - 6x + 5 = (x - 5)(x - 1)$

Example 3 Factorize $x^2 - 4x - 12$

The factors of -12 are,

-12 and 1, 12 and -1, $\boxed{-6 \text{ and } 2}$, 6 and -2, -4 and 3, 4 and -3

$-6 + 2 = -4$ (middle term coefficient)

Hence, $x^2 - 4x - 12 = (x - 6)(x + 2)$

Example 4 Factorize $x^2 + 5x - 14$

The factors of -14 are,

-14 and 1, 14 and -1, -7 and 2, $\boxed{7 \text{ and } -2}$

$7 + -2 = 5$ (middle term coefficient)

Hence, $x^2 + 5x - 14 = (x + 7)(x - 2)$

With plenty of practice, we soon learn to discard the unlikely factors, just concentrating on the obvious ones.

When the coefficient of x^2 is greater than 1, then the factorization process becomes slightly more difficult.

Example 5 Factorize $3x^2 - 11x + 6$

The first term being $3x^2$, is the product of $3x$ and x

Hence, $3x^2 - 11x + 6 = (3x \qquad)(x \qquad)$

The last term is +6, which is the product of,

6 and 1, -6 and -1, 3 and 2, -3 and -2

Hence, all the possible factors are,

$(3x + 6)(x + 1)$	$(3x + 3)(x + 2)$
$(3x - 6)(x - 1)$	$(3x - 3)(x - 2)$
$(3x + 1)(x + 6)$	$(3x + 2)(x + 3)$
$(3x - 1)(x - 6)$	$(3x - 2)(x - 3)$

All these possibilities give $3x^2$ as the first term and +6 as the last term, but the only one which gives $-11x$ as the middle term, is

$$(3x - 2)(x - 3)$$

Hence, $3x^2 - 11x + 6 = (3x - 2)(x - 3)$

Again, with plenty of practice, we find that it is unnecessary to write out all the possibilities.

Example 6 Factorize $4x^2 - 12x + 5$

Note that, in this case, another complication faces us since $4x^2$ can be expressed either in the form $(4x \qquad)(x \qquad)$ or $(2x \qquad)(2x \qquad)$ which, of course, doubles the possible number of factors. Again, however, with some care, and looking for the middle terms of $-12x$, we eventually find that

$$4x^2 - 12x + 5 = (2x - 5)(2x - 1)$$

Example 7 Factorize $6x^2 - 15x + 9$

$$6x^2 - 15x + 9 = 3(2x^2 - 5x + 3)$$
$$= 3(2x - 3)(x - 1)$$

In this case the factor 3, common to all terms, is taken out before the quadratic is factorized. This does, in fact, make the factorization of the function somewhat more simple.

Example 8 Factorize $3x^2 - 2x$

This type of quadratic function is probably the easiest to factorize since all we have to do is to take out a factor of x, i.e.

$$3x^2 - 2x = x(3x - 2)$$

Note There are no number factors to consider.

Activities

1 Rewrite these expressions as the product of two brackets.

(a) $x^2 + 4x + 3$	**(k)** $x^2 + 10x + 21$
(b) $x^2 + 9x + 8$	**(l)** $x^2 - 6x - 7$
(c) $x^2 + 5x + 4$	**(m)** $x^2 - 2x - 15$
(d) $x^2 + 11x + 10$	**(n)** $x^2 - 2x - 8$
(e) $x^2 + 8x + 15$	**(o)** $x^2 - 6x - 16$
(f) $x^2 + 12x + 20$	**(p)** $x^2 - x - 20$
(g) $x^2 + 11x + 18$	**(q)** $x^2 - 13x + 22$
(h) $x^2 + 6x - 7$	**(r)** $x^2 - 2x - 35$
(i) $x^2 + 4x - 5$	**(s)** $x^2 - 4x - 12$
(j) $x^2 + 7x - 8$	**(t)** $x^2 - 13x + 30$

2 Factorize these expressions.

(a) $2x^2 + 3x + 1$	**(k)** $5x^2 - 3x - 2$
(b) $2x^2 + 5x + 3$	**(l)** $11x^2 + 8x - 3$
(c) $2x^2 + 7x + 3$	**(m)** $7x^2 - 2x - 5$
(d) $3x^2 + 10x + 3$	**(n)** $5x^2 + 34x - 7$
(e) $3x^2 + 6x + 3$	**(o)** $4x^2 - 4x + 1$
(f) $5x^2 + 7x + 2$	**(p)** $4x^2 + 11x - 15$
(g) $5x^2 + 16x + 3$	**(q)** $6x^2 - 32x + 10$
(h) $5x^2 + 8x + 3$	**(r)** $6x^2 - 23x + 10$
(i) $7x^2 + 4x - 3$	**(s)** $6x^2 - 7x - 10$
(j) $7x^2 - 4x - 3$	**(t)** $6x^2 - 17x - 10$

3 Factorize the following.

(a) $x^2 - 8x$	**(e)** $6x^2 + 15x$
(b) $2x^2 - 11x$	**(f)** $18x^2 + 12x$
(c) $3x^2 - 9x$	**(g)** $14x^2 - 21x$
(d) $2x^2 + 8x$	**(h)** $5x^2 + 4x$

20.2 Difference between two squares

We must be able to recognize, immediately, this type of quadratic function. As the title suggests, it involves the difference between two perfect squares.

Note There is no middle term involved.

Example 1 Factorize $x^2 - a^2$ (a general case).

We recognize this as a difference of two squares situation, and this factorizes as follows,

$$x^2 - a^2 = (x + a)(x - a)$$

Example 2 Factorize $x^2 - 25$

We can re-write this as $x^2 - 5^2$ and hence, by comparison with Example **1**,

$$x^2 - 25 = (x + 5)(x - 5)$$

Example 3 Factorize $25x^2 - 9y^2$

$$25x^2 - 9y^2 = (5x)^2 - (3y)^2$$

which factorizes to give $(5x + 3y)(5x - 3y)$

We can of course use the difference of two squares factors to enable us to find the value of a numerical example.

Example 4 Find the value of $118^2 - 18^2$

We express this in factor form i.e.

$$\begin{aligned}118^2 - 18^2 &= (118 + 18)(118 - 18)\\ &= 136 \times 100\\ &= 13\,600\end{aligned}$$

This technique can be particularly useful when used in Pythagoras' Theorem problems and also area of rings problems.

Example 5 Find the value of $5.4^2 - 4.6^2$

In factor form,

$$\begin{aligned}5.4^2 - 4.6^2 &= (5.4 + 4.6)(5.4 - 4.6)\\ &= 10 \times 0.8\\ &= 8\end{aligned}$$

Activities

1 Expand and simplify the following.

(a) $(x + 3)(x - 3)$	**(f)** $(2x - 7)(2x + 7)$
(b) $(x + 5)(x - 5)$	**(g)** $(3x + 4)(3x - 4)$
(c) $(x + y)(x - y)$	**(h)** $(5x - 9)(5x + 9)$
(d) $(a - 2b)(a + 2b)$	**(i)** $(a - 1)(a + 1)$
(e) $(2x + y)(2x - y)$	**(j)** $(3a + 8)(3a - 8)$

2 Rewrite these expressions as the product of two brackets.

(a) $x^2 - 100$	**(f)** $4x^2 - y^2$
(b) $x^2 - 64$	**(g)** $a^2 - 36$
(c) $x^2 - 1$	**(h)** $9a^2 - 121$
(d) $x^2 - 144$	**(i)** $36x^2 - 169$
(e) $x^2 - 225$	**(j)** $25x^2 - 81$

3 If $x^2 - y^2 = (x + y)(x - y)$, then use this fact to help you to find the value of the following.

(a) $49^2 - 1^2$	**(f)** $51^2 - 49^2$
(b) $88^2 - 12^2$	**(g)** $63^2 - 37^2$
(c) $54^2 - 4^2$	**(h)** $801^2 - 99^2$
(d) $25^2 - 5^2$	**(i)** $1112^2 - 12^2$
(e) $99^2 - 1^2$	**(j)** $248^2 - 52^2$

4 Now evaluate these more difficult differences.

(a) $3.6^2 - 0.6^2$ **(f)** $(3\frac{1}{4})^2 - (1\frac{3}{4})^2$

(b) $3.6^2 - 1.4^2$ **(g)** $(4\frac{1}{2})^2 - (\frac{1}{2})^2$

(c) $6.5^2 - 3.5^2$ **(h)** $(7\frac{1}{2})^2 - (2\frac{1}{2})^2$

(d) $84.5^2 - 15.5^2$ **(i)** $4.8^2 - 1.2^2$

(e) $2.52^2 - 1.52^2$ **(j)** $7.25^2 - 2.75^2$

20.3 Solution of quadratic equations

In order to solve a quadratic equation, it must always be written in the form

$$ax^2 + bx + c = 0$$

For instance, $x^2 + 2x = 3$ would have to be re-arranged as $x^2 + 2x - 3 = 0$, before starting to solve the equation.

There are 3 accepted methods for solving quadratic equations.

Method 1 – By factorization

We have just learned how to factorize quadratic functions and we use this to help us to solve quadratic equations in the following way.

Example 1 Solve $x^2 + 8x + 12 = 0$

Factorizing, $(x + 6)(x + 2) = 0$

Now, since the product of the two factors is zero, then either one or the other, or even both, factors must be equal to zero.

Hence, either $x + 6 = 0$ or $x + 2 = 0$

if $x + 6 = 0$, then $x = -6$

or, if $x + 2 = 0$, then $x = -2$

Every quadratic equation has two possible answers.

Example 2 Solve $2x^2 - 5x - 18 = 0$

Factorizing, $(2x - 9)(x + 2) = 0$

Hence, $2x - 9 = 0$ which means that $2x = 9$

$\therefore x = 4\frac{1}{2}$

or, $x + 2 = 0$ which means that $x = -2$

So, the solutions are $x = 4\frac{1}{2}$ or $x = -2$

Example 3 Solve $x^2 - 5x = 0$

Factorizing, $x(x - 5) = 0$

In this case, $x = 0$, or $x - 5 = 0$, i.e. $x = 5$

Hence the solutions are $x = 0$ or $x = 5$

Example 4 Solve $x^2 - 9 = 0$

Factorizing, $(x + 3)(x - 3) = 0$
(difference of two squares)

Hence, $x + 3 = 0 \quad \therefore x = -3$

or, $x - 3 = 0 \quad \therefore x = 3$

So the solutions are $x = -3$ or $x = 3$

Method 2 – By formula

If we cannot factorize the quadratic, it is possible to solve the equation because, for any quadratic equation expressed in the form $ax^2 + bx + c = 0$, we can use a formula,

$$x = \frac{-b \pm \sqrt{b^2 - 4ac}}{2a}$$

The values of a, b and c are substituted into the formula (taking great care with the signs of a, b and c). The formula gives us two answers, since the square root of any number can either be positive or negative. This results in the $\pm$ (meaning plus or minus) in the formula.

Example 1 Solve $x^2 - 3x - 5 = 0$ (Give the answers correct to 2 decimal places.)

In this case, $a = 1$, $b = -3$ and $c = -5$

Now, $x = \dfrac{-b \pm \sqrt{b^2 - 4ac}}{2a}$

Hence, $x = \dfrac{-(-3) \pm \sqrt{(-3)^2 - 4 \times 1 \times -5}}{2 \times 1}$

Note $-(-3) = +3$, $(-3)^2 = +9$, $-4 \times 1 \times -5 = +20$

$\therefore \; x = \dfrac{3 \pm \sqrt{9 + 20}}{2} = \dfrac{3 \pm \sqrt{29}}{2}$

So, $x = \dfrac{3 \pm 5.385}{2}$

i.e. $x = \dfrac{3 + 5.385}{2}$ or $\dfrac{3 - 5.385}{2}$

$\therefore \; x = \dfrac{8.385}{2} = 4.19$, or $\dfrac{-2.385}{2} = -1.19$

The two solutions are $x = -1.19$ or $x = 4.19$ (correct to 2 decimal places).

The formula obviously works for quadratics which would factorize; suppose we consider such an example.

Example 2 Solve $3x^2 - 5x - 2 = 0$ (by formula).

In this case $a = 3$, $b = -5$ and $c = -2$

and $x = \dfrac{-b \pm \sqrt{b^2 - 4ac}}{2a}$

Hence, $x = \dfrac{-(-5) \pm \sqrt{(-5)^2 - 4 \times 3 \times -2}}{2 \times 3}$

$\therefore \; x = \dfrac{5 \pm \sqrt{25 + 24}}{6} = \dfrac{5 \pm \sqrt{49}}{6}$

Since 49 is a perfect square, this implies that the equation would in fact have factorized.

However, to continue, $x = \dfrac{5 \pm 7}{6}$

$\therefore \; x = \dfrac{5 + 7}{6} = 2$ or $x = \dfrac{5 - 7}{6} = \dfrac{-2}{6} = \dfrac{-1}{3}$

So, $x = -\frac{1}{3}$ or $x = 2$ are the solutions.

In fact, this quadratic would have factorized as,

$(3x + 1)(x - 2) = 0$

Hence, $3x + 1 = 0 \Rightarrow 3x = -1 \Rightarrow x = -\frac{1}{3}$

or $x - 2 = 0 \Rightarrow x = 2$

as above, by formula.

Note It is very important to learn the formula and always to be very careful in its use.

Activities

Solution of quadratics

1 Solve these, as in the example:

$(x-3)(x+7)=0$
so, $x-3=0$ or $x+7=0$
$\therefore\quad x=3$ or $x=-7$

(a) $(x-2)(x+3)=0$
(b) $(x+5)(x+3)=0$
(c) $(x-4)(x-7)=0$
(d) $(2x-1)(x+2)=0$
(e) $(2x+5)(3x-2)=0$

2 Solve these by first writing each expression as the product of two brackets.

(a) $x^2+4x+3=0$
(b) $x^2+9x+8=0$
(c) $x^2+10x+9=0$
(d) $x^2+5x+4=0$
(e) $x^2+6x-7=0$
(f) $x^2+2x-15=0$
(g) $x^2+3x-18=0$
(h) $x^2+x-20=0$
(i) $x^2-15x+14=0$
(j) $x^2-4x+4=0$
(k) $x^2-2x-15=0$
(l) $x^2-7x-8=0$
(m) $x^2-9x+8=0$
(n) $x^2-9x+20=0$
(o) $x^2-7x+12=0$
(p) $x^2-x-72=0$

3 Use the fact that these are 'the difference of two squares', to solve them.

(a) $x^2-25=0$
(b) $x^2-100=0$
(c) $x^2-4=0$
(d) $x^2-16=0$
(e) $x^2-81=0$
(f) $x^2-\frac{1}{4}=0$
(g) $x^2-9=0$
(h) $4x^2-25=0$
(i) $9x^2-49=0$
(j) $16x^2-144=0$

4 Rearrange these into quadratic form before you solve them.

(a) $x^2-6x=7$
(b) $x^2+21=22x$
(c) $x^2=3(2x+9)$
(d) $x(x-5)-8(x-3)=2$
(e) $x(2x+5)=3(x+8)$
(f) $x+\dfrac{33}{x}=14$

Method 3 – By graphical solution
Drawing graphs of quadratic functions was described in Volume 2, Unit 22.7. This method will produce solutions only as precise as the accuracy of our graph, and is not highly recommended.

Example Draw the graph of $y=2x^2-3x-7$ and use it to solve the equation $2x^2-3x-7=0$. (Use $-2\leqslant x\leqslant 4$)

We require the x-values where $y=0$, i.e. the x-values of the points where the curve cuts the x-axis.

We need to construct a table of values as Table 20.1, and then plot the curve on graph paper, using suitable scales (see Fig. 20.1).

x	−2	−1	0	1	2	3	4
$2x^2$	8	2	0	2	8	18	32
$-3x$	6	3	0	−3	−6	−9	−12
-7	−7	−7	−7	−7	−7	−7	−7
y	7	−2	−7	−8	−5	2	13

Table 20.1

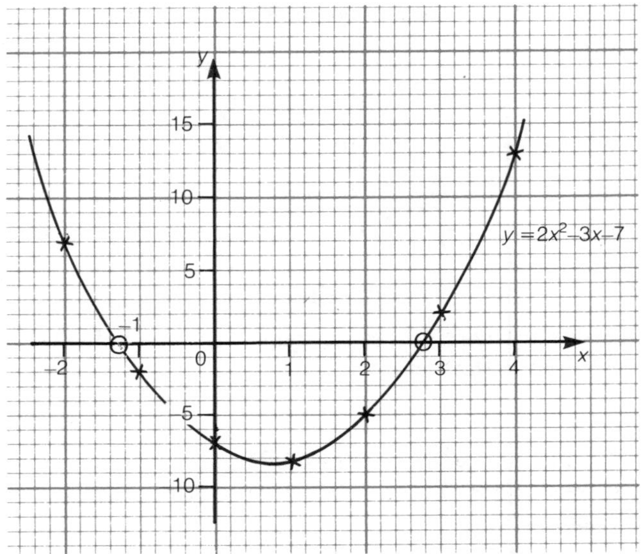

Fig. 20.1

Reading from the graph in Fig. 20.1, the values of x where the curve cuts the x-axis (ringed) are $x=-1.3$ and $x=2.8$.

Hence, the solutions of $2x^2-3x-7=0$ are,

$x=-1.3$ or $x=2.8$.

Activities

1 Complete Table 20.2, and plot the graph of $y=x^2-4x+3$, using axes as shown in Fig. 20.2.

x	0	1	2	3	4
x^2					
$-4x$					
$+3$					
y					

Table 20.2

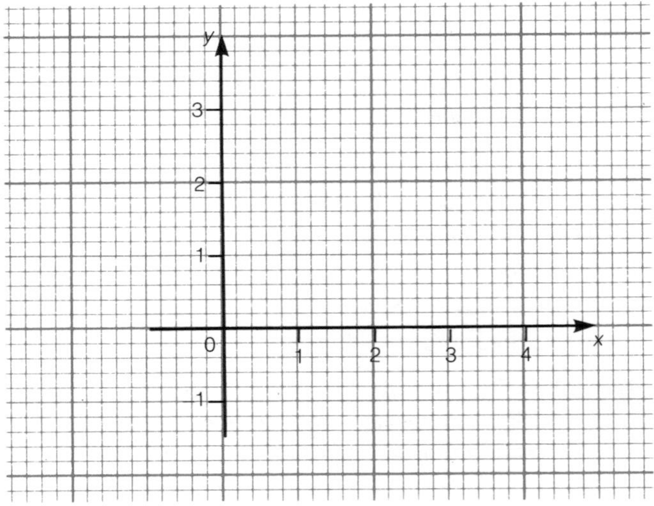

Fig. 20.2

From the graph write down the solutions to $x^2-4x+3=0$.

2 Complete Table 20.3, and plot the graph of $y = x^2 - 3x - 4$, using axes as shown in Fig. 20.3.

x	-1	0	1	2	3	4
x^2						
$-3x$						
-4						
y						

Table 20.3

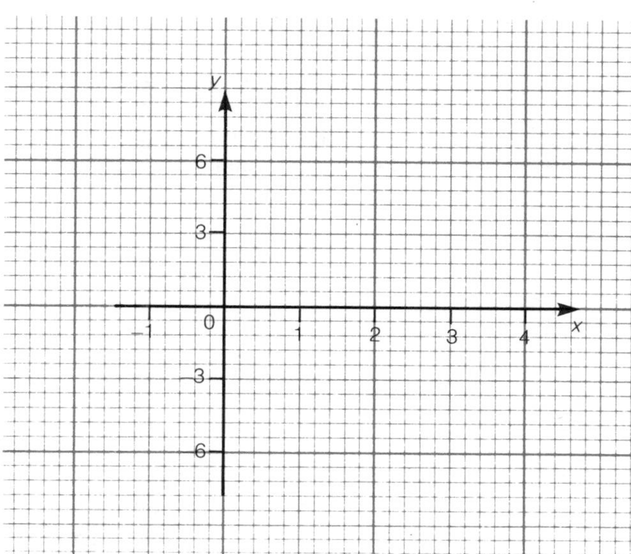

Fig. 20.3

From the graph write down the solutions to $x^2 - 3x - 4 = 0$.

3 Copy and complete Table 20.4, for $y = x^2 - 6x + 5$.

x	0	1	2	3	4	5	6
x^2							
$-6x$							
$+5$							
y							

Table 20.4

(a) plot the graph of $y = x^2 - 6x + 5$
(b) write down the solutions to $x^2 - 6x + 5 = 0$

4 For $0 \leqslant x \leqslant 6$, plot the graph of $y = x^2 - 7x + 10$. Hence, write down the solutions to the equation $x^2 - 7x + 10 = 0$.

5 For $-3 \leqslant x \leqslant 2$, plot the graph of $y = x^2 + x - 4$. Hence, write down the solutions to the equation $x^2 + x - 4 = 0$ (give your answers as decimals).

20.4 Problems involving solution of quadratics

From the data given in the problem, we attempt to build a quadratic equation which we then solve to produce a suitable answer to the problem.

Example The width of a room is 4 m less than the length, and the area is 221 m^2. Find the dimensions of the room.

If we let the length of the room be x m, then the width will be $(x - 4)$ m.

Since area = length × width,

$$221 = x(x - 4)$$

Removing the brackets,

$$x^2 - 4x = 221$$

In quadratic equation form, $x^2 - 4x - 221 = 0$

By factorization, $(x - 17)(x + 13) = 0$

Hence, $x - 17 = 0 \Rightarrow x = 17$ m
or, $x + 13 = 0 \Rightarrow x = -13$ m

Obviously, the length cannot be -13 m and so the length of the room is 17 m.

Check Length 17 m, hence width = 13 m and area = 221 m^2.

Activities

More difficult quadratic equations

1 Solve these by factorizing.

(a) $2x^2 - x - 1 = 0$
(b) $5x^2 + 4x - 1 = 0$
(c) $7x^2 + 26x - 8 = 0$
(d) $4x^2 - 11x - 15 = 0$
(e) $8x^2 + x - 9 = 0$
(f) $5x^2 - 12x + 7 = 0$
(g) $6x^2 - 16x + 10 = 0$
(h) $8x^2 + 26x + 15 = 0$
(i) $4x^2 - 4x + 1 = 0$
(j) $10x^2 - 7x - 12 = 0$

2 Solve these, using the formula,

$$x = \frac{-b \pm \sqrt{b^2 - 4ac}}{2a}$$

Where necessary, give your answers correct to 2 dec pl.

(a) $x^2 - 7x + 10 = 0$
(b) $x^2 + 9x + 13 = 0$
(c) $x^2 + 5x - 21 = 0$
(d) $x^2 + 2x - 5 = 0$
(e) $x^2 + 7x + 2 = 0$
(f) $3x^2 + 7x - 2 = 0$
(g) $2x^2 - 3x - 4 = 0$
(h) $5x^2 - 9x + 3 = 0$
(i) $2x^2 + 11x + 3 = 0$
(j) $4x^2 + 2x - 5 = 0$

3 Solve these problems using quadratic equations.

(a) If the area of the rectangle in Fig. 20.4 is 21 cm^2, find the value of x.

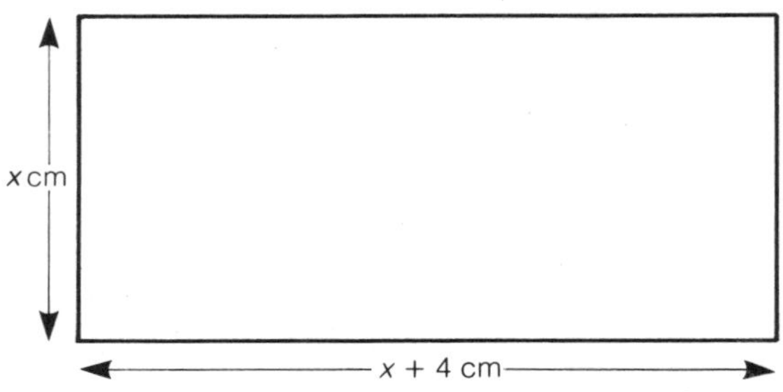

Fig. 20.4

(b) If the area of the triangle in Fig. 20.5 is 18 cm^2, calculate the value of x.

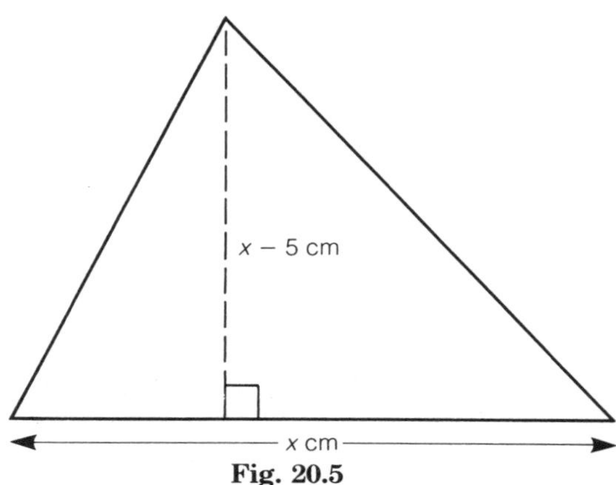

Fig. 20.5

(c) The length of a rectangular garden is 5 metres more than its width. If the area of the garden is 104 m^2, find the width of the garden.

(d) A room is 3 metres high, x metres long and $(x - 4)$ metres wide. If the volume of the room is 180 m^3, find the length of the room.

(e) A rectangular lawn, measuring 20 metres by 15 metres, is surrounded by a path of uniform width. If the total area of the path is 114 m^2, find its width.

Unit 21

Algebraic manipulation

21.1 Simple examples

In our studies of equations, so far, we have discovered that it is quite easy to rearrange or manipulate the equations whenever necessary. It is very difficult to lay down strict rules for performing the manipulation, as every case has to be dealt with on its own merit.

For instance, in each of the following equations, find x in terms of everything else i.e. isolate x.

Example 1 $x + a = b$

$\therefore x = b - a$ (subtract a from both sides)

Example 2 $ax = b$

$\therefore x = \frac{b}{a}$ (divide both sides by a)

Example 3 $a - x = b$

$\therefore a - b = x$ (add x to both sides and subtract b from both sides)

Example 4 $\frac{a}{x} = b$

$\therefore \frac{a}{b} = x$ (multiply both sides by x and divide both sides by b)

Example 5 $mx + nx = y$

$x(m + n) = y$ (take out a factor of x)

$\therefore x = \frac{y}{m + n}$ (divide both sides by $(m + n)$)

Example 6 $a(b - x) = cx$

$ab - ax = cx$ (remove bracket)

$ab = cx + ax$ (add ax to both sides)

$ab = x(c + a)$ (take out a factor of x)

$\frac{ab}{c + a} = x$ (divide both sides by $(c + a)$)

Example 7 $a = \frac{2b + 3x}{3b - 2x}$

$a(3b - 2x) = 2b + 3x$ (multiply both sides by $(3b - 2x)$)

$3ab - 2ax = 2b + 3x$ (remove brackets)

$3ab - 2b = 3x + 2ax$ (rearranging xs to R.H.S.)

$b(3a - 2) = x(3 + 2a)$ (factorizing)

$\frac{b(3a - 2)}{3 + 2a} = x$ (divide both sides by $(3 + 2a)$)

Example 8 $2b = \sqrt{a^2 - x^2}$

$$(2b)^2 = a^2 - x^2 \text{ (squaring both sides)}$$
$$4b^2 = a^2 - x^2$$
$$\therefore x^2 = a^2 - 4b^2 \text{ (rearranging)}$$
$$\therefore x = \sqrt{a^2 - 4b^2} \text{ (taking the square root of both sides)}$$

Example 9 $\frac{x}{x+a} - \frac{a}{x+b} = 1$

Multiply both sides by $(x + a)(x + b)$,

$x(x + b) - a(x + a) = 1(x + a)(x + b)$

$x^2 + bx - ax - a^2 = x^2 + ax + bx + ab$ (removing brackets)

$x^2 - x^2 + bx - ax - bx - ax = a^2 + ab$ (rearranging)

$-2ax = a^2 + ab$ (adding like terms etc)

$$x = \frac{a^2 + ab}{-2a} = \frac{a(a + b)}{-2a}$$

Hence, $x = \frac{-(a + b)}{2}$, in simplest form

Note A few points well worth remembering concerning algebraic manipulation are as follows.

1 Clear fractions, brackets and roots, etc.

2 Rearrange the equation so that all x terms are on one side of the equation, with everything else on the other side.

3 Take a factor of x outside a bracket if more than one term involves x.

4 Divide both sides of the equation by the bracket in order to isolate x, and then simplify as far as possible.

21.2 Further substitution

We can now rearrange an equation in order to find an unknown value, given other values.

Consider, for example, the equation of a straight line. Given the equation of the line and the x co-ordinate, we can find the corresponding y co-ordinate. Likewise, given the equation and the y co-ordinate, we can rearrange the equation and substitute in the y value, giving us the corresponding x value.

Example Find the missing co-ordinates in the following, by using the equation $y = 2x + 3$, and the given co-ordinates. **(i)** $(2, y)$ **(ii)** $(x, 5)$

(i) Substitute $x = 2$ in $y = 2x + 3$

Hence, $y = 4 + 3$

$y = 7$

$\therefore$ the co-ordinates are (2, 7)

(ii) Rearrange $y = 2x + 3$ to give $y - 3 = 2x$

$\therefore \frac{y - 3}{2} = x$

Substitute $y = 5$ in $x = \frac{y - 3}{2}$

So, $x = \frac{5 - 3}{2} = \frac{2}{2} = 1$

$\therefore$ the co-ordinates are (1, 5)

Activities

Algebraic manipulation and substitution

1 Find x in the following.

(a) $3x + a = 2x + b$ **(b)** $ax + bx = 1$

(c) $\frac{a}{x} + \frac{b}{x} = 1$ **(d)** $a(a + x) = b(b + x)$

(e) $\frac{x}{a} + \frac{x}{b} = 1$ **(f)** $\frac{x + a}{x + b} = 2$

(g) $\frac{x}{x + 5} = \frac{a}{b}$ **(h)** $\sqrt{x^2 + b^2} = a$

(i) $a(x - a) = b(x - b)$ **(j)** $\frac{ax + 1}{bx + 1} = \frac{m}{n}$

2 Use the equation of the line, to find the missing co-ordinates in these.

(a) $y = 3x - 5$ **(i)** $(1, y)$ **(ii)** $(-2, y)$ **(iii)** $(x, 12)$ **(iv)** $(x, -20)$

(b) $y = 7 + 2x$ **(i)** $(2, y)$ **(ii)** $(-3, y)$ **(iii)** $(x, 3)$ **(iv)** $(x, 17)$

(c) $2y = 1 - x$ **(i)** $(5, y)$ **(ii)** $(-3, y)$ **(iii)** $(x, -4)$ **(iv)** $(x, -\frac{1}{2})$

(d) $\frac{1}{2}y = \frac{1}{4}x - 2$ **(i)** $(4, y)$ **(ii)** $(-2, y)$ **(iii)** $(x, 1)$ **(iv)** $(x, -6)$

3 Find x in the following.

(a) $2ax + 5bx = 10$ **(b)** $\frac{3}{4}x - \frac{1}{2}x = ab$

(c) $\frac{5ax}{6} - \frac{2ax}{3} = b$ **(d)** $\frac{5}{x} + \frac{2}{3x} = y$

(e) $\frac{9ax}{b} = \frac{3x^2}{ab}$ **(f)** $x(2x - 5) = x(a - x)$

(g) $\frac{x - 5}{a} + \frac{x + 3}{b} = 1$ **(h)** $\frac{2x - 1}{3a} - \frac{x - 2}{a} = 1$

Unit 22

Transformation of formulae

22.1 Change of subject

A formula is basically an equation which gives a general rule for a particular problem.

Example 1 For instance, for the circumference of a circle (C) we use the formula $C = 2\pi r$ (r is the radius of the circle).

It is of course possible to **transform** (change the subject of) the formula $C = 2\pi r$ by dividing both sides by 2π.

Hence, $\dfrac{C}{2\pi} = r$

The radius, r, is now the subject of the formula.

Example 2 The area of a rectangle (A) is Length (L) × Breadth (B).

The formula is quoted as $A = L \times B$

By dividing both sides by L, we can make B the subject, i.e.

$$\frac{A}{L} = B$$

Similarly, by dividing both sides by B, we can make L the subject, i.e.

$$\frac{A}{B} = L$$

Example 3 The surface area of a sphere (S) is given as $S = 4\pi r^2$ (where r is the radius of the sphere).

To make r the subject, firstly isolate r^2 by dividing both sides by 4π.

Hence, $\dfrac{S}{4\pi} = r^2$

$\therefore \sqrt{\dfrac{S}{4\pi}} = r$ (taking the square root of both sides)

Activities

1 In each of the following, change the subject to the letter given in brackets.

(a) $C = 2\pi r$ (r)
(b) $y = mx$ (m)
(c) $A = LB$ (L)
(d) $I = \dfrac{PRT}{100}$ (R)
(e) $A = \frac{1}{2}bh$ (h)
(f) $V = \pi r^2 h$ (h)
(g) $S = VT$ (T)
(h) $y^2 = 4ax$ (x)

2 Make x the subject of the formulae.

Hint Isolate the term in x, first of all.

(a) $S = 2y + 2x$
(b) $2s = x + y + z$
(c) $v^2 = u^2 + 2ax$
(d) $y = mx + c$
(e) $C = 90 - x$
(f) $2A = 3y - 4x$
(g) $Ax + By + c = 0$
(h) $E = x(v^2 - u^2)$

3 Make x the subject of these.

Hint Look to factorize when you have all the xs together.

(a) $V = ax + 2bx$
(b) $Y = 3x - 2ax$
(c) $xg - T = xa$
(d) $a = \dfrac{x}{1+x}$
(e) $ax = bx + C$
(f) $x = ax - b$
(g) $P = \dfrac{x}{x-a}$
(h) $\dfrac{1}{x} + \dfrac{1}{y} = \dfrac{1}{f}$

4 Write x in terms of all the other letters in these examples, some of which are more difficult.

(a) $x = \dfrac{x+a}{b}$
(b) $a = \sqrt{\dfrac{y}{1+x}}$
(c) $a = \dfrac{h}{x}$
(d) $A = \pi x^2$
(e) $y = c\sqrt{x}$
(f) $c^2 y = x^2$
(g) $y = \left(\dfrac{c}{x}\right)^2$
(h) $y = \sqrt{(x+a)}$
(i) $P = m\sqrt{2gx}$
(j) $P = \sqrt{\dfrac{1+x}{1-x}}$

22.2 More substitution

Now that we are able to change the subject of any formula, we are in a position to find an unknown value in any formula, given sufficient information.

Example 1 The area, A, of a triangle is $\frac{1}{2}bh$.
Find the values of (a) A, when $b = 4$ and $h = 6$
(b) b, when $A = 10$ and $h = 4$
(c) h, when $A = 15$ and $b = 6$

(a) Substitute $b = 4$ and $h = 6$ into $A = \frac{1}{2}bh$.
This gives $A = \frac{1}{2} \times 4 \times 6$
$= 12$ *square units*

(b) Rearrange $A = \frac{1}{2}bh$, to make b the subject.
$2A = bh$ (multiply both sides by 2)
$\dfrac{2A}{h} = b$ (divide both sides by h)

Substitute $A = 10$ and $h = 4$

Then, $\dfrac{20}{4} = b$, i.e. $b = 5$

(c) Rearrange $A = \frac{1}{2}bh$ to make h the subject.
$2A = bh$ (multiply both sides by 2)
$\dfrac{2A}{b} = h$ (divide both sides by b)

Substitute $A = 15$ and $b = 6$

Then, $\dfrac{30}{6} = h$, i.e. $h = 5$

Example 2 The formula connecting temperature in °C with temperature in °F is given as $C = \frac{5}{9}(F - 32)$. Convert 30°C into °F.

We have to make F the subject of the formula $C = \frac{5}{9}(F - 32)$.

$9C = 5(F - 32)$ (multiply both sides by 9)

$9C = 5F - 160$ (remove the brackets)

$9C + 160 = 5F$ (add 160 to both sides)

$\frac{9C + 160}{5} = F$ (divide both sides by 5)

Substitute $C = 30$,

then, $\frac{270 + 160}{5} = \frac{430}{5} = F$, i.e. $F = 86°$

Activities

Evaluating formulae

1 Use $A = LB$, to find

(a) A, when $L = 7$, $B = 5$
(b) L, when $A = 72, B = 18$
(c) B, when $A = 28$, $L = 3.5$

2 Use $I = \frac{PRT}{100}$ to find

(a) I, when $P = 250$, $R = 8$, $T = 6$
(b) P, when $I = 60$, $R = 5$, $T = 2$
(c) T, when $I = 9$, $P = 30$, $R = 3$

3 Use $V = U + AT$, to find

(a) V, when $U = 12, A = 3$, $T = 4$
(b) U, when $V = 88$, $A = 2\frac{1}{2}$, $T = 30$
(c) T, when $V = 95$, $U = 50$, $A = 4.5$

4 Use $v^2 = u^2 + 2as$, to find

(a) v, when $u = 5$, $a = 2$, $s = 6$
(b) u, when $v = 12$, $a = 4$, $s = 5.5$
(c) a, when $v = 20$, $u = 10$, $s = 25$

5 Use $A = \pi r^2$, to find

(a) A, when $\pi = 3.14$, $r = 5$
(b) r, when $A = 38.5$, $\pi = \frac{22}{7}$

6 Use $V = \frac{1}{3}\pi r^2 h$, to find

(a) V, when $\pi = 3.14$, $r = 10$, $h = 15$
(b) h, when $\pi = \frac{22}{7}$, $V = 330$, $r = 3$
(c) r, when $\pi = \frac{22}{7}$, $V = 208$, $h = 6$

7 Use $y = mx + c$, to find

(a) y, when $m = 6$, $x = 3$, $c = -5$
(b) m, when $y = 10$, $x = 4$, $c = 2$
(c) c, when $y = 15$, $m = \frac{3}{4}$, $x = 12$

8 Use $y^2 = 4ax$, to find

(a) y, when $a = 10$, $x = 10$
(b) x, when $y = 15$, $a = 6.25$
(c) a, when $y = 10$, $x = 1.25$

Various exercises

1 Simplify these.

(a) $\frac{3x}{5} + \frac{2x}{3} + \frac{x}{2}$ **(b)** $\frac{3x - 5}{4} + \frac{2x + 1}{3}$

2 Solve for x,

(a) $\frac{2x}{3} - \frac{x}{2} + \frac{5x}{6} = 3$ **(b)** $\frac{x - 2}{2} - \frac{2x - 1}{5} = 5$

3 Find the solution set for the following,

(a) $3x - 2 > 7$ **(b)** $15 - 2x < 7$
(c) $3(2x - 5) \geqslant 9$ **(d)** $\frac{3}{4}x \leqslant 15$

4 Solve these for x and y.

(a) $\left.\begin{aligned} 3x - y &= 5 \\ 2x + 2y &= 14 \end{aligned}\right\}$ **(b)** $\left.\begin{aligned} 4x + 3y &= 5 \\ x + y &= -1 \end{aligned}\right\}$

5 Solve these simultaneous equations by graphical methods.

(a) $\left.\begin{aligned} y &= 2x - 1 \\ y &= \tfrac{1}{2}x + 2 \end{aligned}\right\}$ **(b)** $\left.\begin{aligned} 3x + 2y &= 12 \\ y &= 2x - 1 \end{aligned}\right\}$

6 Factorize these.

(a) $5p^2 - 20p$ **(b)** $q^2 - 25$ **(c)** $x^2 - 4x - 5$

7 Solve these for x.

(a) $x^2 - 2x - 48 = 0$ **(b)** $x^2 + 4x + 3 = 0$

8 Make x the subject of these formulae.

(a) $V = lwx$ **(b)** $V = \frac{1}{3}r^2x$ **(c)** $P = 2(x + y)$

9 A newspaper costs x pence and a magazine costs y pence. If together they cost 46p and the magazine costs 10p more than the newspaper, find the cost of both.

10 3 choc ices and 2 lollipops cost 96p and 2 choc ices and 3 lollipops cost 89p. Find the cost of each.

Unit 23

Matrix algebra

23.1 Introduction

A matrix is a set of numbers arranged in rows and columns as shown.

$$\begin{matrix} \text{col. 1} & \text{col. 2} & \text{col. 3} & \\ \end{matrix}$$
$$\begin{pmatrix} 6 & 5 & 4 \\ 3 & 2 & 1 \end{pmatrix} \begin{matrix} \text{row 1} \\ \text{row 2} \end{matrix}$$

This matrix has two rows and three columns. We say that this matrix has **order** 2 by 3 (written 2×3).

We must remember that only matrices (plural of matrix) of the same order may be added or subtracted.

23.2 Addition of matrices

In the addition of matrices, we add corresponding elements of the matrices together, which gives us a matrix of the same order.

General case

$$\begin{pmatrix} a & b \\ c & d \end{pmatrix} + \begin{pmatrix} e & f \\ g & h \end{pmatrix} = \begin{pmatrix} a+e & b+f \\ c+g & d+h \end{pmatrix}$$

Add the following matrices.

Example 1

$$\begin{pmatrix} 4 & 2 \\ 3 & 5 \end{pmatrix} + \begin{pmatrix} 0 & 1 \\ 2 & 2 \end{pmatrix} = \begin{pmatrix} 4+0 & 2+1 \\ 3+2 & 5+2 \end{pmatrix} = \begin{pmatrix} 4 & 3 \\ 5 & 7 \end{pmatrix}$$

Example 2

$$\begin{pmatrix} 3 & -1 & 2 \\ -4 & 2 & 1 \end{pmatrix} + \begin{pmatrix} -2 & 4 & -3 \\ 4 & -1 & 2 \end{pmatrix} = \begin{pmatrix} 1 & 3 & -1 \\ 0 & 1 & 3 \end{pmatrix}$$

Example 3

$$\begin{pmatrix} -4 \\ 2 \end{pmatrix} + \begin{pmatrix} -2 \\ -3 \end{pmatrix} = \begin{pmatrix} -6 \\ -1 \end{pmatrix}$$

Example 4

$$\begin{pmatrix} \frac{2}{3} & \frac{1}{4} \\ -2 & 0 \end{pmatrix} + \begin{pmatrix} \frac{4}{3} & -\frac{3}{4} \\ 1 & -2 \end{pmatrix} = \begin{pmatrix} 2 & -\frac{1}{2} \\ -1 & -2 \end{pmatrix}$$

Example 5

$$\begin{pmatrix} 2m & 3n \\ 4m & -2n \end{pmatrix} + \begin{pmatrix} -m & n \\ m & -3n \end{pmatrix} = \begin{pmatrix} m & 4n \\ 5m & -5n \end{pmatrix}$$

Example 6

If $P = \begin{pmatrix} 3 & 2 \\ 1 & 4 \end{pmatrix}$ $Q = \begin{pmatrix} 5 & -2 \\ -1 & 3 \end{pmatrix}$ $R = \begin{pmatrix} 3 & -4 \\ 2 & -1 \end{pmatrix}$ find,

(i) $P + Q + R$

i.e. $\begin{pmatrix} 3 & 2 \\ 1 & 4 \end{pmatrix} + \begin{pmatrix} 5 & -2 \\ -1 & 3 \end{pmatrix} + \begin{pmatrix} 3 & -4 \\ 2 & -1 \end{pmatrix} = \begin{pmatrix} 11 & -4 \\ 2 & 6 \end{pmatrix}$

(ii) $P + Q = \begin{pmatrix} 3 & 2 \\ 1 & 4 \end{pmatrix} + \begin{pmatrix} 5 & -2 \\ -1 & 3 \end{pmatrix} = \begin{pmatrix} 8 & 0 \\ 0 & 7 \end{pmatrix}$

(iii) $Q + P = \begin{pmatrix} 5 & -2 \\ -1 & 3 \end{pmatrix} + \begin{pmatrix} 3 & 2 \\ 1 & 4 \end{pmatrix} = \begin{pmatrix} 8 & 0 \\ 0 & 7 \end{pmatrix}$

Parts **(ii)** and **(iii)** show us that matrix addition is a **commutative** operation.

Example 7 $\begin{pmatrix} 5 & 4 \\ 3 & 2 \\ 1 & 0 \end{pmatrix} + \begin{pmatrix} 0 & 1 & 2 \\ 3 & 4 & 5 \end{pmatrix}$

Since these two matrices are not of the same order (i.e. 3×2 and 2×3), it is absolutely impossible for us to add them together.

Activities

1 State the order of each of the following matrices.

(a) $\begin{pmatrix} 2 & 1 & 3 \\ 2 & 3 & 5 \end{pmatrix}$ **(b)** $\begin{pmatrix} 5 & 1 \\ 2 & 4 \\ 1 & 7 \end{pmatrix}$ **(c)** $\begin{pmatrix} 2 & 5 & 9 \end{pmatrix}$

(d) $\begin{pmatrix} 4 \\ 3 \\ 5 \end{pmatrix}$ **(e)** $\begin{pmatrix} -1 & -3 \\ 3 & 6 \end{pmatrix}$ **(f)** $\begin{pmatrix} 1 & 4 & 8 \\ 3 & 5 & 6 \\ 5 & 4 & 0 \end{pmatrix}$

2 Find the sums of these matrices.

(a) $\begin{pmatrix} 1 \\ 4 \end{pmatrix} + \begin{pmatrix} 4 \\ 7 \end{pmatrix}$ **(b)** $\begin{pmatrix} 2 & 4 \end{pmatrix} + \begin{pmatrix} 3 & 1 \end{pmatrix}$

(c) $\begin{pmatrix} 5 & -3 \end{pmatrix} + \begin{pmatrix} -1 & 2 \end{pmatrix}$ **(d)** $\begin{pmatrix} -4 \\ 1 \end{pmatrix} + \begin{pmatrix} 5 \\ 2 \end{pmatrix}$

(e) $\begin{pmatrix} a & c \end{pmatrix} + \begin{pmatrix} 3a & -2c \end{pmatrix}$ **(f)** $\begin{pmatrix} c \\ e \end{pmatrix} + \begin{pmatrix} d \\ b \end{pmatrix}$

(g) $\begin{pmatrix} 3 & 5 \\ 2 & 1 \end{pmatrix} + \begin{pmatrix} 4 & 6 \\ 3 & 1 \end{pmatrix}$ **(h)** $\begin{pmatrix} -1 & 4 \\ 2 & 0 \end{pmatrix} + \begin{pmatrix} 2 & 5 \\ -1 & 6 \end{pmatrix}$

(i) $\begin{pmatrix} 1\frac{1}{2} & 3 \\ 5 & 2 \end{pmatrix} + \begin{pmatrix} 2\frac{1}{2} & -1 \\ -3 & 3\frac{1}{2} \end{pmatrix}$ **(j)** $\begin{pmatrix} \frac{3}{4} & -1 \\ \frac{2}{3} & 0 \end{pmatrix} + \begin{pmatrix} \frac{1}{2} & -\frac{1}{4} \\ \frac{1}{3} & -1 \end{pmatrix}$

(k) $\begin{pmatrix} a & 2c \\ 2a & -c \end{pmatrix} + \begin{pmatrix} 3a & -c \\ 5a & 0 \end{pmatrix}$

(l) $\begin{pmatrix} 3x & 4y \\ -x & 2y \end{pmatrix} + \begin{pmatrix} -x & -2y \\ 3x & -y \end{pmatrix}$

3 Given, $A = \begin{pmatrix} 4 & 0 \\ 5 & 3 \end{pmatrix}$ $B = \begin{pmatrix} -2 & -3 \\ 7 & 2 \end{pmatrix}$ $C = \begin{pmatrix} 0 & 3 \\ 5 & -1 \end{pmatrix}$

find the following matrices.

(a) $A + B$ **(b)** $C + B$ **(c)** $B + A$
(d) $A + B + C$

4 Given,

$X = \begin{pmatrix} -1 & 0 \\ 2 & 3 \end{pmatrix}$ $Y = \begin{pmatrix} -2 & -1 \\ -5 & 0 \end{pmatrix}$ $Z = \begin{pmatrix} 3 & 0 \\ -2 & 5 \end{pmatrix}$

find the following matrices.

(a) $X + Y$ **(b)** $Y + Z$ **(c)** $X + Z$
(d) $(X + Y) + Z$ **(e)** $X + (Y + Z)$

What law for addition of matrices does this verify?

23.3 Subtraction of matrices

General case

$$\begin{pmatrix} a & b \\ c & d \end{pmatrix} - \begin{pmatrix} e & f \\ g & h \end{pmatrix} = \begin{pmatrix} a-e & b-f \\ c-g & d-h \end{pmatrix}$$

In performing the subtraction, we must be very careful indeed to take note of the signs of each of the elements, and to apply our knowledge of directed number in dealing with them.

Example 1

$$\begin{pmatrix} 7 & 4 \\ 5 & 3 \end{pmatrix} - \begin{pmatrix} 2 & 3 \\ 2 & 3 \end{pmatrix} = \begin{pmatrix} 7-2 & 4-3 \\ 5-2 & 3-3 \end{pmatrix} = \begin{pmatrix} 5 & 1 \\ 3 & 0 \end{pmatrix}$$

Example 2

$$\begin{pmatrix} -7 & 3 \\ 1 & -2 \end{pmatrix} - \begin{pmatrix} 2 & -4 \\ 3 & -5 \end{pmatrix} = \begin{pmatrix} -7-2 & 3--4 \\ 1-3 & -2--5 \end{pmatrix}$$
$$= \begin{pmatrix} -9 & 7 \\ -2 & 3 \end{pmatrix}$$

Check $-7 \ -2 = -9$; $\quad 3 - -4 = 3 + 4 = 7$;
$1 - \ 3 = -2$; $\quad -2 - -5 = 3$

Example 3

$$\begin{pmatrix} 15 & 6 & 1 \\ 2 & 3 & -9 \end{pmatrix} - \begin{pmatrix} 2 & -8 & 6 \\ 4 & 3 & 10 \end{pmatrix} = \begin{pmatrix} 13 & 14 & -5 \\ -2 & 0 & -19 \end{pmatrix}$$

Example 4

$$\begin{pmatrix} 4 \\ -3 \end{pmatrix} - \begin{pmatrix} -2 \\ 1 \end{pmatrix} = \begin{pmatrix} 6 \\ -4 \end{pmatrix}$$

Example 5

$$\begin{pmatrix} -2a & 3b \\ -c & 2d \end{pmatrix} - \begin{pmatrix} 3a & 4b \\ -4c & -2d \end{pmatrix} = \begin{pmatrix} -5a & -b \\ 3c & 4d \end{pmatrix}$$

Example 6

If $P = \begin{pmatrix} 3 & 2 \\ 1 & 4 \end{pmatrix}$ $Q = \begin{pmatrix} 5 & -2 \\ -1 & 3 \end{pmatrix}$ $R = \begin{pmatrix} 3 & -4 \\ 2 & -1 \end{pmatrix}$ find,

(i) $P - Q = \begin{pmatrix} 3 & 2 \\ 1 & 4 \end{pmatrix} - \begin{pmatrix} 5 & -2 \\ -1 & 3 \end{pmatrix} = \begin{pmatrix} -2 & 4 \\ 2 & 1 \end{pmatrix}$

(ii) $Q - R = \begin{pmatrix} 5 & -2 \\ -1 & 3 \end{pmatrix} - \begin{pmatrix} 3 & -4 \\ 2 & -1 \end{pmatrix} = \begin{pmatrix} 2 & 2 \\ -3 & 4 \end{pmatrix}$

(iii) $P - R = \begin{pmatrix} 3 & 2 \\ 1 & 4 \end{pmatrix} - \begin{pmatrix} 3 & -4 \\ 2 & -1 \end{pmatrix} = \begin{pmatrix} 0 & 6 \\ -1 & 5 \end{pmatrix}$

Example 7 $\begin{pmatrix} 2 \\ -3 \end{pmatrix} - (3 \quad 2)$

This cannot possibly be done since the matrices are of different orders (i.e. 2×1 and 1×2).

It is possible to solve some reasonably simple equations involving addition and subtraction of matrices by following normal algebraic rules.

Example 8 Solve $A + \begin{pmatrix} 3 & -5 \\ 2 & -1 \end{pmatrix} = \begin{pmatrix} 9 & 4 \\ -2 & -3 \end{pmatrix}$

$$A = \begin{pmatrix} 9 & 4 \\ -2 & -3 \end{pmatrix} - \begin{pmatrix} 3 & -5 \\ 2 & -1 \end{pmatrix}$$

Hence, $A = \begin{pmatrix} 6 & 9 \\ -4 & -2 \end{pmatrix}$

Activities

1 Simplify each of these.

(a) $\begin{pmatrix} 5 \\ 4 \end{pmatrix} - \begin{pmatrix} 1 \\ 2 \end{pmatrix}$ **(b)** $\begin{pmatrix} 2 \\ 3 \end{pmatrix} - \begin{pmatrix} 5 \\ 9 \end{pmatrix}$ **(c)** $\begin{pmatrix} -1 \\ 2 \end{pmatrix} - \begin{pmatrix} -3 \\ -4 \end{pmatrix}$

(d) $\begin{pmatrix} 4 \\ 3 \end{pmatrix} - \begin{pmatrix} -1 \\ -5 \end{pmatrix}$ **(e)** $\begin{pmatrix} -2 \\ -2 \end{pmatrix} - \begin{pmatrix} 0 \\ 4 \end{pmatrix}$

2 Simplify these (2×2) matrices.

(a) $\begin{pmatrix} 6 & 4 \\ 3 & 2 \end{pmatrix} - \begin{pmatrix} 2 & 2 \\ 1 & 0 \end{pmatrix}$ **(b)** $\begin{pmatrix} 4 & -2 \\ 5 & 8 \end{pmatrix} - \begin{pmatrix} 0 & -2 \\ -3 & 0 \end{pmatrix}$

(c) $\begin{pmatrix} 2 & 3 \\ -3 & 1 \end{pmatrix} - \begin{pmatrix} 5 & -1 \\ -2 & 3 \end{pmatrix}$ **(d)** $\begin{pmatrix} -1 & 0 \\ 3 & 1 \end{pmatrix} - \begin{pmatrix} -2 & -3 \\ -2 & -1 \end{pmatrix}$

(e) $\begin{pmatrix} 2x & y \\ x & 2y \end{pmatrix} - \begin{pmatrix} x & 3y \\ -x & -y \end{pmatrix}$

(f) $\begin{pmatrix} 0 & 4h \\ -g & h \end{pmatrix} - \begin{pmatrix} g & 2h \\ -3g & -h \end{pmatrix}$

3 Given, $A = \begin{pmatrix} 1 & 2 \\ 3 & 4 \end{pmatrix}$ $B = \begin{pmatrix} -3 & 4 \\ 1 & 0 \end{pmatrix}$ $C = \begin{pmatrix} 4 & 1 \\ -1 & 2 \end{pmatrix}$
find the following matrices.

(a) $A + B$ **(b)** $A + C$ **(c)** $A - B$
(d) $C - B$ **(e)** $(A + B) - (A + C)$

4 Solve these equations for the (2×2) matrix X.

(a) $X - \begin{pmatrix} 2 & 1 \\ 3 & 1 \end{pmatrix} = \begin{pmatrix} 1 & 0 \\ 0 & -1 \end{pmatrix}$

(b) $\begin{pmatrix} 2 & 3 \\ -1 & 4 \end{pmatrix} - X = \begin{pmatrix} 4 & 1 \\ 3 & 2 \end{pmatrix}$

(c) $X + \begin{pmatrix} 2 & 1 \\ 1 & -1 \end{pmatrix} = \begin{pmatrix} -3 & 1 \\ 3 & 2 \end{pmatrix}$

(d) $X - \begin{pmatrix} 1 & 4 \\ -1 & -2 \end{pmatrix} = \begin{pmatrix} 3 & 7 \\ 9 & 4 \end{pmatrix}$

23.4 Multiplying a matrix by a scalar

Here we multiply the matrix by a given fixed number. Each element of the matrix is, in turn, multiplied by this number.

General case

$$k\begin{pmatrix} a & b \\ c & d \end{pmatrix} = \begin{pmatrix} ka & kb \\ kc & kd \end{pmatrix}$$

Example 1

$$2\begin{pmatrix} 3 & 1 \\ 0 & 2 \end{pmatrix} = \begin{pmatrix} 2 \times 3 & 2 \times 1 \\ 2 \times 0 & 2 \times 2 \end{pmatrix} = \begin{pmatrix} 6 & 2 \\ 0 & 4 \end{pmatrix}$$

Example 2

$$3\begin{pmatrix} -4 & 2 \\ 1 & -3 \\ 0 & -1 \end{pmatrix} = \begin{pmatrix} -12 & 6 \\ 3 & -9 \\ 0 & -3 \end{pmatrix}$$

Example 3

$$-4\begin{pmatrix} 1 & -3 \\ -2 & 1 \end{pmatrix} = \begin{pmatrix} -4 & 12 \\ 8 & -4 \end{pmatrix}$$

Example 4

$$-\tfrac{1}{4}\begin{pmatrix}-3 & 4\\ 2 & -5\end{pmatrix}=\begin{pmatrix}\frac{3}{4} & -1\\ -\frac{1}{2} & \frac{5}{4}\end{pmatrix}$$

It is of course possible to solve reasonably simple matrix equations.

Example 5

Solve, $4A=\begin{pmatrix}16\\-8\\12\end{pmatrix}$

$$\therefore A=\begin{pmatrix}\frac{16}{4}\\ \frac{-8}{4}\\ \frac{12}{4}\end{pmatrix}=\begin{pmatrix}4\\-2\\3\end{pmatrix}$$

Example 6

Solve, $3B+\begin{pmatrix}5 & 8\\ 2 & -1\end{pmatrix}=\begin{pmatrix}8 & 2\\ -1 & 5\end{pmatrix}$

$$3B=\begin{pmatrix}8 & 2\\ -1 & 5\end{pmatrix}-\begin{pmatrix}5 & 8\\ 2 & -1\end{pmatrix}=\begin{pmatrix}3 & -6\\ -3 & 6\end{pmatrix}$$

$$\therefore B=\begin{pmatrix}1 & -2\\ -1 & 2\end{pmatrix}$$

Activities

1 Work out the following.

(a) $4\begin{pmatrix}1\\2\end{pmatrix}$ **(b)** $3\begin{pmatrix}4\\2\\1\end{pmatrix}$ **(c)** $2(1\quad 3\quad 5)$

(d) $3\begin{pmatrix}2 & 5\\ 3 & 1\end{pmatrix}$ **(e)** $\frac{1}{2}\begin{pmatrix}2 & 4\\ 6 & 8\end{pmatrix}$ **(f)** $-2\begin{pmatrix}1 & -2\\ 3 & 1\end{pmatrix}$

2 If $X=\begin{pmatrix}2 & 5\\ 1 & 3\end{pmatrix}$ then find these matrices.

(a) $2X$ **(b)** $3X$ **(c)** $5X$ **(d)** $-2(X)$

3 If $Y=\begin{pmatrix}-2 & 3\\ 1 & 2\end{pmatrix}$ then find these (2×2) matrices.

(a) $2Y+3Y$ **(b)** $3Y-4Y$ **(c)** $6Y-2Y$
(d) Do these examples follow the normal rules of algebra?

4 If $A=\begin{pmatrix}2 & -3\\ 4 & 0\end{pmatrix}$ and $B=\begin{pmatrix}-3 & 4\\ 2 & -1\end{pmatrix}$ simplify,

(a) $2A$ **(b)** $2B$ **(c)** $3A$
(d) $A+B$ **(e)** $2(A+B)$ **(f)** $2A+2B$
(g) $A-B$ **(h)** $2(A-B)$ **(i)** $2A-2B$
(j) What do equal matrices suggest?

5 Solve each of these.

(a) $3X=\begin{pmatrix}12\\-9\\-6\end{pmatrix}$ **(b)** $2X+\begin{pmatrix}3\\5\\7\end{pmatrix}=\begin{pmatrix}7\\1\\9\end{pmatrix}$

(c) $3X=\begin{pmatrix}6 & 15\\ -3 & 9\end{pmatrix}$ **(d)** $2X+\begin{pmatrix}3 & 1\\ 4 & 2\end{pmatrix}=\begin{pmatrix}9 & 5\\ 2 & 8\end{pmatrix}$

(e) $2X-\begin{pmatrix}5 & 3\\ -2 & 0\end{pmatrix}=\begin{pmatrix}-1 & 2\\ 1 & 3\end{pmatrix}$

23.5 Multiplication of two matrices

We can only multiply two matrices together if the number of columns in the first matrix is the same as the number of rows in the second matrix.

The resulting matrix will have the same number of rows as the first matrix and the same number of columns as the second matrix. Hence, a (3×2) matrix multiplied by a (2×4) matrix produces a (3×4) matrix result.

We shall restrict our study of matrix multiplication to the following pairs,

(a) (1×2) multiplied by (2×1)
(b) (2×2) multiplied by (2×1)
(c) (2×2) multiplied by (2×2)

(a) General case

$$\begin{pmatrix}\overset{\text{1st}}{a} & \overset{\text{2nd}}{b}\end{pmatrix}\begin{pmatrix}\overset{\text{1st}}{c}\\ \overset{\text{2nd}}{d}\end{pmatrix}=(ac+bd)$$

$(1\times 2)\times(2\times 1)$ gives a (1×1) result.

Note the sequence of the operation:
First element of the first matrix × first element of the second matrix; **plus**, second element of the first matrix × second element of the second matrix.

Example 1

$$(4\quad 3)\begin{pmatrix}-2\\4\end{pmatrix}=((4\times -2)+(3\times 4))$$
$$=(-8+12)=(4)$$

(b) General case

$$\begin{pmatrix}\overset{\text{1st}}{a} & \overset{\text{2nd}}{b}\\ \overset{\text{3rd}}{c} & \overset{\text{4th}}{d}\end{pmatrix}\begin{pmatrix}\overset{\text{1st}}{e}\\ \overset{\text{2nd}}{f}\end{pmatrix}=\begin{pmatrix}ae+bf\\ ce+df\end{pmatrix}$$

$(2\times 2)\times(2\times 1)$ gives a (2×1) result.

Note the sequence of the operation:
First element of the first matrix × first element of second matrix **plus**, second element of first matrix × second element of second matrix. This gives the top (first) element of the result.

Then, third element of first matrix × first element of second matrix, **plus**, fourth element of first matrix × second element of second matrix.

Example 2

$$\begin{pmatrix}2 & 3\\ -1 & 4\end{pmatrix}\begin{pmatrix}-2\\5\end{pmatrix}=\begin{pmatrix}(2\times -2)+(3\times 5)\\ (-1\times -2)+(4\times 5)\end{pmatrix}$$
$$=\begin{pmatrix}-4+15\\ 2+20\end{pmatrix}=\begin{pmatrix}11\\22\end{pmatrix}$$

(c) General case

$$\underset{A}{\begin{pmatrix}\overset{\text{1st}}{a} & \overset{\text{2nd}}{b}\\ \overset{\text{3rd}}{c} & \overset{\text{4th}}{d}\end{pmatrix}}\underset{B}{\begin{pmatrix}\overset{\text{1st}}{e} & \overset{\text{2nd}}{f}\\ \overset{\text{3rd}}{g} & \overset{\text{4th}}{h}\end{pmatrix}}=\begin{pmatrix}ae+bg & af+bh\\ ce+dg & cf+dh\end{pmatrix}$$

$(2\times 2)\times(2\times 2)$ gives a (2×2) result.

Note the sequence of the operation:
As in the previous simpler cases, this technique depends on multiplying the elements of the rows of the first matrix by the elements of the columns of the second matrix.

Hence the first element of matrix $A \times$ the first element of matrix B, added to the second element of matrix $A \times$ the third element of matrix B, gives the first element of the result.

Then, (first element of $A \times$ second element of B) + (second element of $A \times$ fourth element of B) gives the second element of the result.

Then, (third element of $A \times$ first element of B) + (fourth element of $A \times$ third element of B) gives the third element of the result.

And, (third element of $A \times$ second element of B) + (fourth element of $A \times$ fourth element of B) gives the fourth element of the result.

Example 3

$$\begin{pmatrix}2 & 3\\4 & 1\end{pmatrix}\begin{pmatrix}1 & 4\\5 & 2\end{pmatrix} = \begin{pmatrix}(2\times 1)+(3\times 5) & (2\times 4)+(3\times 2)\\(4\times 1)+(1\times 5) & (4\times 4)+(1\times 2)\end{pmatrix}$$

$$= \begin{pmatrix}2+15 & 8+6\\4+\ 5 & 16+2\end{pmatrix} = \begin{pmatrix}17 & 14\\9 & 18\end{pmatrix}$$

Example 4

$$\begin{pmatrix}-2 & 0\\3 & 1\end{pmatrix}\begin{pmatrix}4 & -2\\-1 & 6\end{pmatrix}$$

$$= \begin{pmatrix}(-2\times 4)+(0\times -1) & (-2\times -2)+(0\times 6)\\(\ 3\times 4)+(1\times -1) & (\ 3\times -2)+(1\times 6)\end{pmatrix}$$

$$= \begin{pmatrix}-8+0 & 4+0\\12-1 & -6+6\end{pmatrix}$$

$$= \begin{pmatrix}-8 & 4\\11 & 0\end{pmatrix}$$

Example 5 $A = \begin{pmatrix}3 & -1\\2 & 2\end{pmatrix}$ $B = \begin{pmatrix}4 & 2\\-1 & 0\end{pmatrix}$

Find, **(a)** $A.B$ **(b)** $B.A$

(a) $A.B = \begin{pmatrix}3 & -1\\2 & 2\end{pmatrix}\begin{pmatrix}4 & 2\\-1 & 0\end{pmatrix}$

$$= \begin{pmatrix}(3\times 4)+(-1\times -1) & (3\times 2)+(-1\times 0)\\(2\times 4)+(\ 2\times -1) & (2\times 2)+(\ 2\times 0)\end{pmatrix}$$

$$= \begin{pmatrix}12+1 & 6+0\\8-2 & 4+0\end{pmatrix}$$

$$= \begin{pmatrix}13 & 6\\6 & 4\end{pmatrix}$$

(b) $B.A = \begin{pmatrix}4 & 2\\-1 & 0\end{pmatrix}\begin{pmatrix}3 & -1\\2 & 2\end{pmatrix}$

$$= \begin{pmatrix}(\ 4\times 3)+(2\times 2) & (\ 4\times -1)+(2\times 2)\\(-1\times 3)+(0\times 2) & (-1\times -1)+(0\times 2)\end{pmatrix}$$

$$= \begin{pmatrix}12+4 & -4+4\\-3+0 & 1+0\end{pmatrix}$$

$$= \begin{pmatrix}16 & 0\\-3 & 1\end{pmatrix}$$

Note If we compare the results obtained from $A.B$ and $B.A$ we can see that they are completely different.

Thus, since $AB \neq BA$, then obviously matrix multiplication is **non-commutative**.

In the case of three or more matrices being multiplied together, the order in which the problem is tackled is vitally important.

Hence, for $A \times B \times C$, we can perform this calculation in two ways and achieve the correct result, either by doing $(A \times B) \times C$, i.e. multiply the first two together and then multiply the result by the third, or $A \times (B \times C)$, i.e. multiply the second and third together and pre-multiply the result by the first.

Activities

1 Find the following products.

(a) $(1\ \ 3)\begin{pmatrix}4\\2\end{pmatrix}$ **(b)** $(2\ \ 5)\begin{pmatrix}1\\4\end{pmatrix}$ **(c)** $(1\ \ -2)\begin{pmatrix}4\\1\end{pmatrix}$

(d) $(-1\ \ -2)\begin{pmatrix}-2\\3\end{pmatrix}$ **(e)** $\begin{pmatrix}1 & 2\\0 & 1\end{pmatrix}\begin{pmatrix}3\\4\end{pmatrix}$

(f) $\begin{pmatrix}2 & 5\\1 & 3\end{pmatrix}\begin{pmatrix}1\\2\end{pmatrix}$ **(g)** $\begin{pmatrix}-2 & 1\\1 & -1\end{pmatrix}\begin{pmatrix}5\\1\end{pmatrix}$

(h) $\begin{pmatrix}-2 & \frac{1}{2}\\\frac{1}{2} & 3\end{pmatrix}\begin{pmatrix}4\\2\end{pmatrix}$ **(i)** $\begin{pmatrix}3 & -2\\-2 & -3\end{pmatrix}\begin{pmatrix}-1\\4\end{pmatrix}$

(j) $\begin{pmatrix}3 & 4\\0 & -2\end{pmatrix}\begin{pmatrix}4\\-3\end{pmatrix}$

2 Calculate,

(a) $\begin{pmatrix}2 & 1\\3 & 0\end{pmatrix}\begin{pmatrix}1 & 3\\1 & 4\end{pmatrix}$ **(b)** $\begin{pmatrix}3 & 2\\1 & 5\end{pmatrix}\begin{pmatrix}5 & 0\\2 & 3\end{pmatrix}$

(c) $\begin{pmatrix}0 & 5\\1 & 0\end{pmatrix}\begin{pmatrix}3 & 7\\2 & 4\end{pmatrix}$ **(d)** $\begin{pmatrix}4 & 3\\1 & 0\end{pmatrix}\begin{pmatrix}2 & 6\\0 & 5\end{pmatrix}$

(e) $\begin{pmatrix}-1 & 8\\4 & -2\end{pmatrix}\begin{pmatrix}2 & 5\\3 & 0\end{pmatrix}$ **(f)** $\begin{pmatrix}2 & -3\\-1 & -3\end{pmatrix}\begin{pmatrix}3 & 2\\-1 & 5\end{pmatrix}$

(g) $\begin{pmatrix}0 & 2\\3 & 1\end{pmatrix}\begin{pmatrix}4 & -1\\-2 & 3\end{pmatrix}$ **(h)** $\begin{pmatrix}-1 & 2\\0 & 3\end{pmatrix}\begin{pmatrix}-1 & 2\\0 & 3\end{pmatrix}$

3 Given that, $G = \begin{pmatrix}2 & 5\\3 & 1\end{pmatrix}$ $H = \begin{pmatrix}-5 & 2\\2 & 4\end{pmatrix}$

find, **(a)** GH **(b)** HG

4 Given,

$A = \begin{pmatrix}-2 & 0\\5 & -2\end{pmatrix}$ $B = \begin{pmatrix}1 & 3\\3 & -1\end{pmatrix}$ $C = \begin{pmatrix}-2 & 6\\4 & 0\end{pmatrix}$

find, **(a)** AB **(b)** BA **(c)** AC **(d)** BC **(e)** $AB + AC$ **(f)** $A(B + C)$

5 Calculate,

(a) $\begin{pmatrix}-3 & -2\\2 & -1\end{pmatrix}\begin{pmatrix}-4 & -1\\-1 & 0\end{pmatrix}$ **(b)** $\begin{pmatrix}0 & 2\\2 & 0\end{pmatrix}\begin{pmatrix}0 & 1\\0 & 3\end{pmatrix}$

23.6 The identity matrix

If we multiply any (2×2) matrix by $\begin{pmatrix}1 & 0\\0 & 1\end{pmatrix}$ the matrix is unaltered.

General case

$\begin{pmatrix}a & b\\c & d\end{pmatrix}\begin{pmatrix}1 & 0\\0 & 1\end{pmatrix}$ gives the result $\begin{pmatrix}a & b\\c & d\end{pmatrix}$

Having this special quality, we say that

$$\begin{pmatrix}1 & 0\\0 & 1\end{pmatrix}$$

is the **identity matrix** (I) for matrix multiplication and, in general, $A.I = A$.

It is interesting to note that $I.A$ also equals A, which produces an obvious exception to the non-commutative rule.

We can see this for ourselves when attempting the examples in the Activities following, by reversing the pairings and showing that the results are indeed the same.

Suppose we now consider the following.

If $A = \begin{pmatrix} 11 & 5 \\ 2 & 1 \end{pmatrix}$ and $B = \begin{pmatrix} 1 & -5 \\ -2 & 11 \end{pmatrix}$ find $A.B$

$\begin{pmatrix} 11 & 5 \\ 2 & 1 \end{pmatrix}\begin{pmatrix} 1 & -5 \\ -2 & 11 \end{pmatrix}$ gives the result $\begin{pmatrix} 1 & 0 \\ 0 & 1 \end{pmatrix}$

Hence, in this case, $A.B = I$

From this result, we say that matrix B is the inverse of matrix A (written A^{-1}) i.e. $B = A^{-1}$.

In general terms, a matrix multiplied by its inverse gives the identity matrix result. Thus,

$$A.A^{-1} = I$$

By reversing the two matrices and multiplying them together, we still obtain the identity matrix I, which of course implies that $A = B^{-1}$ and that also, $A^{-1}.A = I$ (another exception to the non-commutative nature of matrix multiplication).

Activities

1 Calculate

(a) $\begin{pmatrix} 1 & 0 \\ 0 & 1 \end{pmatrix}\begin{pmatrix} 2 & 3 \\ 1 & 5 \end{pmatrix}$ (b) $\begin{pmatrix} 1 & 0 \\ 0 & 1 \end{pmatrix}\begin{pmatrix} -2 & 3 \\ 3 & -2 \end{pmatrix}$

(c) $\begin{pmatrix} -2 & 5 \\ 3 & 1 \end{pmatrix}\begin{pmatrix} 1 & 0 \\ 0 & 1 \end{pmatrix}$ (d) $\begin{pmatrix} 2 & a \\ a & 5 \end{pmatrix}\begin{pmatrix} 1 & 0 \\ 0 & 1 \end{pmatrix}$

2 Fill in the missing figures in these.

(a) $\begin{pmatrix} ? & 4 \\ 5 & 2 \end{pmatrix}\begin{pmatrix} 1 & 0 \\ 0 & 1 \end{pmatrix} = \begin{pmatrix} 2 & ? \\ ? & ? \end{pmatrix}$

(b) $\begin{pmatrix} 1 & 0 \\ 0 & 1 \end{pmatrix}\begin{pmatrix} -2 & 5 \\ ? & 3 \end{pmatrix} = \begin{pmatrix} ? & ? \\ 2 & ? \end{pmatrix}$

3 Calculate,

(a) $\begin{pmatrix} 3 & 2 \\ 7 & 5 \end{pmatrix}\begin{pmatrix} 5 & -2 \\ -7 & 3 \end{pmatrix}$ (b) $\begin{pmatrix} -1 & 2 \\ -3 & 5 \end{pmatrix}\begin{pmatrix} 5 & -2 \\ 3 & -1 \end{pmatrix}$

(c) $\begin{pmatrix} 3 & 2 \\ 1 & 1 \end{pmatrix}\begin{pmatrix} 1 & -2 \\ -1 & 3 \end{pmatrix}$ (d) $\begin{pmatrix} 1 & 1 \\ 1 & 2 \end{pmatrix}\begin{pmatrix} 2 & -1 \\ -1 & 1 \end{pmatrix}$

4 Study the pattern in Question **3**. Now, in each case, below, try to write down the matrix that will give you the identity matrix as your answer when you multiply.

(a) $\begin{pmatrix} 2 & 1 \\ 1 & 1 \end{pmatrix}\begin{pmatrix} ? & ? \\ ? & ? \end{pmatrix} = \begin{pmatrix} 1 & 0 \\ 0 & 1 \end{pmatrix}$

(b) $\begin{pmatrix} 2 & 3 \\ 3 & 5 \end{pmatrix}\begin{pmatrix} ? & ? \\ ? & ? \end{pmatrix} = \begin{pmatrix} 1 & 0 \\ 0 & 1 \end{pmatrix}$

(c) $\begin{pmatrix} 4 & 3 \\ 9 & 7 \end{pmatrix}\begin{pmatrix} ? & ? \\ ? & ? \end{pmatrix} = \begin{pmatrix} 1 & 0 \\ 0 & 1 \end{pmatrix}$

23.7 The inverse of a matrix

Not all matrices have inverses and so we need a method of determining whether, or not, a matrix actually has an inverse.

We do this by finding the **determinant** of the matrix in the following way.

The determinant (det.) of $\begin{pmatrix} a & b \\ c & d \end{pmatrix} = ad - bc$

If the determinant $= 0$, then the matrix does **not** have an inverse.

Whereas, if the determinant $\neq 0$ (whether positive or negative) then the matrix has an inverse.

Example 1 Determine whether the following matrices have an inverse.

(a) $\begin{pmatrix} 3 & 6 \\ 1 & 2 \end{pmatrix}$ (b) $\begin{pmatrix} 4 & 6 \\ 3 & 5 \end{pmatrix}$ (c) $\begin{pmatrix} -2 & -3 \\ -5 & 4 \end{pmatrix}$

(a) The det. of $\begin{pmatrix} 3 & 6 \\ 1 & 2 \end{pmatrix} = 3 \times 2 - 6 \times 1$
$= 6 - 6$
$= 0$

Hence, $\begin{pmatrix} 3 & 6 \\ 1 & 2 \end{pmatrix}$ does not have an inverse matrix.

(b) The det. of $\begin{pmatrix} 4 & 6 \\ 3 & 5 \end{pmatrix} = 4 \times 5 - 6 \times 3$
$= 20 - 18$
$= 2$

Hence, $\begin{pmatrix} 4 & 6 \\ 3 & 5 \end{pmatrix}$ has an inverse matrix.

(c) The det. of $\begin{pmatrix} -2 & -3 \\ -5 & 4 \end{pmatrix} = -2 \times 4 - -3 \times -5$
$= -8 - 15$
$= -23$

Hence, $\begin{pmatrix} -2 & -3 \\ -5 & 4 \end{pmatrix}$ also has an inverse matrix.

Now having established that the matrix does have an inverse, we proceed as follows. We rearrange the matrix

$\begin{pmatrix} a & b \\ c & d \end{pmatrix}$ to be $\begin{pmatrix} d & -b \\ -c & a \end{pmatrix}$ and multiply this by $\frac{1}{\text{det.}}$

leading diagonal

i.e. we exchange the elements of the leading diagonal and reverse the signs of the elements of the other diagonal, multiplying the result by $\frac{1}{\text{det.}}$.

Example 2 Find A^{-1} if $A = \begin{pmatrix} 9 & 5 \\ 7 & 4 \end{pmatrix}$

Det. of $A = 36 - 35 = 1$

Hence, $A^{-1} = \frac{1}{1}\begin{pmatrix} 4 & -5 \\ -7 & 9 \end{pmatrix} = \begin{pmatrix} 4 & -5 \\ -7 & 9 \end{pmatrix}$

Of course, we have an obvious method of checking our result, since $A.A^{-1} = I$

We calculate $\begin{pmatrix} 9 & 5 \\ 7 & 4 \end{pmatrix}\begin{pmatrix} 4 & -5 \\ -7 & 9 \end{pmatrix}$ the result being $\begin{pmatrix} 1 & 0 \\ 0 & 1 \end{pmatrix}$

So, $\begin{pmatrix} 4 & -5 \\ -7 & 9 \end{pmatrix}$ is the inverse of $\begin{pmatrix} 9 & 5 \\ 7 & 4 \end{pmatrix}$

Example 3 Find B^{-1} if $B = \begin{pmatrix} 4 & 2 \\ -5 & -3 \end{pmatrix}$

Det. of $B = (4 \times -3) - (2 \times -5) = -12 + 10 = -2$

Hence, $B^{-1} = -\frac{1}{2} \begin{pmatrix} -3 & -2 \\ 5 & 4 \end{pmatrix}$

$= \begin{pmatrix} \frac{3}{2} & 1 \\ -\frac{5}{2} & -2 \end{pmatrix}$ (leave in improper fraction form)

Check $B.B^{-1} = \begin{pmatrix} 4 & 2 \\ -5 & -3 \end{pmatrix} \begin{pmatrix} \frac{3}{2} & 1 \\ -\frac{5}{2} & -2 \end{pmatrix}$

$$= \begin{pmatrix} (4 \times \frac{3}{2}) + (2 \times -\frac{5}{2}) & (4 \times 1) + (2 \times -2) \\ (-5 \times \frac{3}{2}) + (-3 \times -\frac{5}{2}) & (-5 \times 1) + (-3 \times -2) \end{pmatrix}$$

$$= \begin{pmatrix} 6 - 5 & 4 - 4 \\ -\frac{15}{2} + \frac{15}{2} & -5 + 6 \end{pmatrix}$$

$$= \begin{pmatrix} 1 & 0 \\ 0 & 1 \end{pmatrix}$$

Hence, inverse of $\begin{pmatrix} 4 & 2 \\ -5 & -3 \end{pmatrix}$ is $\begin{pmatrix} \frac{3}{2} & 1 \\ -\frac{5}{2} & -2 \end{pmatrix}$

Activities

1 Calculate the determinant for each of these.

(a) $\begin{pmatrix} 3 & 4 \\ 2 & 3 \end{pmatrix}$ **(b)** $\begin{pmatrix} 2 & 1 \\ 4 & 3 \end{pmatrix}$ **(c)** $\begin{pmatrix} 3 & 2 \\ 1 & 2 \end{pmatrix}$

(d) $\begin{pmatrix} 2 & -3 \\ -2 & -2 \end{pmatrix}$ **(e)** $\begin{pmatrix} 4 & -1 \\ 6 & 1 \end{pmatrix}$ **(f)** $\begin{pmatrix} 2 & -3 \\ 3 & 4 \end{pmatrix}$

2 Use your answers in Question **1** to find the inverse of the matrices.

3 Show that each of the following matrices is its own inverse.

(a) $\begin{pmatrix} -1 & 0 \\ 0 & 1 \end{pmatrix}$ **(b)** $\begin{pmatrix} 1 & 0 \\ 0 & -1 \end{pmatrix}$ **(c)** $\begin{pmatrix} 0 & -1 \\ -1 & 0 \end{pmatrix}$

4 Given, $A = \begin{pmatrix} 2 & 5 \\ 1 & 3 \end{pmatrix}$ and $B = \begin{pmatrix} 1 & 2 \\ 1 & 4 \end{pmatrix}$ calculate,

(a) AB **(b)** BA **(c)** A^{-1}
(d) B^{-1} **(e)** $(AB)^{-1}$ **(f)** $A^{-1}B^{-1}$

5 Given, $X = \begin{pmatrix} -1 & 3 \\ -1 & 4 \end{pmatrix}$ and $Y = \begin{pmatrix} 0 & -2 \\ 2 & 5 \end{pmatrix}$ calculate,

(a) XY **(b)** YX **(c)** X^{-1}
(d) Y^{-1} **(e)** $(XY)^{-1}$ **(f)** $X^{-1}Y^{-1}$

6 Why does the matrix $\begin{pmatrix} 3 & 12 \\ 2 & 8 \end{pmatrix}$ have no inverse?

7 If $A = \begin{pmatrix} 0 & -1 \\ 1 & 0 \end{pmatrix}$ find A^2 and A^3.

(Remember, $A^2 = A.A$ etc).
Hence, find the inverses of A^2 and A^3.

23.8 Matrix solutions to simultaneous equations

We can use matrices to solve simultaneous equations in the following way.

Example 1 Solve $2x + y = 1$
$5x + 3y = -1$

We re-write this in matrix form as

$$\begin{pmatrix} 2 & 1 \\ 5 & 3 \end{pmatrix} \begin{pmatrix} x \\ y \end{pmatrix} = \begin{pmatrix} 1 \\ -1 \end{pmatrix}$$

We find the inverse of $\begin{pmatrix} 2 & 1 \\ 5 & 3 \end{pmatrix}$ to be $\begin{pmatrix} 3 & -1 \\ -5 & 2 \end{pmatrix}$

Pre-multiplying the equation (both sides) by the inverse matrix gives,

$$\begin{pmatrix} 3 & -1 \\ -5 & 2 \end{pmatrix} \begin{pmatrix} 2 & 1 \\ 5 & 3 \end{pmatrix} \begin{pmatrix} x \\ y \end{pmatrix} = \begin{pmatrix} 3 & -1 \\ -5 & 2 \end{pmatrix} \begin{pmatrix} 1 \\ -1 \end{pmatrix}$$

$$\begin{pmatrix} 1 & 0 \\ 0 & 1 \end{pmatrix} \begin{pmatrix} x \\ y \end{pmatrix} = \begin{pmatrix} 4 \\ -7 \end{pmatrix}$$

$$\therefore \begin{pmatrix} x \\ y \end{pmatrix} = \begin{pmatrix} 4 \\ -7 \end{pmatrix}$$

Hence, the solution is $x = 4, y = -7$

Example 2 Solve $x + 3y = 1$
$4x - y = -2$

In matrix form, $\begin{pmatrix} 1 & 3 \\ 4 & -1 \end{pmatrix} \begin{pmatrix} x \\ y \end{pmatrix} = \begin{pmatrix} 1 \\ -2 \end{pmatrix}$

We find the inverse of $\begin{pmatrix} 1 & 3 \\ 4 & -1 \end{pmatrix}$ to be $-\frac{1}{13} \begin{pmatrix} -1 & -3 \\ -4 & 1 \end{pmatrix}$

i.e. $\begin{pmatrix} \frac{1}{13} & \frac{3}{13} \\ \frac{4}{13} & -\frac{1}{13} \end{pmatrix}$

Then, pre-multiplying both sides by the inverse gives,

$$\begin{pmatrix} \frac{1}{13} & \frac{3}{13} \\ \frac{4}{13} & -\frac{1}{13} \end{pmatrix} \begin{pmatrix} 1 & 3 \\ 4 & -1 \end{pmatrix} \begin{pmatrix} x \\ y \end{pmatrix} = \begin{pmatrix} \frac{1}{13} & \frac{3}{13} \\ \frac{4}{13} & -\frac{1}{13} \end{pmatrix} \begin{pmatrix} 1 \\ -2 \end{pmatrix}$$

$$\begin{pmatrix} 1 & 0 \\ 0 & 1 \end{pmatrix} \begin{pmatrix} x \\ y \end{pmatrix} = \begin{pmatrix} -\frac{5}{13} \\ \frac{6}{13} \end{pmatrix}$$

$$\begin{pmatrix} x \\ y \end{pmatrix} = \begin{pmatrix} -\frac{5}{13} \\ \frac{6}{13} \end{pmatrix}$$

Hence, the solution is $x = -\frac{5}{13}, y = \frac{6}{13}$

Note This is obviously a very useful method for finding the solution of a pair of simultaneous equations, but it cannot be used if the initial matrix does not have an inverse.

i.e. $7x + 14y = 5$
$x + 2y = 1$

Since $\begin{pmatrix} 7 & 14 \\ 1 & 2 \end{pmatrix}$ has no inverse (i.e. det. = 0), then we cannot solve the equations by this method.

Activities

1 Write down the pair of simultaneous equations given by the matrix $\begin{pmatrix}2 & 1\\1 & 1\end{pmatrix}\begin{pmatrix}x\\y\end{pmatrix} = \begin{pmatrix}11\\7\end{pmatrix}$.

By pre-multiplying both sides of the matrix equation by the matrix $\begin{pmatrix}1 & -1\\-1 & 2\end{pmatrix}$, find $\begin{pmatrix}x\\y\end{pmatrix}$.

2 Write in matrix form, the pair of equations,

$$3x + 2y = 9$$
$$x + y = 4$$

Pre-multiply both sides of the matrix equation by $\begin{pmatrix}1 & -2\\-1 & 3\end{pmatrix}$ and hence find x and y.

3 Use the method of matrices to solve for x and y,

(a) $2x + y = 1$, $5x + 3y = 3$ **(b)** $3x + 2y = 4$, $7x + 5y = 9$

(c) $2x + y = 10$, $3x + 2y = 17$ **(d)** $7x + 3y = -3$, $2x + y = 2$

4 Use the matrix method to solve these, but be careful in calculating the inverses.

(a) $2x + y = 11$, $x + 4y = 23$ **(b)** $2x + y = 1$, $x + 4y = 4$

(c) $2x - y = 1$, $3x - 2y = 2$ **(d)** $x - 3y = -1$, $x + 2y = 3$

5 Rearrange the following equations and then solve them by matrix methods.

(a) $2x = 9 - y$, $3x = 2(7 - y)$ **(b)** $2x = 4 - 3y$, $2 - x = 5y$

Unit 24

Mappings

24.1 Relations and mappings

A **relation** is a pairing of an element of one set A (the object or domain set), with an element of another set B (the image, co-domain or range set).

A **mapping** is a relation between two sets which links the elements of the domain with the elements of the range.

There are 3 types of mapping we should consider.

(a) One-to-one mappings, in which each element of the domain links with just one element in the range (see Fig. 24.1).

one-to-one

domain range

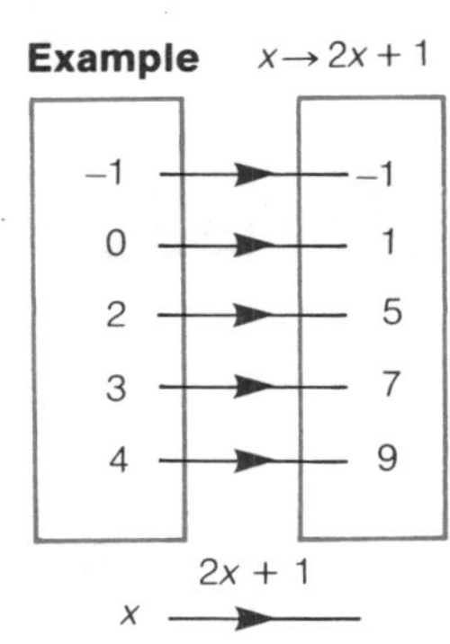

Fig. 24.1

(b) Many-to-one mappings, in which more than one element of the domain links with just one element of the range (see Fig. 24.2).

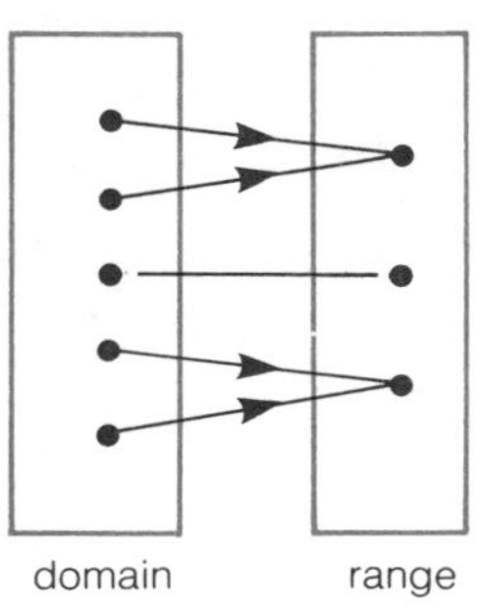

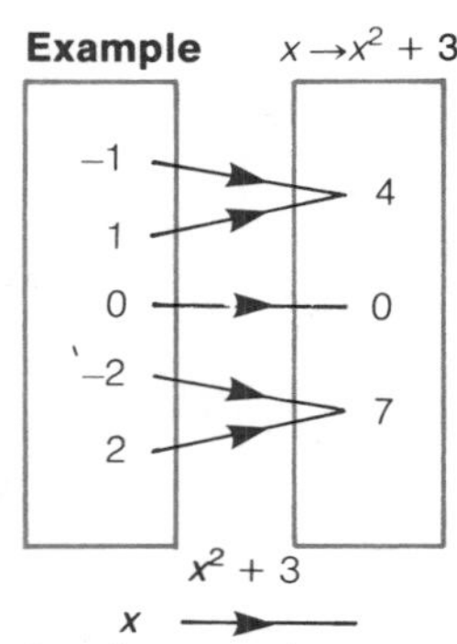

Fig. 24.2

(c) One-to-many mappings, in which an element of the domain links with more than one element in the range (see Fig. 24.3).

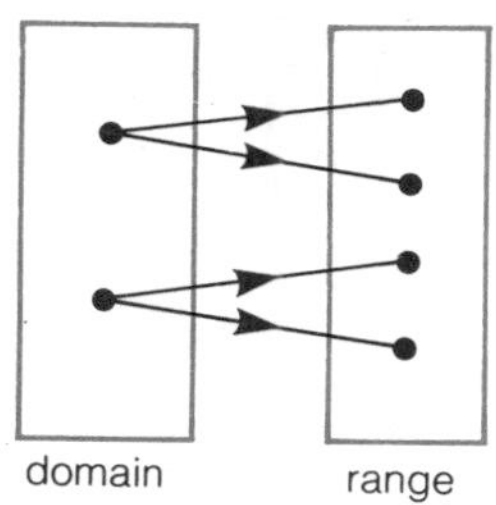

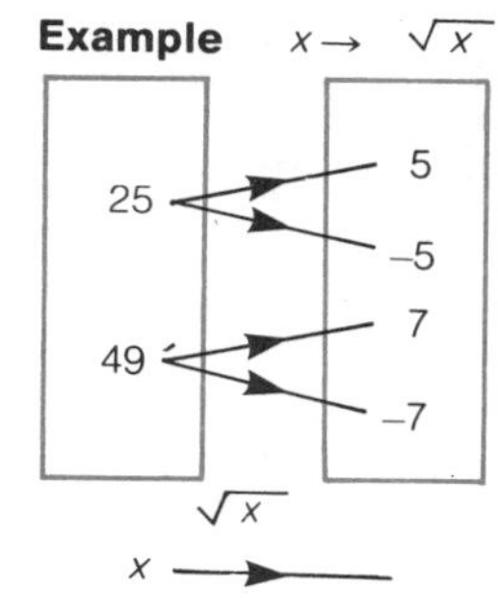

domain mapping range

Fig. 24.3

Activities

1 Draw an arrow diagram for each set, given the operations,

(a)	$\{1, 2, 3, 4, 5,\}$	$\rightarrow$	is 5 less than
(b)	$\{1, 3, 5, 7, 9,\}$	$\rightarrow$	is a quarter of
(c)	$\{1, 2, 3, 4, 5,\}$	$\rightarrow$	is the square root of
(d)	$\{\frac{1}{2}, \frac{3}{4}, \frac{1}{4}, 1\frac{1}{2}\}$	$\rightarrow$	is the same value as

2 Joan and Jean are tall, Jean and Mary are teenagers and Joan and Mary are prefects. Draw an arrow diagram to show the relationship between the set of girls and the set of characteristics.

3

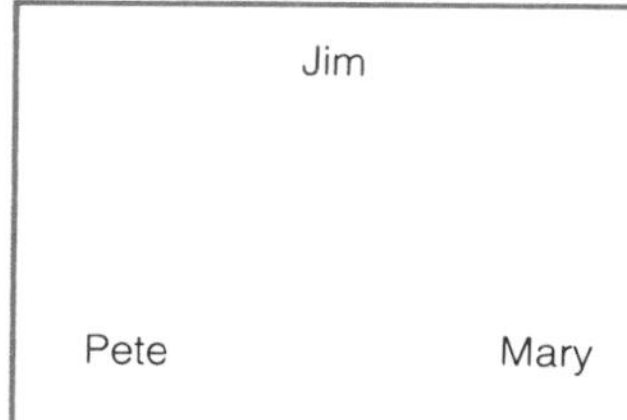

Fig. 24.4

Complete Fig. 24.4, using arrows to show the relationship 'is the brother of', if Mary, Pete and Jim are in the same family.

4 Describe in words, the relationship between the following pairs of sets.

(a)	$\{4, 9, 16\ 25\}$	$\{2, 3, 4, 5\}$
(b)	$\{\frac{1}{2}, 1, 1\frac{1}{2}, 2\}$	$\{2, 4, 6, 8\}$
(c)	$\{5, 10, 15, 20\}$	$\{1, 2, 3, 4\}$

5 Each of the arrow diagrams in Fig. 24.5, shows a relationship from one set to another. State which of these are mappings, and what kind of mapping they are.

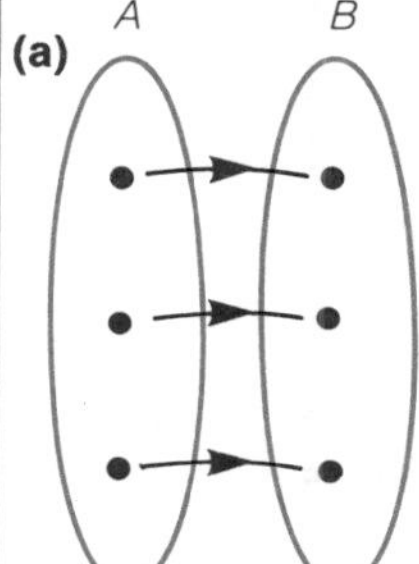

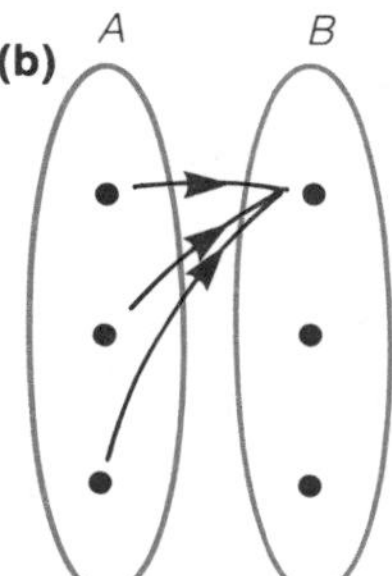

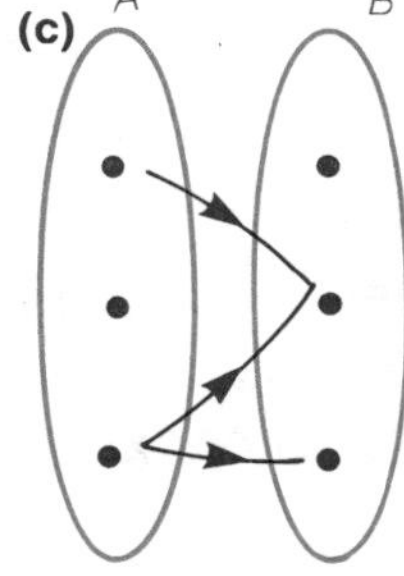

Fig. 24.5

24.2 Functions

Mappings that are one-to-one or many-to-one are called **functions**, but a one-to-many mapping is **not** a function.

The letters f, g, h are generally used to represent functions and we can write, for example, as follows.

1 $f(x) = 3x + 5$

where f is the name, or label of the function and $f(x)$ is the image of x when using f.

We can express $f(x) = 3x + 5$ in another way i.e. $f{:}x \rightarrow 3x + 5$, which we read as,

'f is a function such that x maps onto $3x + 5$'

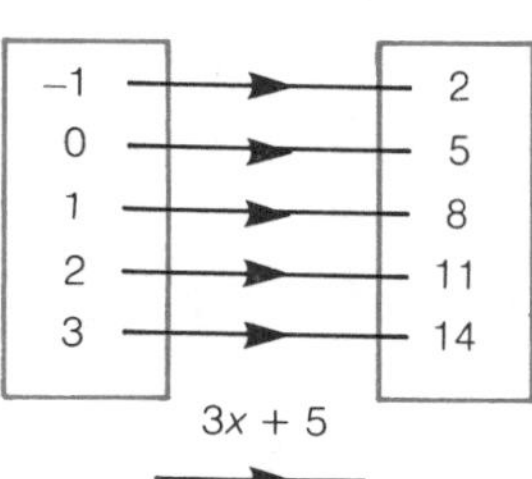

domain mapping range

Fig. 24.6

Hence, see Fig. 24.6,
$f(3)$, the image of 3, is 14
$f(1)$, the image of 1, is 8
$f(-1)$, the image of -1, is 2
and so on.

2 $g{:}x \rightarrow x^2 - x$

Use a mapping diagram to show the following,

(a) $g(2)$, **(b)** $g(10)$, **(c)** $g(-3)$, **(d)** $g(0)$

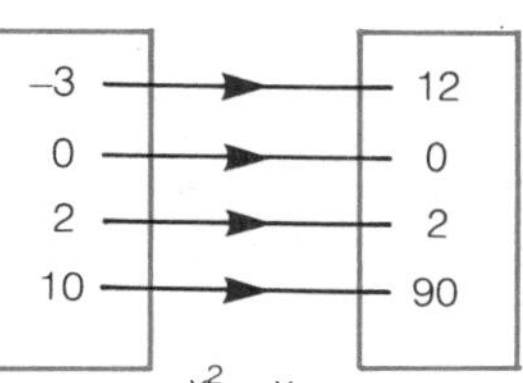

domain mapping range

Fig. 24.7

Hence, see Fig. 24.7,
(a) $g(2) = 2$
(b) $g(10) = 90$
(c) $g(-3) = 12$
(d) $g(0) = 0$

It is possible for us to look at the problem from another viewpoint.

For instance, if $f(x) = 3x + 8$, find the values of x if,

(a) $f(x) = 20$, **(b)** $f(x) = 5$

This is best done by solving the respective equations.

(a) $f(x) = 3x + 8$
Hence, $20 = 3x + 8$
$12 = 3x$ i.e. $x = 4$ is the solution

(b) $f(x) = 3x + 8$
Hence, $5 = 3x + 8$
$-3 = 3x$ i.e. $x = -1$ is the solution

This serves, in fact, as an introduction to inverse functions, which follow. (See Example 2, Unit 24.4 for an alternative approach.)

Activities

1 Using the domain $\{1, 2, 3, 4, 5\}$ find the range for the following functions.

(a) $f{:}x \rightarrow 3x$ **(b)** $f{:}x \rightarrow x + 3$
(c) $f{:}x \rightarrow 2x + 1$ **(d)** $f{:}x \rightarrow 3x - 2$

2 Using the domain $\{1, 3, 5, 7\}$ find the range for the following functions.

(a) $f{:}x \to 2x$ **(b)** $f{:}x \to x - 4$
(c) $f{:}x \to 5x - 3$ **(d)** $f{:}x \to 3(x - 4)$

3 Using the domain $\{-2, -1, 0, 1, 2\}$ find the range for the following functions.

(a) $f{:}x \to 4x$ **(b)** $f{:}x \to 2x - 3$
(c) $f{:}x \to 2(x + 1)$ **(d)** $f{:}x \to 7 - x$

4 For each of the arrow diagrams in Fig. 24.8, try to establish the function.

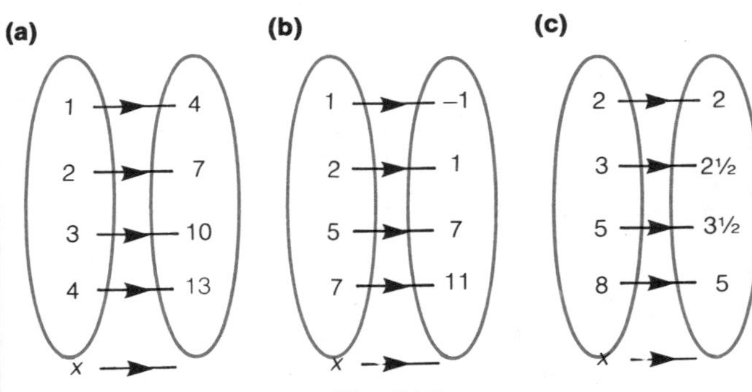

Fig. 24.8

5 Draw an arrow diagram for the given rule and domain for the following.

(a) $g(x) = 3x + 5$ $\{0, 1, 4, 9\}$
(b) $g(x) = 2 - 5x$ $\{3, 5, 7, 9\}$
(c) $g(x) = \frac{1}{2}x + 3$ $\{2, 4, 6, 8\}$
(d) $g(x) = x^2 + 1$ $\{-1, 2, 5, 8\}$

6 If $f{:}x \to 2x + 7$, find,

(a) $f(2)$ **(b)** $f(5)$ **(c)** $f(0)$ **(d)** $f(-3)$

7 If $h{:}x \to 3x + 2$, find x when,

(a) $h(x) = 8$ **(b)** $h(x) = -7$

24.3 Inverse functions

The **inverse function** takes us from the range back to the domain (see Fig. 24.9).

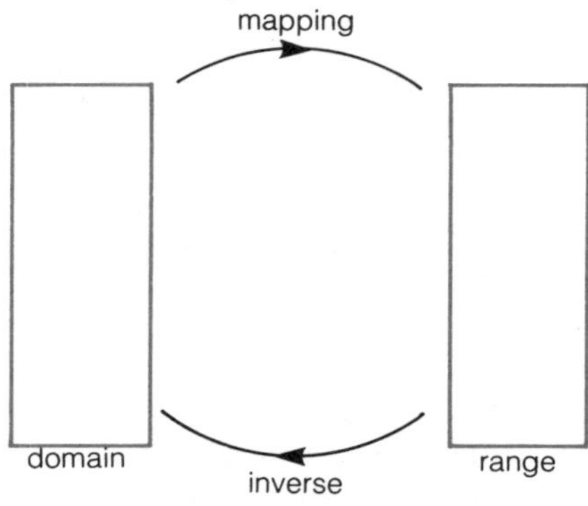

Fig. 24.9

One-to-one mappings have inverses that are functions, but the inverses of many-to-one mappings are not functions.

24.4 Finding the inverse of a function

Probably the best way of finding the inverse of a function is to use a **flowchart**.

Example 1 $f{:}x \to 2x - 5$

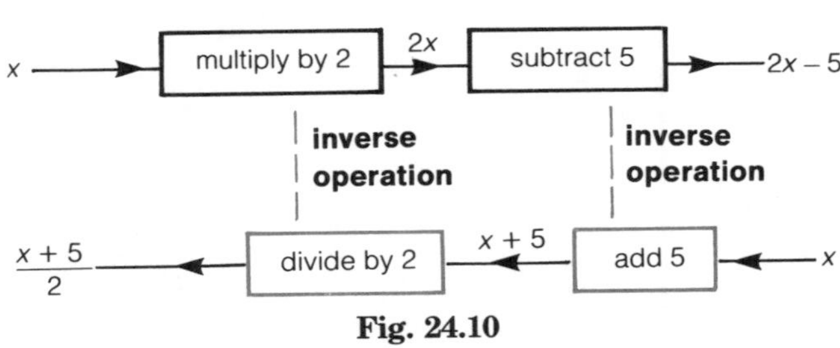

Fig. 24.10

See Fig. 24.10. The inverse function (written as f^{-1}) is,

$$f^{-1}{:}x \to \frac{x+5}{2}, \text{ or even, } f^{-1}(x) = \frac{x+5}{2}$$

We can easily check to see whether this works, or not, by using some particular values of x. For instance,

$$f(3) = (2 \times 3) - 5 = 6 - 5 = 1 \quad \text{i.e. } f(3) = 1 \text{ and,}$$

$$f^{-1}(1) = \frac{1+5}{2} = \frac{6}{2} = 3 \quad \text{i.e. } f^{-1}(1) = 3$$

Example 2 $g(x) = 3(x - 2)$

Find $g^{-1}(x)$ and hence find the value of x, if $g(x) = 18$

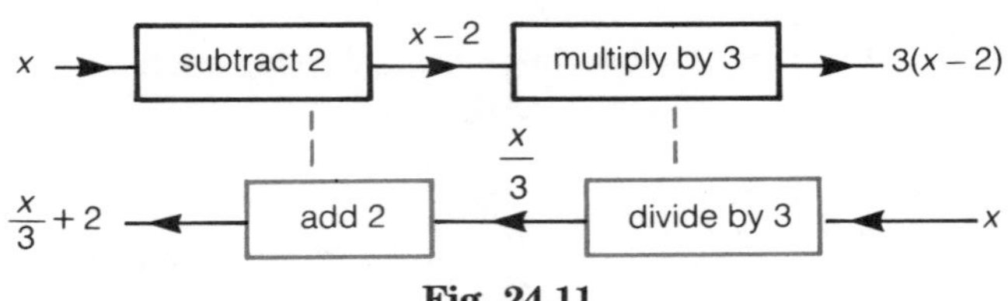

Fig. 24.11

See Fig. 24.11.

$$g^{-1}(x) = \frac{x}{3} + 2$$

Since $g(x) = 18$, we require to find $g^{-1}(18)$.

$$g^{-1}(18) = \frac{18}{3} + 2 = 6 + 2 = 8$$

Hence, the value of x is 8

Activities

Functions and inverse functions

1 Write down the inverses of each rule,

(a) $x \to 5x + 2$ **(b)** $x \to 4x - 1$ **(c)** $x \to \frac{1}{2}x - 3$

2 If $f{:}x \to 3x - 9$ find,

(a) f^{-1} **(b)** $f(2)$ **(c)** $f^{-1}(2)$

3 If $f{:}x \to 3(x - 3)$ find,

(a) f^{-1} **(b)** $f(1)$ **(c)** $f^{-1}(1)$

4 If $g(x) = 4x - 5$, then find,

(a) $g(3)$ **(b)** $g(10)$ **(c)** value of x, if $g(x) = 15$

5 If $f(x) = 5(x + 2)$, then find,

(a) $f(-1)$ **(b)** $f(3)$ **(c)** value of x, if $f(x) = 100$

6 If $h(x) = \frac{2x-1}{5}$, then find

(a) $h(0)$ **(b)** $h(-2)$ **(c)** value of x, if $h(x) = 3$

7 If $g(x) = x^2 - 5$, then find

(a) $g(-2)$ **(b)** $g(\frac{1}{2})$ **(c)** value of x, if $g(x) = 44$

8 If $f(x) = \frac{5}{x}$, then find

(a) $f(5)$ **(b)** $f(-2)$ **(c)** value of x, if $f(x) = -10$

9 If $h(x) = x^2 - 3x$, then find

(a) $h(-1)$ **(b)** $h(2)$ **(c)** values of x, if $h(x) = 0$

24.5 Composite functions

If we wish to apply two (or more) functions, one after the other, to an element of the domain, we write the composite function (the joint function) as $fg(x)$.

In this case, we apply g first, and then apply f to the result.

In the case of $gf(x)$, we apply f first, and then apply g to the result.

Hence the order in which the functions are written is very important.

Example $f{:}x \to 5x+1$ $g{:}x \to \frac{1}{2}(x-3)$

Find **(a)** $fg(9)$, **(b)** $gf(9)$, **(c)** $ff(9)$, **(d)** $gg(9)$

(a) $fg(9) = f(\frac{1}{2}(9-3)) = f(3) = (5 \times 3) + 1 = 16$

(b) $gf(9) = g((5 \times 9) + 1) = g(46) = \frac{1}{2}(46-3) = 21\frac{1}{2}$

(c) $ff(9) = f((5 \times 9) + 1) = f(46) = (5 \times 46) + 1 = 231$

(d) $gg(9) = g(\frac{1}{2}(9-3)) = g(3) = \frac{1}{2}(3-3) = 0$

It is possible to draw a flowchart, in order to find a single function h, that is the same as the composite function fg.

Activities

1 Draw an arrow diagram for the domain {1, 2, 3, 4, 5} to show,

(a) $x \to x^2$, followed by $x \to x+5$
(b) $x \to x+7$, followed by $x \to 3x$
(c) $x \to 4x$, followed by $x \to x-5$

2 Write down the composite of,

(a) $x \to 2x-5$, followed by $x \to 7x$
(b) $x \to 5x$, followed by $x \to 5-x$
(c) $x \to x-3$, followed by $x \to x^2$
(d) $x \to 6x-5$, followed by $x \to \frac{1}{x}$

3 If $f{:}x \to 3x+1$ and $g{:}x \to x^2$, then find,

(a) $f(3)$ **(b)** $g(5)$ **(c)** $gf(3)$ **(d)** $fg(3)$
(e) $gf(5)$ **(f)** $fg(5)$

4 If $f{:}x \to 2x-7$ and $g{:}x \to 3x+5$, then find,

(a) $gf(4)$ **(b)** $fg(1)$ **(c)** $gf(0)$ **(d)** $fg(-2)$

5 If $f{:}x \to x^2$ and $g{:}x \to 4x+1$, then find,

(a) $fg(2)$ **(b)** $gf(2)$ **(c)** $ff(2)$ **(d)** $gg(2)$

6 If $f(x) = \frac{2x+1}{5}$, then find the value of,

(a) $f(7)$ **(b)** $f(-3)$ **(c)** $ff(7)$ **(d)** $ff(-3)$

7 If $f(x) = 2x+1$ and $g(x) = 3x-2$, find x when,

(a) $fg(x) = 19$ **(b)** $gf(x) = 27$

8 If $f(x) = x^2$ and $g(x) = 2x+1$, find x when,

(a) $fg(x) = 33$ **(b)** $gf(x) = 25$

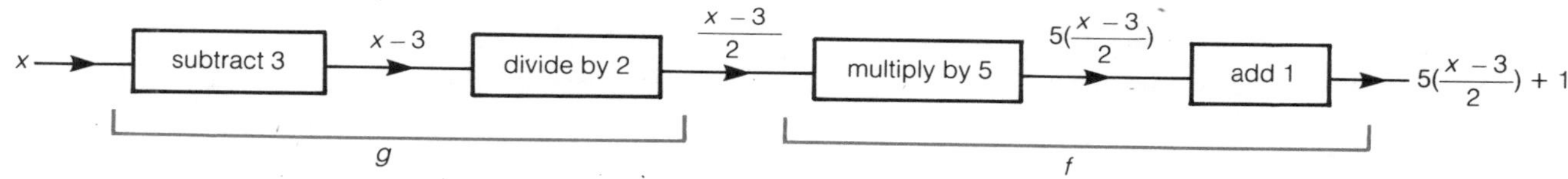

Fig. 24.12

From Fig. 24.12,

$$fg(x) = 5\left(\frac{x-3}{2}\right) + 1 = \frac{5x-15+2}{2}$$

Hence, $h(x) = \frac{5x-13}{2}$

Check Try $h(9)$, which is in fact $fg(9)$, i.e. **(a)** above,

$$h(9) = \frac{(5 \times 9) - 13}{2} = \frac{45-13}{2} = \frac{32}{2}$$

Hence, $h(9) = 16$, the same result as in **(a)** above.

Note It is also worthwhile to note that, if we apply a function and its inverse to an element (or vice versa), the result will be the original element.

Hence, $ff^{-1}(x) = f^{-1}f(x) = x$

Unit 25

Set problems – algebraic solutions

As we saw in Volume 2, Unit 19, it is possible to solve problems with the aid of sets and Venn diagrams. However, some of the problems are best solved with algebraic assistance.

The basic idea involved is to use a letter x to represent the unknown quantity.

Example 1 In a form of 25 pupils, 10 learn French and 5 learn Spanish. If 2 pupils learn both languages, how many learn neither?

Fig. 25.1 shows the Venn diagram.

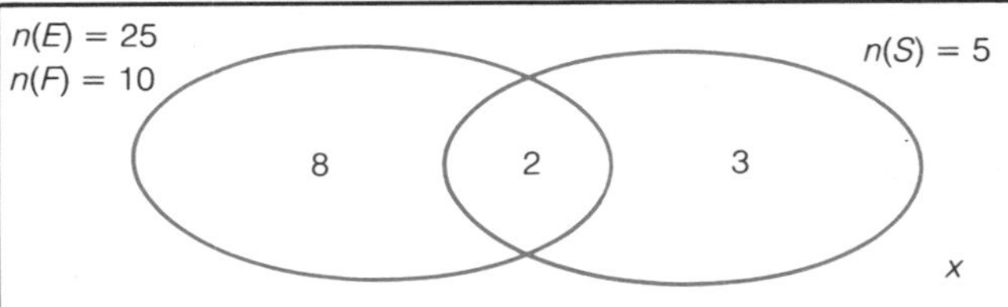

Fig. 25.1

Let the number of pupils studying neither French nor Spanish be x.

Since 2 pupils study both languages, then 8 study French only and 3 study Spanish only.

We can now build-up an equation, i.e.

$$8 + 2 + 3 + x = 25$$
$$13 + x = 25$$
$$\therefore \; x = 12$$

Hence, 12 pupils study neither language.

Example 2 In a group of 10 sixth-form students, 6 are studying Maths, 5 Physics and 7 French. 3 study Maths and Physics, 2 study Physics and French and 4 study French and Maths. Each student studies at least one of these subjects. How many are studying all three subjects?

See Fig. 25.2.

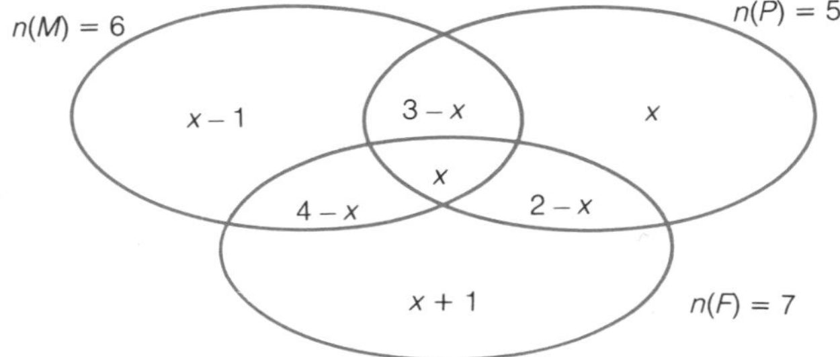

Fig. 25.2

Let x students study all three subjects.

Since the number studying Maths and Physics is 3 students, then $3 - x$ students study Maths and Physics only.

Similarly $2 - x$ students study Physics and French only, and $4 - x$ students study Maths and French only.

Now, number of students studying Maths only will be

$$6 - ((3x - x) + x + 4 - x)$$
$$= 6 - (7 - x) = 6 - 7 + x$$

i.e. $x - 1$ study Maths only.

We then repeat the exercise for the Physics only, and French only, and we find x students study Physics only, and $x + 1$ students study French only.

Finally, since all 10 students are involved, we can add all the algebraic terms together to form an equation which is easily solved, i.e.

$$(x - 1) + (3 - x) + x + (4 - x) + x + (2 - x) + (x + 1) = 10$$

So, $x + 9 = 10 \quad \therefore x = 1$

Hence, one student studies all three subjects.

Note The result can easily be checked by substitution of $x = 1$ in the Venn diagram, Fig. 25.2, which proves correct.

Activities

Problems with sets

In solving these problems you will find it helpful to draw a Venn diagram and then use algebra.

1 In a group of 32 students, 17 studied Maths, 13 studied English and 7 studied neither. How many students studied both Maths and English?

2 In a group of 40 adults, 31 drank tea, 23 drank coffee and 5 drank neither. How many drank both tea and coffee?

3 In a group of 50 football supporters, there were 36 with scarves in their team's colours, 22 with hats and 11 with neither. Let x be the number of supporters with both hat and scarf.

(a) Form an equation in x and solve it.
(b) How many supporters had just a hat?
(c) How many had just a scarf?

4 Out of 136 sixth-formers in a school, 60 studied Latin, 100 studied French and 48 studied Spanish. If 28 took Latin and French, 44 took French and Spanish and 20 took Latin and Spanish, draw a Venn diagram showing three overlapping sets, and let x represent the students who studied all three languages.

(a) Write an equation for x and solve it.
(b) How many studied Latin and French **only**?
(c) How many studied French and Spanish **only**?
(d) How many studied Latin and Spanish **only**?

5

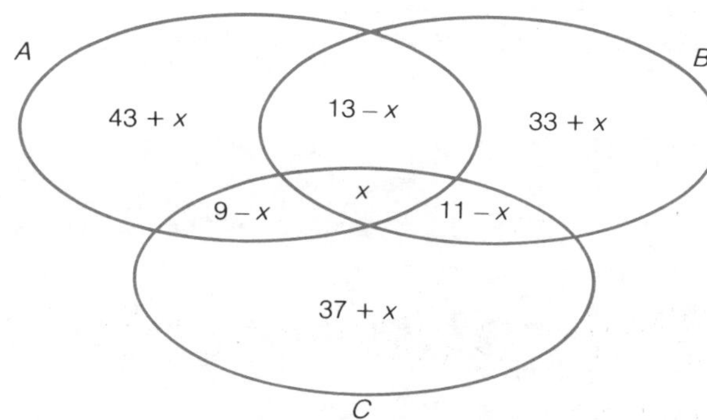

Fig. 25.3

Fig. 25.3 shows the number of elements in the regions of a Venn diagram.

If $n(A \cup B \cup C) = 152$, find,

(a) $n(A \cap B \cap C)$ **(b)** $n(A)$
(c) $n(B)$ **(d)** $n(C)$
(e) $n(A \cap B)$ **(f)** $n(B \cap C)$
(g) $n(A \cap C)$

6 The Venn diagram, in Fig. 25.4, shows the number of players at a Sport's Club who took part in various activities.

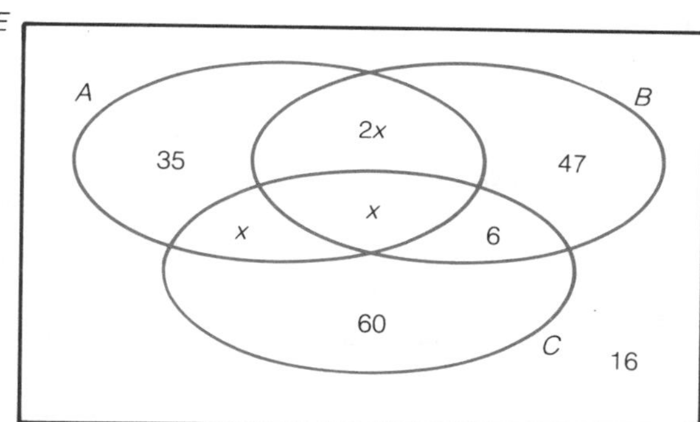

Fig. 25.4

A = {Members who took part in Athletics}
B = {Members who play Badminton}
C = {Members who play Squash}

If there are 200 members, find the number who,

(a) play squash **(b)** play just badminton
(c) take part in more than one activity
(d) take part in one activity only

7 There are 85 houses in a street. The newspaper boy delivered 40 copies of the *Sun*, 31 copies of the *Star* and 49 copies of the *Express*. 22 houses had the *Sun* and the *Star*, 36 had the *Sun* and the *Express*, and 26 had the *Star* and the *Express*. If x houses had all three papers and 27 had none at all, form an equation in x and solve it. Hence find out how many houses,

(a) had two newspapers delivered
(b) had just the *Sun* **(c)** had just the *Star*
(d) did not have the *Express*

GEOMETRY/ TRIGONOMETRY

Unit 26

Trigonometric ratios

26.1 Introduction

We discovered in Volume 2, Unit 23, that for any right-angled triangle there was a relationship between the lengths of the three sides. This relationship is known as Pythagoras' Theorem which states that, for any right-angled triangle, the square of the hypotenuse (longest side) is equal to the sum of the squares of the other two sides.

We may now extend this idea to include the relationships between side lengths and angle sizes, but we must remember that these apply, once again, only to right-angled triangles.

Any right-angled triangle may be labelled as shown in Fig. 26.1.

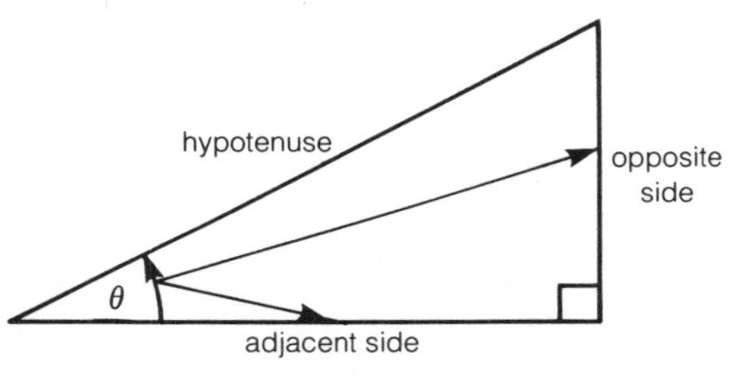

or

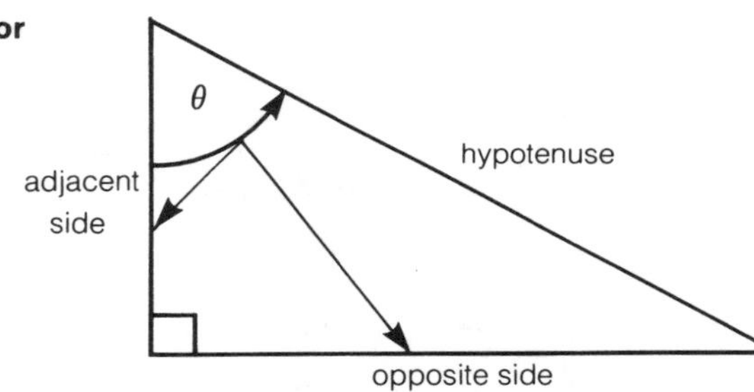

Fig. 26.1

(a) The **hypotenuse** is the longest side of a right-angled triangle and is always opposite the right angle.
(b) The **adjacent side** is the side from which the angle $\theta°$ is measured.
(c) The **opposite side** is the side opposite the angle $\theta°$.

As we shall shortly discover, there are three general relationships between sides and angles in a right-angled triangle, and these are known as the **trigonometric (trig.) ratios**.

26.2 The tangent of an angle ($\tan\theta$)

This ratio links an angle with the opposite and adjacent side lengths in the following way (see Fig. 26.2).

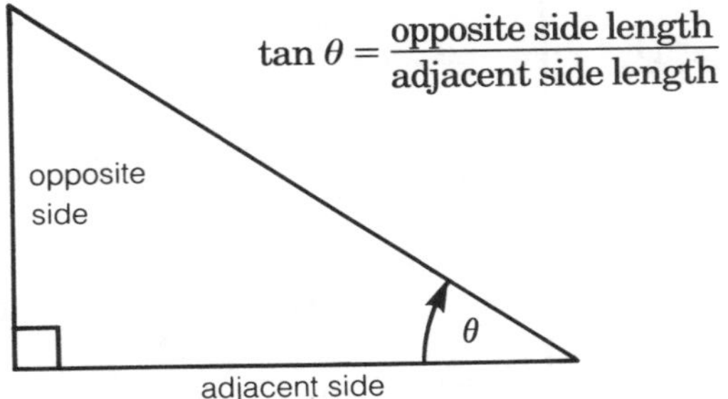

$$\tan\theta = \frac{\text{opposite side length}}{\text{adjacent side length}}$$

Fig. 26.2

We can now use our scientific calculator to find the value of the tangent of an angle.

Example 1 Find the value of the tangent of 35°, correct to 3 significant figures.

Enter 35 onto the display and key [tan]. The reading on the display is 0.7002075 which, corrected to 3 significant figures, is 0.700.

Hence, $\tan 35° = 0.7$ (to 3 sig figs)

Example 2 Find the value of the tangent of 68.4°, correct to 3 sig figs.

Enter 68.4 onto the display and key [tan]. The reading on the display is 2.5257117 which, corrected to 3 sig figs, is 2.53.

Hence, $\tan 68.4° = 2.53$ (to 3 sig figs)

26.3 Calculations using the tangent ratio

We are now in a position to be able to calculate the length of an opposite side, given the necessary angle and its adjacent side length.

Example See Fig. 26.3. Find the length of the side AB, correct to 3 sig figs.

AB is the opposite side (opp) to $\angle C$
BC is the adjacent side (adj) to $\angle C$

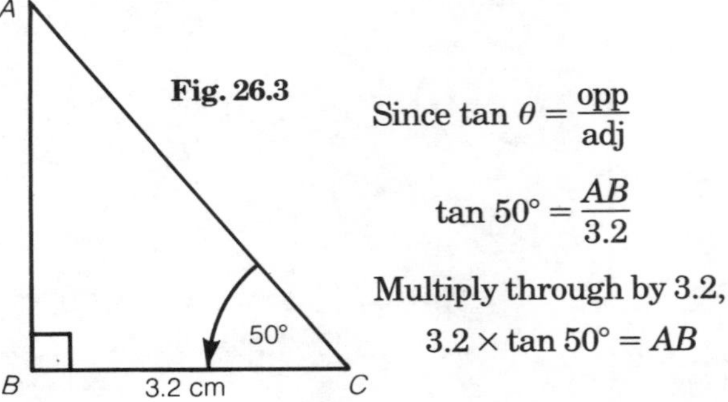

Fig. 26.3

Since $\tan\theta = \dfrac{\text{opp}}{\text{adj}}$

$$\tan 50° = \frac{AB}{3.2}$$

Multiply through by 3.2,

$$3.2 \times \tan 50° = AB$$

We now use our calculator to work out the problem. Enter 50 onto the display and key [tan] (as we did, above) and multiply the result by 3.2.

Hence,
$$\begin{aligned} AB &= 3.2 \times 1.1917536 \\ &= 3.8136115 \\ &= 3.81 \text{ cm (correct to 3 sig figs)} \end{aligned}$$

Note It would also be possible to solve the problem by considering $\angle A = 40°$. Side AB would then be the adjacent and BC would be the opposite side.

Hence, $\tan 40° = \dfrac{3.2}{AB}$

which we would rearrange to give,

$$AB = \frac{3.2}{\tan 40°} = 3.81 \text{ cm}$$

although the calculation is slightly more awkward.

The process for finding the value of an angle, given its tangent, is quite straightforward using the calculator.

Example Find, to the nearest tenth of a degree, the angle whose tangent is 0.68. (Sometimes written as $\theta = \tan^{-1} 0.68$.)

Enter 0.68 onto the display and key $\boxed{\tan^{-1}}$ giving 34.215702 which, to the nearest tenth of a degree, will be 34.2°.

Hence, $\theta = \tan^{-1} 0.68 = 34.2°$

Note On some calculators, $\boxed{\tan^{-1}}$ is in the second function.

Now, given the two necessary side lengths, we can find the tangent of an angle and hence the value of the angle itself.

Example Find the value of θ in Fig. 26.4.

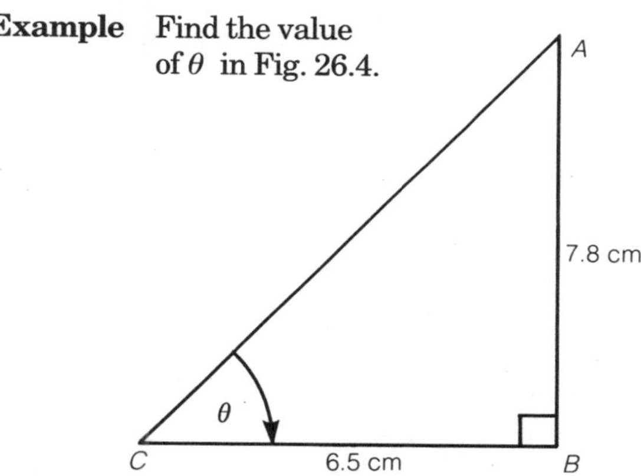

Fig. 26.4

AB is the opposite side length.
BC is the adjacent side length.

Hence, $\tan \theta = \dfrac{7.8}{6.5}$

i.e. $\tan \theta = 1.2$

$\therefore \theta = \tan^{-1} 1.2$

Enter 1.2 onto the display and key $\boxed{\tan^{-1}}$ giving 50.194429 which, to the nearest tenth of a degree, will be 50.2°.

Hence, $\theta = 50.2°$

Activities

1 Find the tangents of the following angles, correct to 3 significant figures.

(a) 25° **(b)** 51° **(c)** 70° **(d)** 42°
(e) 22.6° **(f)** 37.9° **(g)** 9.3° **(h)** 63.5°

2 Find the angles, to the nearest tenth of a degree, whose tangents are given as follows.

(a) $\tan^{-1} 0.45$ **(b)** $\tan^{-1} 1.36$ **(c)** $\tan^{-1} 2.037$
(d) $\tan^{-1} 0.984$ **(e)** $\tan^{-1} 3.025$ **(f)** $\tan^{-1} 0.192$

3 From Fig. 26.5, find the lengths of AB, correct to 3 sig figs.

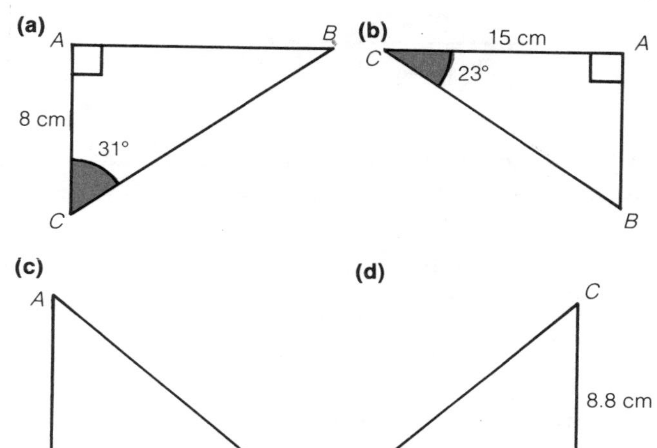

Fig. 26.5

4 Find angles A, in Fig. 26.6, correct to $\frac{1}{10}$°.

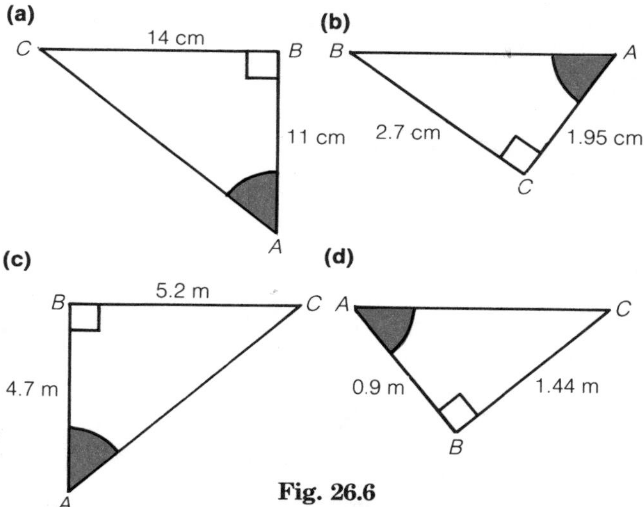

Fig. 26.6

5 In $\triangle ABC, \hat{B} = 90°, AB = 12$ cm, $BC = 11$ cm. Find $\hat{A}$.

6 In $\triangle XYZ, \hat{X} = 90°, XY = 3.5$ m, $XZ = 2.6$ m. Find $\hat{Y}$.

7 In $\triangle PQR, \hat{Q} = 90°, PQ = 10$ cm, $\hat{P} = 24.8°$. Find QR.

8 In $\triangle DEF, \hat{F} = 90°, DF = 13$ cm, $\hat{D} = 58°$. Find EF.

26.4 The sine of an angle (sin θ)

This ratio links an angle with the opposite and hypotenuse side lengths in the following way (see Fig. 26.7).

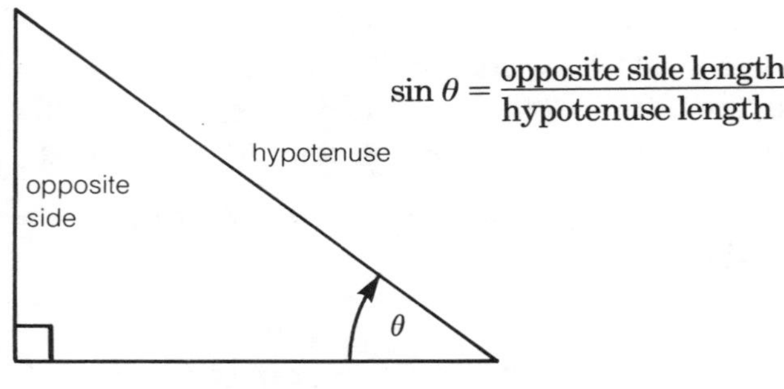

Fig. 26.7

In a similar manner to that for the tangent ratio, we again use our scientific calculator to find the values of $\sin\theta$ and $\sin^{-1}$.

Example 1 Find the sine of 25.2°, correct to 3 significant figures.

$\sin 25.2° = 0.4257792$

Hence, $\sin 25.2° = 0.426$ (correct to 3 sig figs)

Example 2 Find, to the nearest tenth of a degree, the angle whose sine is 0.6532.

$\sin\theta = 0.6532$
$\therefore \theta = \sin^{-1} 0.6532$
$\theta = 40.783305$

Hence, $\theta = 40.8°$ (to the nearest tenth of a degree)

26.5 Calculations using the sine ratio

Example 1 From Fig. 26.8, find the length of the side AB, correct to 3 sig figs.

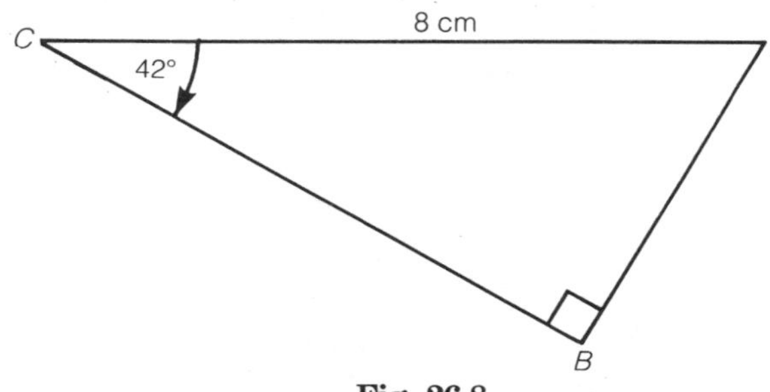

Fig. 26.8

AC is the hypotenuse length
AB is the opposite side length

Now, $\sin\theta = \dfrac{AB}{AC}$, hence $\sin 42° = \dfrac{AB}{8}$

Rearranging gives, $8 \times \sin 42° = AB$

Using the calculator, $AB = 5.3530449$

and so $AB = 5.35$ cm (to 3 sig figs)

Example 2 In a $\triangle PQR$, $\angle Q = 90°$, $PQ = 3.8$ cm and $PR = 4.4$ cm. Find $\angle R$ (to the nearest tenth of a degree).

Draw a diagram displaying the given information (see Fig. 26.9). Let $\angle R$ be θ, PR is the hypotenuse length, PQ is the opposite side length.

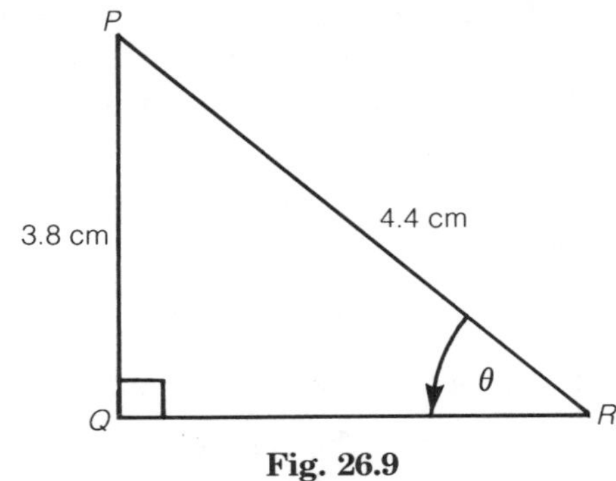

Fig. 26.9

$\sin\theta = \dfrac{PQ}{PR} = \dfrac{3.8}{4.4} = 0.8636363$

and $\theta = \sin^{-1} 0.8636363$
$\theta = 59.727358°$

So, $\angle R = 59.7°$ (to the nearest $\frac{1}{10}$°)

Activities

1 Find the sines of the following angles correct to 3 sig figs.

(a) 17° **(b)** 41° **(c)** 69° **(d)** 73°
(e) 33.4° **(f)** 48.9° **(g)** 62.7° **(h)** 81.2°

2 Find the angle, to the nearest tenth of a degree, whose sine is given by,

(a) $\sin^{-1} 0.224$ **(b)** $\sin^{-1} 0.3678$ **(c)** $\sin^{-1} 0.451$
(d) $\sin^{-1} 0.5056$ **(e)** $\sin^{-1} 0.722$ **(f)** $\sin^{-1} 0.884$

3 From Fig. 26.10, find the lengths of AB, correct to 3 sig figs.

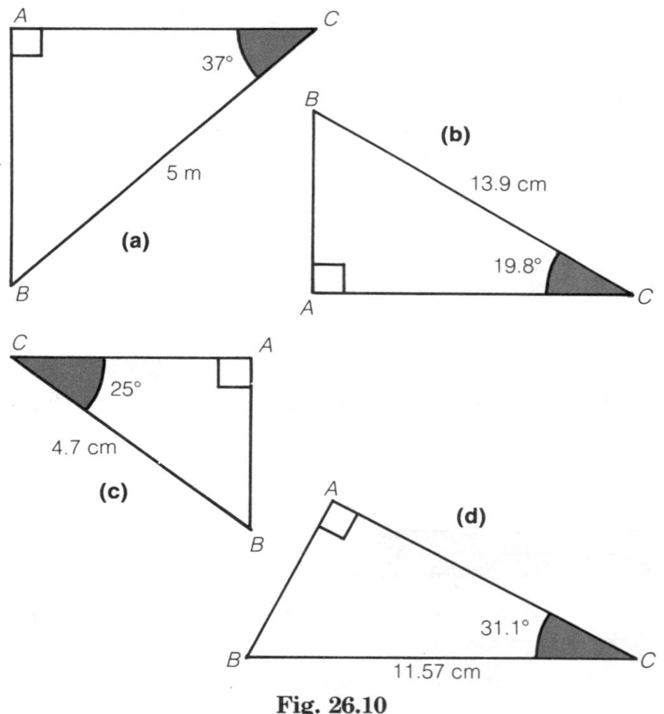

Fig. 26.10

4 Find angles A, in Fig. 26.11, correct to $\frac{1}{10}°$.

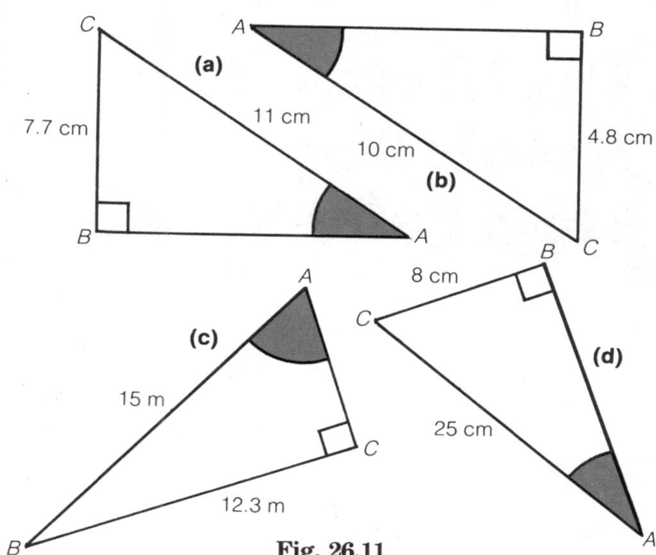

Fig. 26.11

5 In $\triangle ABC, \hat{B} = 90°, \hat{C} = 38°, AC = 4.5$ cm. Find AB.

6 In $\triangle PQR, \hat{R} = 90°, PQ = 8$ cm, $\hat{P} = 66.8°$. Find QR.

7 In $\triangle ABC, \hat{B} = 90°, AB = 3.4$ cm, $AC = 4.2$ cm. Find $\hat{C}$.

8 In $\triangle XYZ, \hat{X} = 90°, YZ = 3.5$ cm, $\hat{Z} = 60.9°$. Find XY.

26.6 The cosine of an angle (cos θ)

This ratio links an angle with the adjacent and hypotenuse side lengths, in the following way (see Fig. 26.12).

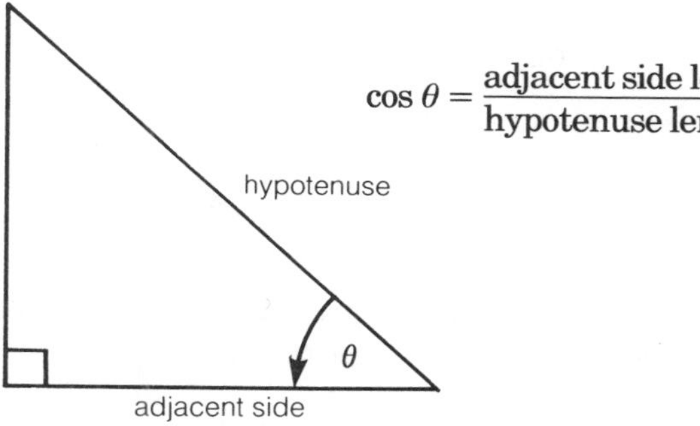

$$\cos\theta = \frac{\text{adjacent side length}}{\text{hypotenuse length}}$$

Fig. 26.12

Once again, in a similar manner to those for the tangent and sine ratios, we use our scientific calculator to find the values of cos θ and $\cos^{-1}$.

26.7 Calculations using the cosine ratio

Example In a $\triangle XYZ, \angle Z = 90°, XY = 7.2$ cm, $XZ = 5.1$ cm. Find $\angle X$ (to the nearest tenth of a degree).

Draw a diagram of the given information (see Fig. 26.13) and let $\angle X$ be θ.

XZ is the adjacent side length
XY is the hypotenuse length

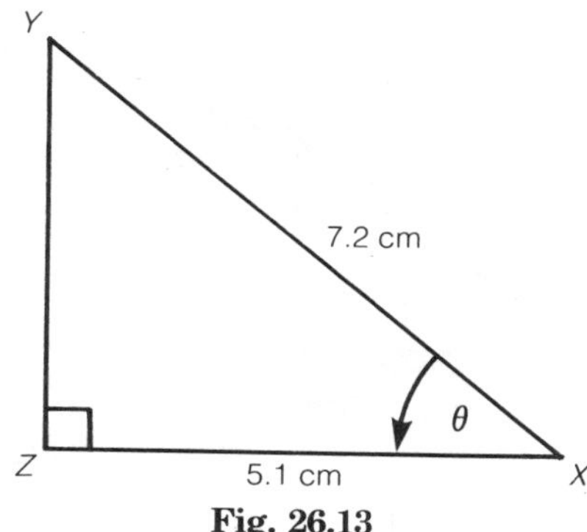

Fig. 26.13

$$\cos\theta = \frac{XZ}{XY} = \frac{5.1}{7.2} = 0.7083333$$

and $\theta = \cos^{-1} 0.7083333$
$\theta = 44.900529°$

So, $\angle X = 44.9°$ (to the nearest $\frac{1}{10}°$)

Note Since there is a similarity between all three ratios, we have to be careful in applying the correct ratio to the information given in the problem.

Activities

1 Find the cosines of the following angles correct to 3 significant figures.

(a) 52° **(b)** 39° **(c)** 71° **(d)** 54°
(e) 39.2° **(f)** 27.9° **(g)** 66.5° **(h)** 22.8°

2 Find the angles, to the nearest tenth of a degree, whose cosines are given as follows,

(a) $\cos^{-1} 0.234$ **(b)** $\cos^{-1} 0.561$ **(c)** $\cos^{-1} 0.772$
(d) $\cos^{-1} 0.8751$ **(e)** $\cos^{-1} 0.898$ **(f)** $\cos^{-1} 0.9123$

3 From Fig. 26.14, find the lengths of AB, correct to 3 sig figs.

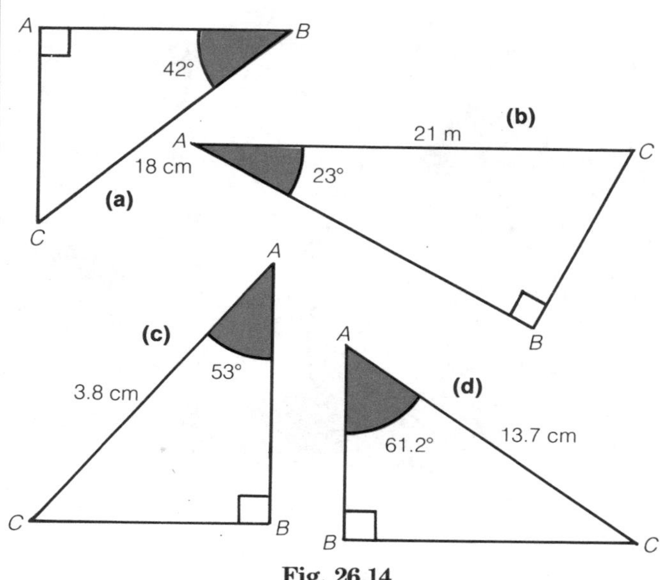

Fig. 26.14

4 Find angles A, in Fig. 26.15, correct to $\frac{1}{10}°$.

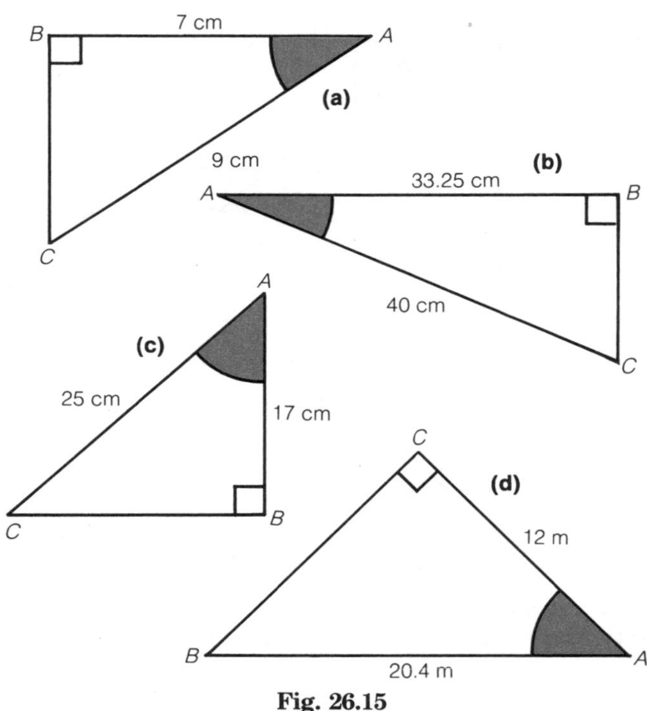

Fig. 26.15

5 In $\triangle ABC, \hat{B} = 90°, \hat{A} = 32°, AC = 10$ cm. Find AB.

6 In $\triangle PQR, \hat{P} = 90°, \hat{Q} = 32.4°, RQ = 6$ m. Find PQ.

7 In $\triangle XYZ, \hat{Z} = 90°, XY = 4$ cm, $XZ = 3.3$ cm. Find $\hat{X}$.

8 In $\triangle ABC, \hat{B} = 90°, AC = 8.2$ cm, $AB = 6.15$ cm. Find $\hat{A}$.

Unit 27

Problems involving trig. ratios

27.1 Introduction

We can now apply our trig. knowledge to specific problems such as the angle a ladder makes with a wall, or the height of a cliff, or even the distance from the shore of a boat out at sea.

However, before we can consider such problems we need to be aware of a few technical terms.

27.2 Angles of elevation and depression

See Fig. 27.1.

(a) The **angle of elevation** is the angle between the horizontal and the object (when the object is above the observer).

(b) The **angle of depression** is the angle between the horizontal and the object (when the object is below the observer).

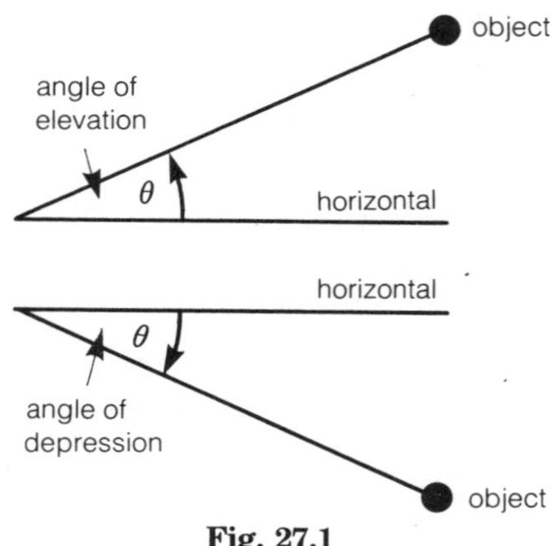

Fig. 27.1

For any given situation, the angle of elevation is equal to the angle of depression (alternate angles).

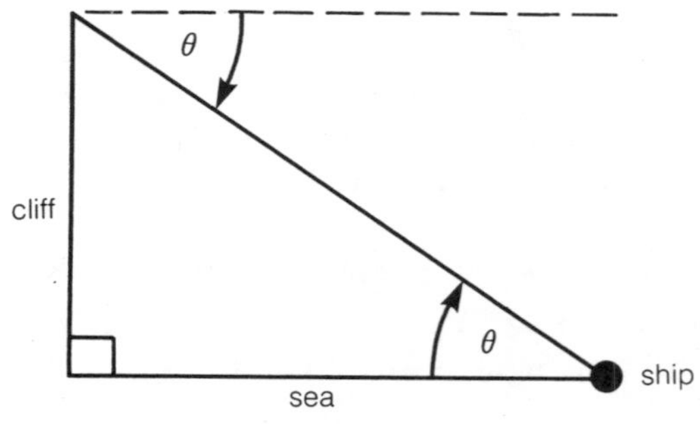

Fig. 27.2

Hence (see Fig. 27.2), the angle of elevation of the top of the cliff from the ship ($\theta°$) is the same as the angle of depression of the ship from the top of the cliff ($\theta°$).

27.3 Bearings

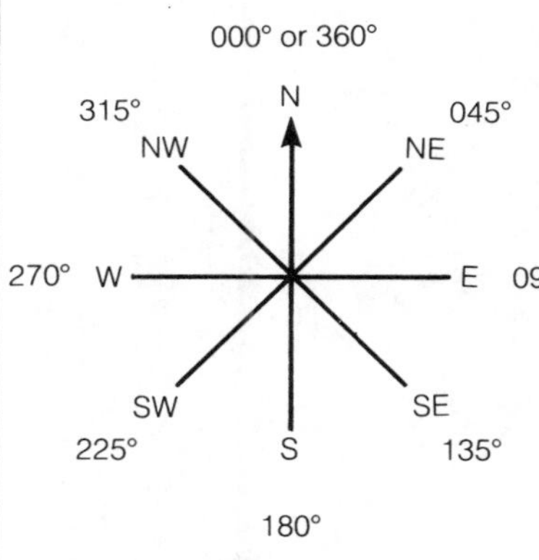

Fig. 27.3

See Fig. 27.3.

The directions given by the compass are known as **bearings** measured in degrees from 0° to 360°.

They are measured in a clockwise direction from N, North, and are given in 3-figure form.

Hence, a bearing of 5° is actually written 005°. A bearing of 55° is written 055° and a bearing of 155° is written 155° etc.

27.4 Typical trig. problems

Example 1 How far up a wall will a ladder, 5 m long, reach if the ladder makes an angle of 38° with the horizontal ground.

See Fig. 27.4. Let the height the ladder reaches up the wall be h m.

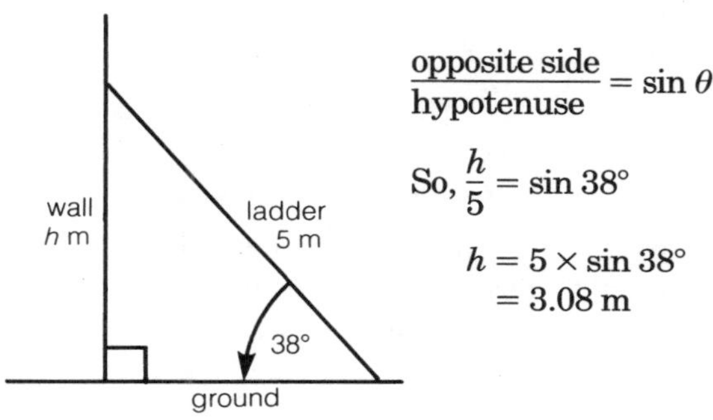

Fig. 27.4

$$\frac{\text{opposite side}}{\text{hypotenuse}} = \sin\theta$$

So, $\frac{h}{5} = \sin 38°$

$h = 5 \times \sin 38°$
$= 3.08$ m

Hence, the ladder will reach 3.08 m up the wall.

Example 2 Find the angle of elevation of the top of a tree 20 m high, from a point on the ground 15 m away from the tree.

See Fig. 27.5. Let the angle of elevation be θ.

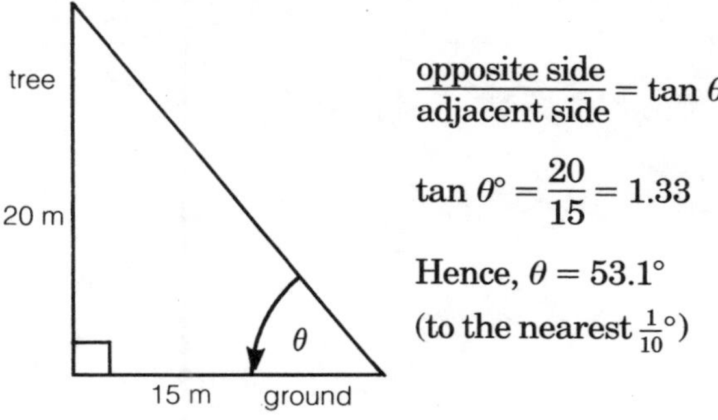

Fig. 27.5

$$\frac{\text{opposite side}}{\text{adjacent side}} = \tan\theta$$

$$\tan\theta° = \frac{20}{15} = 1.33$$

Hence, $\theta = 53.1°$

(to the nearest $\frac{1}{10}$°)

So the angle of elevation of the top of the tree from a point on the ground is 53.1°.

Example 3 A ship sails from a point A to a point C, on a bearing of 050° (a distance of 80 km). Point B is due north of A and due west of C. Find the distance from A to B.

See Fig. 27.6. Let the distance AB be x km.

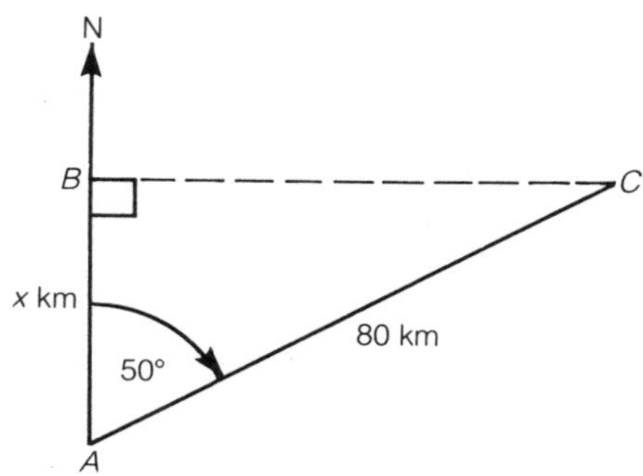

Fig. 27.6

Since $\cos\theta = \frac{\text{adjacent side}}{\text{hypotenuse}}$ then $\frac{x}{80} = \cos 50°$

Hence, rearranging, $x = 80 \times \cos 50°$
$= 51.4$ km

So, B is 51.4 km due north of A.

Activities

Angles of elevation & depression

1 See Fig. 27.7. From a point A on the ground, which is 50 m from the base of a tree, the angle of elevation of the top of the tree is 22°. Find the height of the tree.

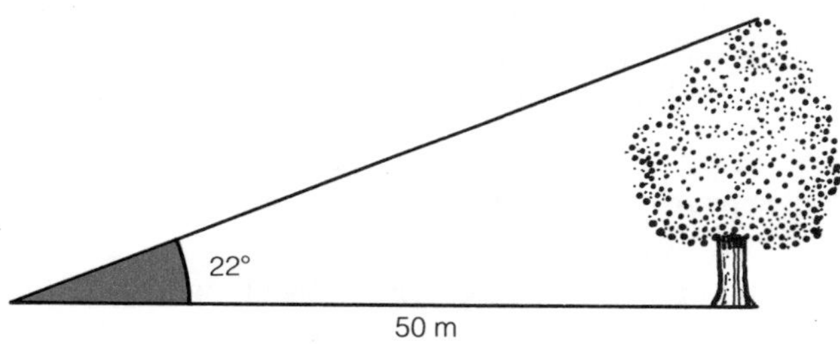

Fig. 27.7

2 From a point P on the ground, which is 200 m from the base of a tower, the angle of elevation of the top of the tower is 30°. Find the height of the tower.

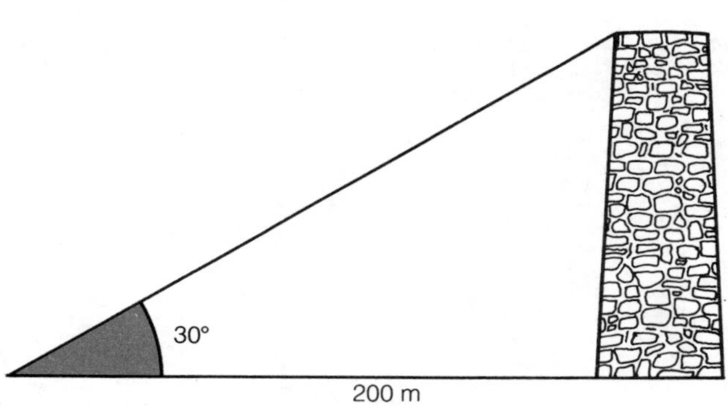

Fig. 27.8

3 From the top of a hill, which is 400 m above sea level, the angle of depression of a boat out at sea is 20°. What is the distance of the boat from the top of the hill?

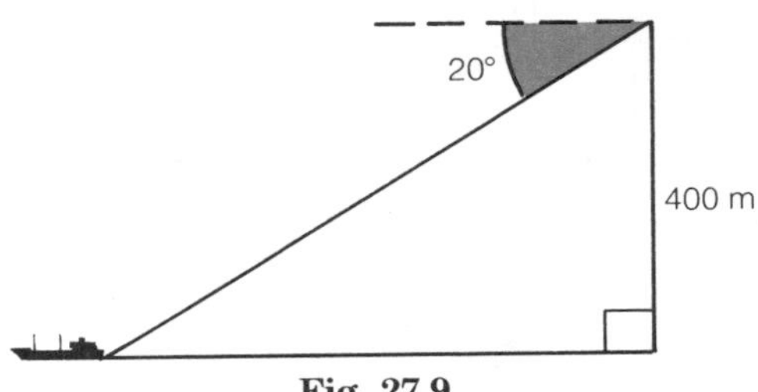

Fig. 27.9

4 An aircraft flying at a height of 5000 m, measures the angle of depression of a farmhouse to be 17°. How much farther has the plane to fly before it passes over the farmhouse?

5 A telephone mast is 50 m high. What is the angle of elevation of the top of the mast from a distance of 150 m from the base of the mast?

6 A man standing on the edge of a cliff 200 m above sea level, spies a boat 1 kilometre out to sea. What is the angle of depression of the boat?

7 From the opposite side of the road, the angle of elevation of the top of my house is 28°. If the distance from the opposite side of the road to my house is 11 m, how high is my house?

Bearings

1 A ship sails from port along a bearing of 035° for a distance of 15 km and drops anchor.

(a) How far east of port is the ship?
(b) How far north of the port is the ship?

2 An aeroplane takes off from Glasgow and flies along a bearing of 155° for a distance of 60 km. At this point, calculate,

(a) how far south of Glasgow is the plane.
(b) how far east of Glasgow is the plane.

3 A car leaves town and travels north for 10 km. It then turns due east and travels for a further 12 km. What is the car's present bearing from the town from where it started?

4 A boat sails due south from port for a distance of 14 km. It then sails due west for a further 8 km. What is the boat's bearing from port at this point?

5 Two ships sail from port at the same time. Ship A travels 15 km due north. In the same time, Ship B travels 12 km due east. What is the bearing of Ship B from Ship A at this point?

6 At noon, two ships sail from port. Ship X sails at 25 km per hour along a bearing of 072°. Ship Y sails north at 18 km per hour. At 1400 hours, calculate,

(a) how far Ship X is east of Ship Y
(b) how far Ship X is south of Ship Y

Trig. problems

1 In rectangle $ABCD$, $AB = 10$ cm and $BC = 6$ cm. Find $C\widehat{A}B$.

2 $EFGH$ is a rectangle with $EF = 5.2$ cm and $EG = 7.1$ cm. Find $G\widehat{E}F$ and the acute angles between the diagonals.

3 A ladder leans against a vertical wall (see Fig. 27.10). The ladder is 3 m long and its top is 2.2 m above the foot of the wall. Find the angle that the ladder makes with the ground.

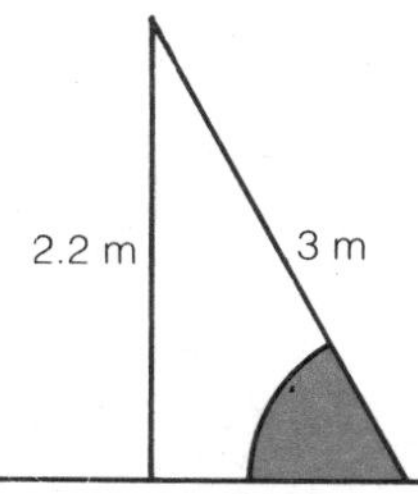

Fig. 27.10

4 See Fig. 27.11. C is the centre of a circle of radius 18 cm. Angle $ACB = 80°$. Find the length of the chord AB.

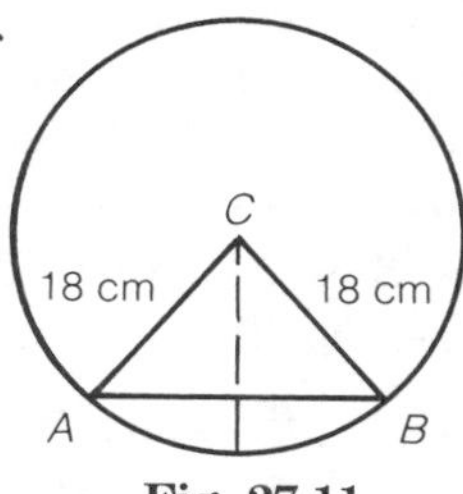

Fig. 27.11

5 In triangle ABC, $AB = AC = 14$ cm and $B = 59°$. Find the height of the triangle.

6 Fig. 27.12 shows triangle XYZ. $XY = XZ = 5$ cm and $YZ = 8$ cm. Find the angles of the triangle.

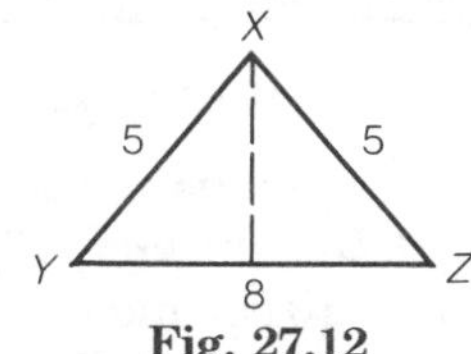

Fig. 27.12

7 The angles of elevation from two points A to B, which are at either side of a flagpole, are 28° and 37°, respectively. If the flagpole is 50 m tall, then what is the distance between the points A and B?

8 A man on the top of an 80 m high cliff, spots two boats out to sea in direct line with each other. If the angles of depression of the boats are 19° and 25°, respectively, then what is the distance between the two boats?

9 The bearing of town A from town B is 044°. A is 16 km north of B. How far east of B is it?

10 The diagonals of a rhombus are 24 cm and 32 cm. Calculate the angles of the rhombus.

Unit 28

Three-dimensional trigonometry (3-D trig.)

28.1 Problems involving cubes and cuboids

Up to now, we have only considered trig. problems in two dimensions. However, it is possible to apply the same trig. ratios to 3-dimensional problems, providing we can identify some right-angled triangles to work with.

Example In a room 28 m long, 21 m wide and 12 m high find,

(a) the diagonal length from a corner on the floor to the corner on the ceiling,

(b) the angle that the above diagonal makes with the floor.

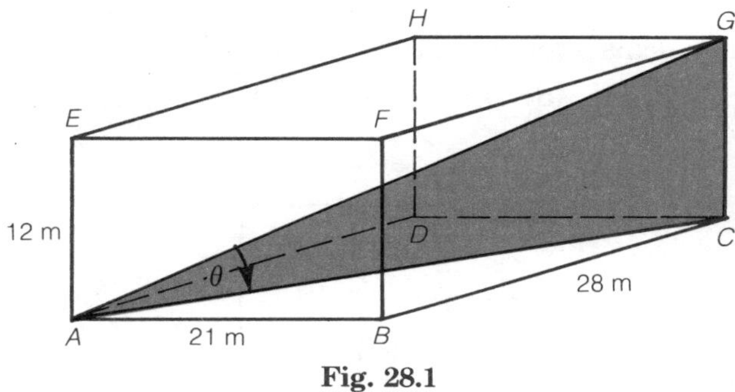

Fig. 28.1

See Fig. 28.1.

(a) The distance required is the distance AG

(b) The angle required is $\theta°$ i.e. $G\widehat{A}C$

(a) Finding the distance AG

In order to find AG, we must consider the right-angled triangle ACG, in which we know only that the height of the room, $CG = 12$ m.

We can, however, calculate the diagonal distance across the floor, AC, by applying Pythagoras' Theorem to the right-angled triangle ABC (see Fig. 28.2).

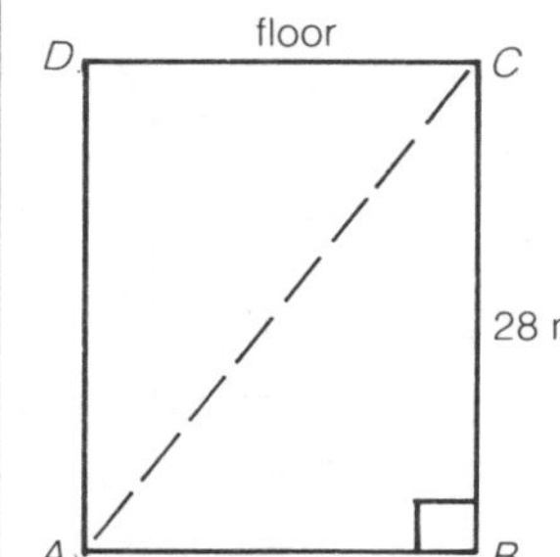

Fig. 28.2

Using Pythagoras' Theorem to find AC

$$AC^2 = 21^2 + 28^2 = 441 + 784 = 1225$$

$$\therefore AC = \sqrt{1225} = 35 \text{ m}$$

Now consider $\triangle ACG$. We use Pythagoras' Theorem again to find AG, as required. (See Fig. 28.3.)

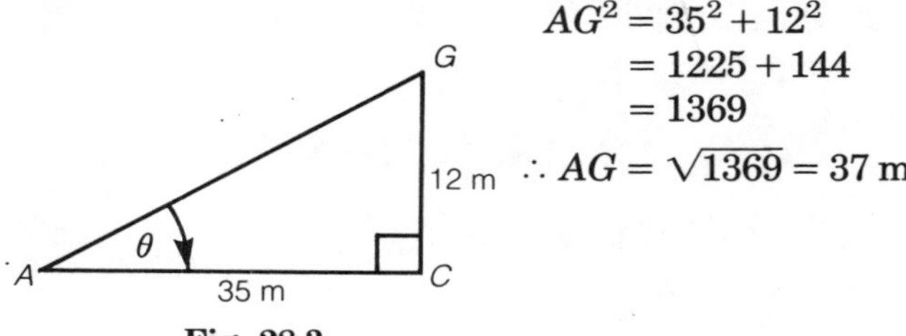

Fig. 28.3

$$AG^2 = 35^2 + 12^2$$
$$= 1225 + 144$$
$$= 1369$$
$$\therefore AG = \sqrt{1369} = 37 \text{ m}$$

Hence, the required diagonal length is 37 m.

(b) Finding $G\hat{A}C$ (i.e. θ)

We simply apply the appropriate trig. ratio to the problem

$$\text{Hence, } \tan\theta = \frac{12}{35} = 0.3428571$$
$$\therefore \theta = \tan^{-1} 0.3428571$$
$$= 18.9°$$

So, the angle the above diagonal makes with the floor is 18.9°.

Activities

1 In the cube $ABCDEFGH$, shown in Fig. 28.4, the edges are 8 cm long. Calculate these lengths,

(a) BD **(b)** BH

and calculate these angles,

(c) $D\hat{B}H$ **(d)** $D\hat{A}H$ **(e)** $C\hat{G}A$

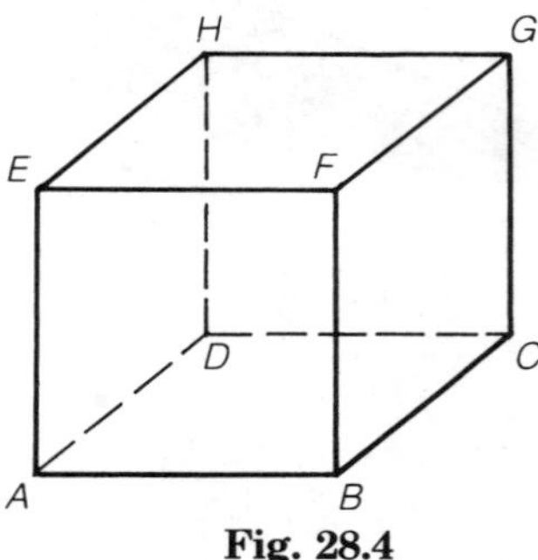

Fig. 28.4

2 In the cuboid $ABCDEFGH$, shown in Fig. 28.5, $AB = 12$ cm, $BC = 9$ cm and $BF = 5$ cm. Find,

(a) length EB **(b)** length BG
(c) length EG **(d)** length EC
(e) angle EHA **(f)** angle EFA
(g) angle EGA **(h)** angle BHF

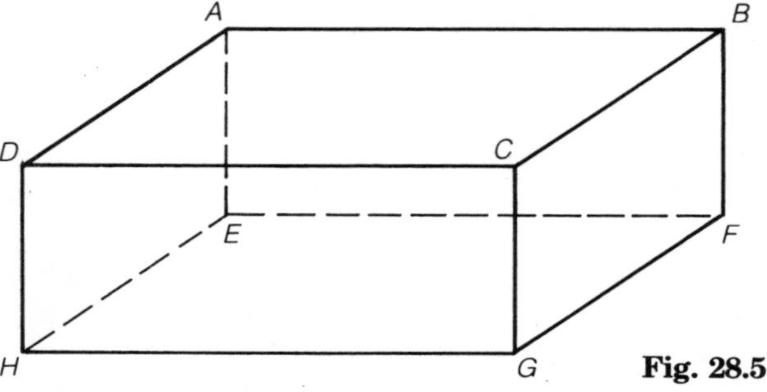

Fig. 28.5

28.2 Problems involving pyramids and cones

We are also now in a position to tackle problems involving square-based and rectangular-based pyramids, and also cones.

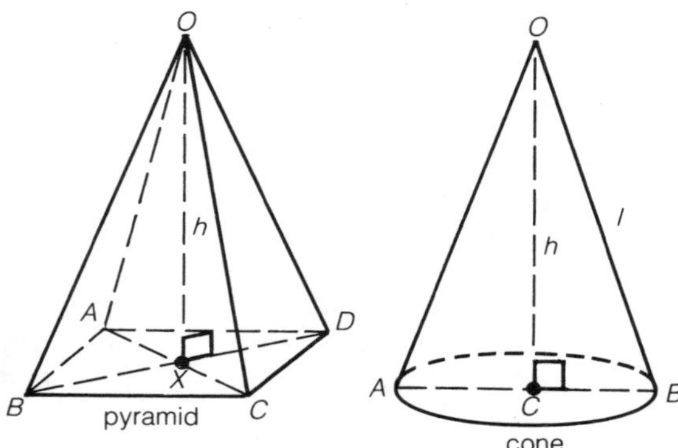

Fig. 28.6

The procedure is very much the same as for the cuboid example in Unit 28.1, where we used Pythagoras' Theorem to find diagonal base lengths etc, in order to give us sufficient information to calculate slant heights, vertical heights and a variety of angles. See Fig. 28.6.

$XD = \frac{1}{2}BD$ and $BD^2 = BC^2 + CD^2$
$OB^2 = OC^2 + CB^2$ and so on.

Note The whole basis of this exercise is to form the necessary right-angled triangles to enable us to find the required information.

Activities

Answer all calculations correct to 3 significant figures.

1 In the square-based pyramid $ABCDE$, shown in Fig. 28.7, $AB = 10$ cm and the vertical height $= 12$ cm. Find,

(a) DB **(b)** DE
(c) $E\hat{A}C$ **(d)** $D\hat{E}B$

Fig. 28.7

2 In the rectangular-based pyramid $VABCD$, shown in Fig. 28.8, $AB = 15$ cm $BC = 20$ cm and $VX = 16$ cm. Find,

(a) DB **(b)** VB **(c)** $V\hat{A}D$
(d) $V\hat{B}X$ **(e)** $C\hat{V}D$
(f) $C\hat{V}B$ **(g)** $D\hat{V}B$

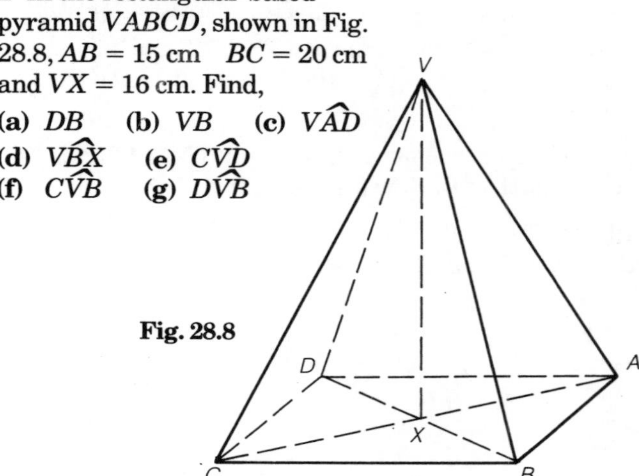

Fig. 28.8

3 For the cone in Fig. 28.9, find,
(a) slant height VA
(b) $A\widehat{B}V$ **(c)** $A\widehat{V}B$
(d) $A\widehat{V}X$

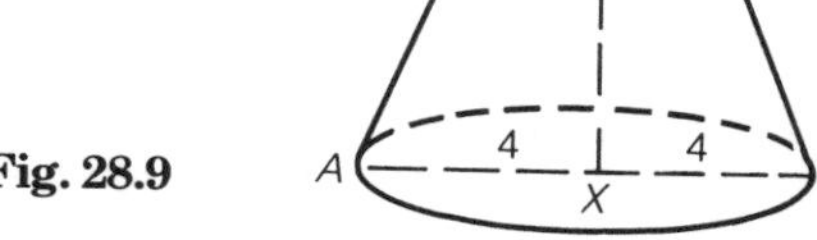

Fig. 28.9

4 Fig. 28.10 shows a tent whose end faces, ABC and EFG, are isosceles triangles.
The height of the tent pole, AD, is 2 m. Calculate,
(a) length AC **(b)** length GD
(c) length GA **(d)** $A\widehat{G}D$

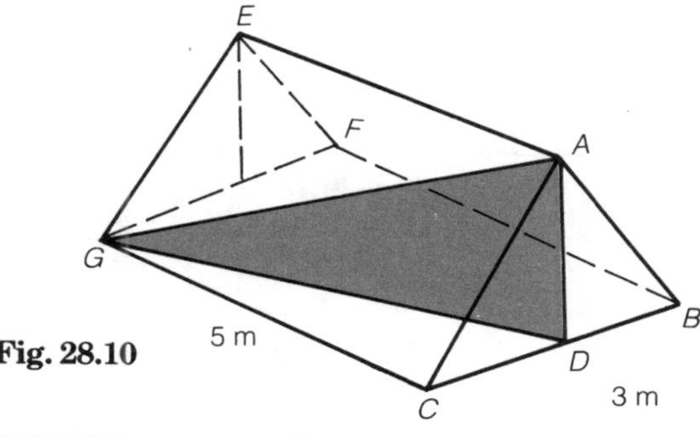

Fig. 28.10

5 $VABCD$ is a pyramid on a square base $ABCD$, with the vertex V vertically above A. If $AB = 20$ cm and $VA = 24$ cm, find the lengths of the slant edges and the angle each makes with $ABCD$.

6 $VJKLM$ is a pyramid on a rectangular base $JKLM$, with V directly above J. If $JK = 9$ cm, $JM = 12$ cm and $VK = 15$ cm, then calculate the lengths of the slant edges and the angle each makes with the base.

7 From a point A, due south of a tower, the angle of elevation of the top of the tower is 24°. From a point B, due east of the tower, the elevation of the top of the tower is 32°. If the tower is 30 m tall, find the distance AB.

8 In the wedge $ABCDEF$ shown in Fig. 28.11, $CDEF$ is perpendicular to $ABCD$. The surface, $ABFE$, is inclined at 35° to the base, $ABCD$. Angle $EAF = 30°$ and $FC = 12$ cm. Calculate,
(a) the length of AE
(b) the length of AF **(c)** angle FAC

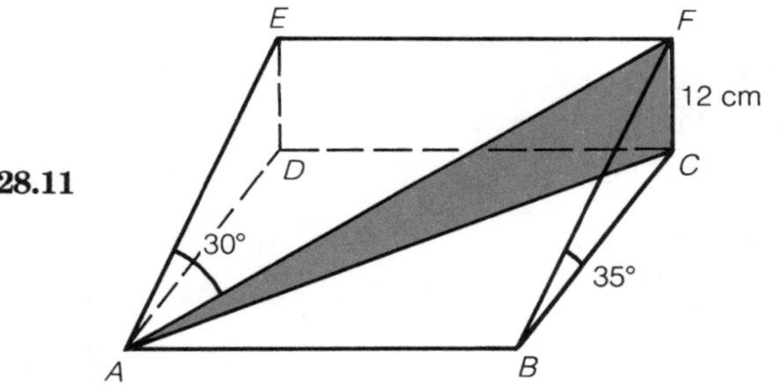

Fig. 28.11

Unit 29

Gradients

29.1 The gradient of a line

As we saw in Volume 2, Unit 22.5, the gradient of a line is found by constructing a right-angled triangle, using part or all of the line as the hypotenuse. The value of the gradient is found by dividing the vertical height by the horizontal length. This is, in fact, the tangent of the angle θ, that the line makes with the horizontal,

i.e. $\dfrac{\text{opposite side}}{\text{adjacent side}} = \text{the gradient of the line} = \tan\theta$

Example 1

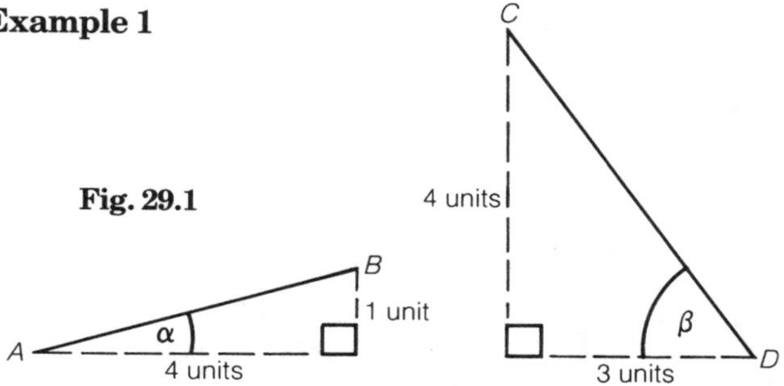

Fig. 29.1

See Fig. 29.1.

The line AB has a gradient of $\tan\alpha = \dfrac{1}{4}$

The line CD has a gradient of $-\tan\beta = \dfrac{-4}{3}$

(As explained in Volume 2, lines sloping in the same direction as AB have +ve gradients and lines sloping in the same direction as CD have −ve gradients.)

Example 2 Plot the line joining the points (2,1) and (4,3) and find its gradient.

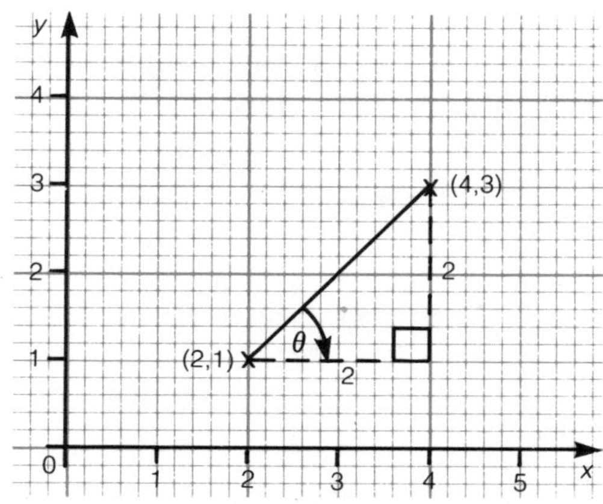

Fig. 29.2

See Fig. 29.2.

Gradient of this line $= \tan\theta = \dfrac{2}{2}$

Hence, gradient = 1

Example 3 Plot the graph of $y = 3x + 1$ for $0 \leqslant x \leqslant 4$. See Table 29.1 and Fig. 29.3.

x	0	1	2	3	4
$3x$ $+1$	0 1	3 1	6 1	9 1	12 1
y	1	4	7	10	13

Table 29.1

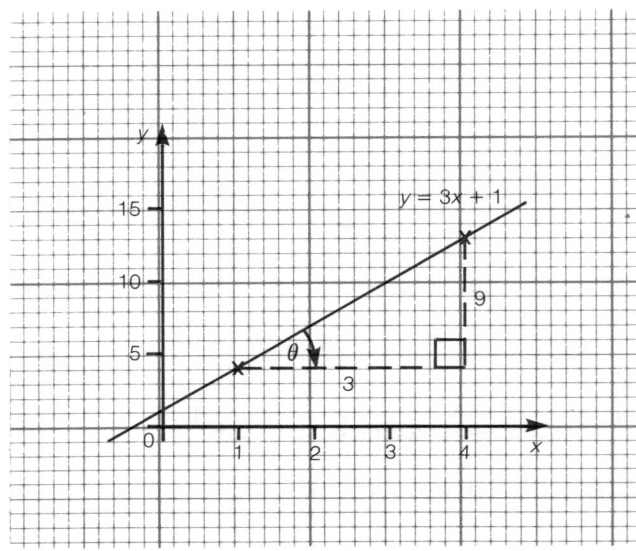

Fig. 29.3

From the graph in Fig. 29.3,

$\tan\theta = \dfrac{9}{3} = 3$

$y = mx + c$ and $y = 3x + 1$

Confirming that m (the gradient) = 3

We can find the gradient of a line joining two points, without plotting the points, simply from,

$$\text{gradient} = \frac{\text{difference in the } y\text{-values}}{\text{difference in the } x\text{-values}}$$

Example 4 Find the gradient of the line joining the points (4,3) and (−2,4).

$$\text{gradient} = \frac{3-4}{4-(-2)} = \frac{-1}{6}$$

Hence, the gradient $= -\dfrac{1}{6}$

Activities

1 Calculate the gradient of each line shown in Fig. 29.4.

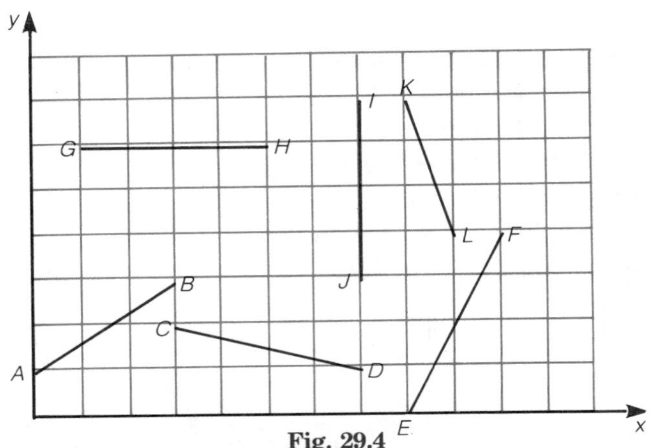

Fig. 29.4

2 Plot the following pairs of points and find the gradient of the straight line through each pair.

(a) (4,2) (5,7) **(b)** (6,−2) (7,8)

(c) (−4,−2) (−9,−2) **(d)** (4,4) (6,0)

(e) (−2,5) (−4,0) **(f)** (6,1) (6,−2)

3 Plot the following graphs for $0 \leqslant x \leqslant 4$. Then, in each case, construct a right-angled triangle and find $\tan\theta$.

(a) $y = 2x - 1$ **(b)** $y = 3x - 2$

(c) $2y = x + 4$ **(d)** $y = \frac{1}{2}x + 5$

(Check to see that $\tan\theta$ = gradient.)

4 Without plotting the points, calculate the gradient of the line joining each of the following pairs of points.

(a) (−1,−4) (5,−2) **(b)** (1,3) (4,2)

(c) (6,5) (−2,3) **(d)** (−2,7) (2,5)

(e) (0,3) (7,1) **(f)** (2,−4) (−3,1)

(g) (1,4) (3,3) **(h)** (−1,−5) (0,−2)

29.2 The gradient of a curve at a particular point

Since the gradient of a curve is constantly changing, we are only able to find the gradient of the curve at specific points. We do this by constructing a **tangent** to the curve at the required point, and then we find the gradient of this line.

Example Find the gradient of the curve $y = x^2 - 3x + 2$ $(-2 \leqslant x \leqslant 4)$ at the point P (3,2) and the point Q (−1,6).

See Fig. 29.5.

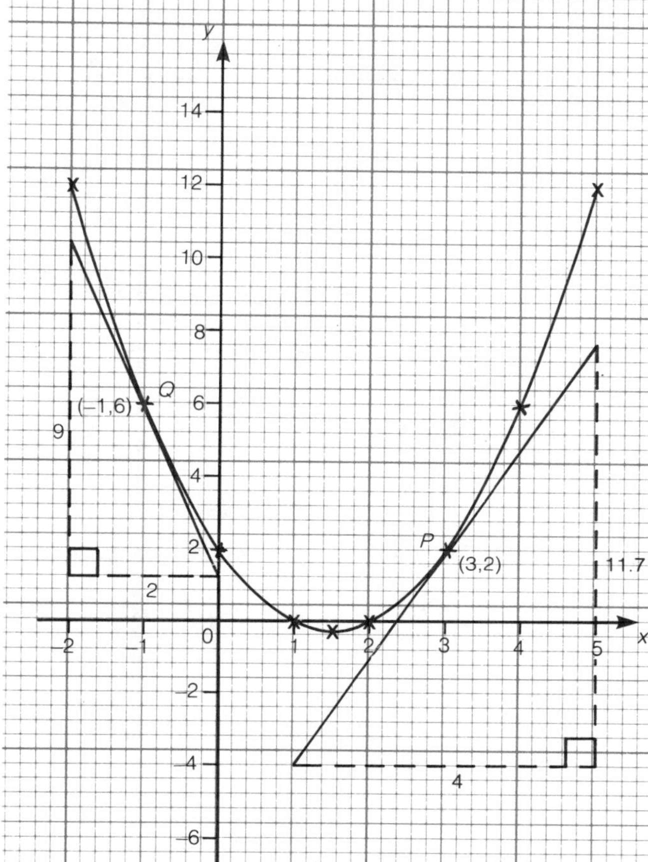

Fig. 29.5

$$\text{Gradient of tangent at point } P\ (3,2) = \frac{11.7}{4} = 2.9$$

$$\text{Gradient of tangent at point } Q\ (-1,6) = \frac{-9.2}{2} = -4.6$$

Note Obviously, these values are only approximate because they will only be as accurate as the curve itself and the accuracy of the tangent drawn to it. In fact, the actual gradients (by calculation) are,

gradient at $P = 3$, gradient at $Q = -5$

So, we must allow ourselves some degree of tolerance when using the graphical method.

Activities

1 By drawing a suitable tangent to the curve at P (see Fig. 29.6), we can find the gradient of the curve at the point (5,3). What is this gradient?

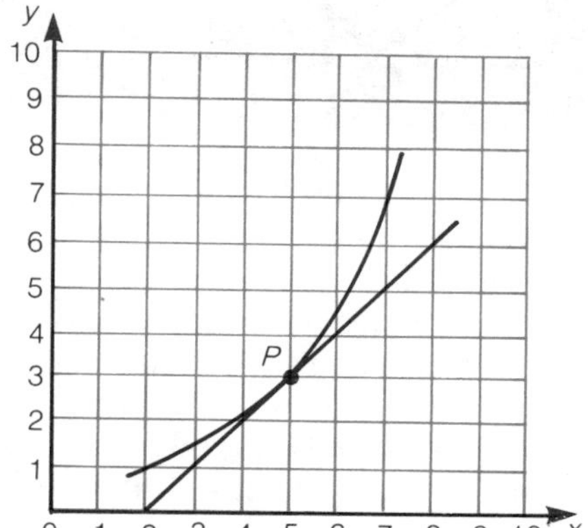

Fig. 29.6

2 In Fig. 29.7, by drawing suitable tangents at the points $P(6,6)$ and $Q(-3,4\frac{1}{2})$, find the approximate gradient of the curve at these points.

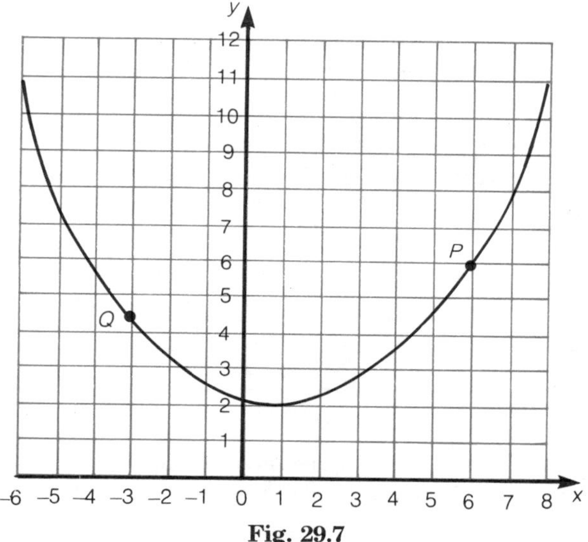

Fig. 29.7

3 Taking a suitable scale, plot on graph paper the points in Table 29.2 and draw a smooth curve through them.

x	0	1	2	3	4	5	6
y	0	0.25	1	2.25	4	6.25	9

Table 29.2

(a) Draw the tangents to the curve at the points where $x = 2$ and $x = 4$.

(b) Find the approximate gradient of the curve at each of these points.

4 Draw the graph of $y = \dfrac{20}{x}$ for $0 < x \leqslant 10$.

Find the approximate gradients of the curve at the points where $x = 2$ and $x = 4$.

Unit 30

Congruent triangles

Congruent triangles are triangles which are identical in every respect. Unfortunately, triangles sometimes look congruent when in fact they are not. Much depends on how much information concerning side lengths and sizes of angles is given, before we are able to say that two triangles are congruent.

Two triangles can only be said to be **congruent** if one of the following conditions is satisfied.

1 Corresponding sides are equal; sometimes called 'side-side-side' (S.S.S.). See Fig. 30.1.

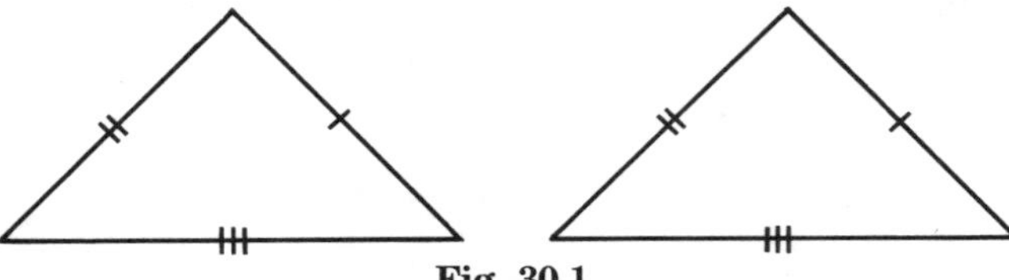

Fig. 30.1

2 Two sides and the included angle, are equal; sometimes called 'side-angle-side' (S.A.S.). See Fig. 30.2.

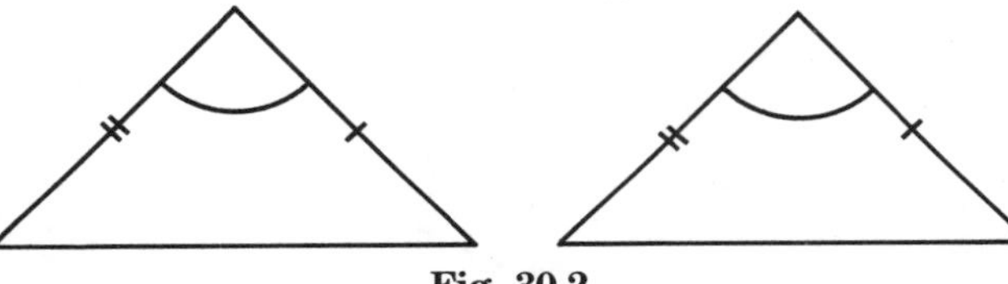

Fig. 30.2

3 Two angles and one corresponding side are equal; sometimes called 'angle-side-angle' (A.S.A. or A.A.S.). See Fig. 30.3.

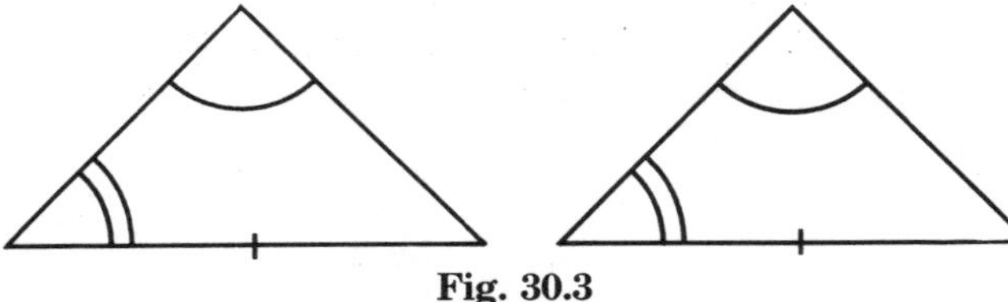

Fig. 30.3

4 For right-angled triangles, the hypotenuse and one pair of corresponding sides must be equal; sometimes called 'right angle-hypotenuse-side' (R.H.S.). See Fig. 30.4.

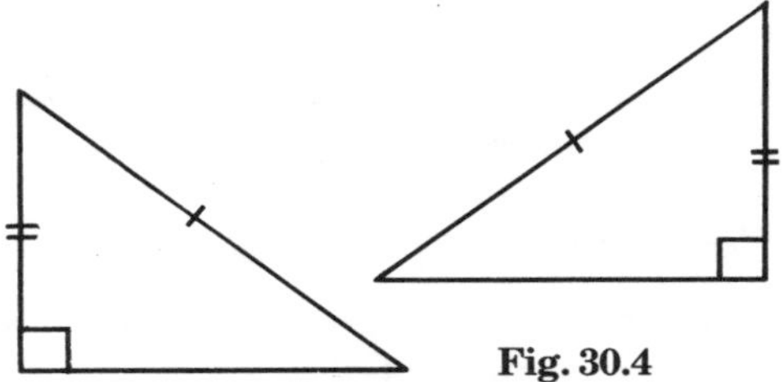

Fig. 30.4

Hence, by applying the above conditions to a pair of triangles, we can say that they are **(a)** congruent, **(b)** not necessarily congruent or **(c)** non-congruent.

Activities

1 State whether the pairs of triangles in Fig. 30.5 are congruent, giving reasons for your answers.

Note Drawings are **not** to scale.

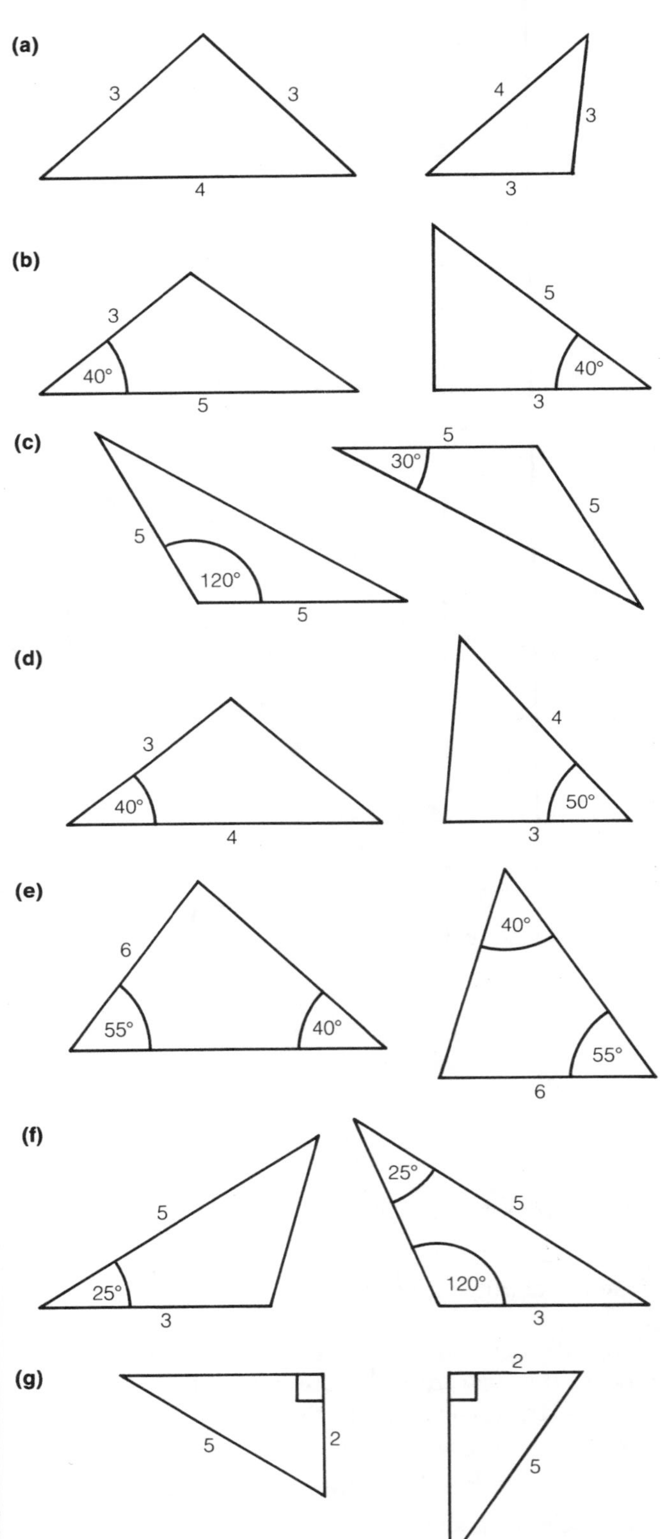

Fig. 30.5

Unit 31

Similar triangles

If two triangles are **similar** then,

(a) corresponding angles are equal (A.A.A.)

and **(b)** the ratio of corresponding side lengths is the same.

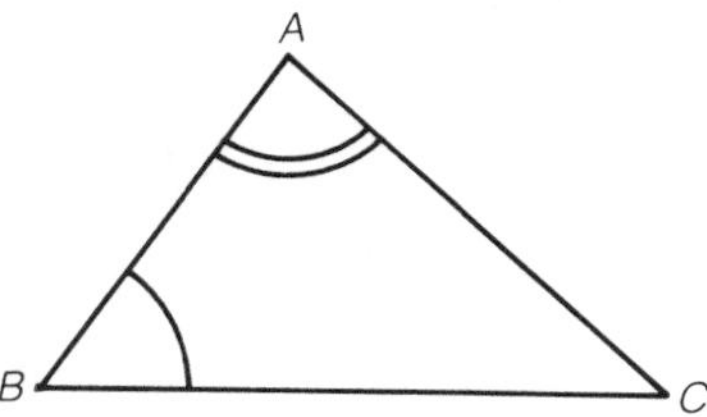

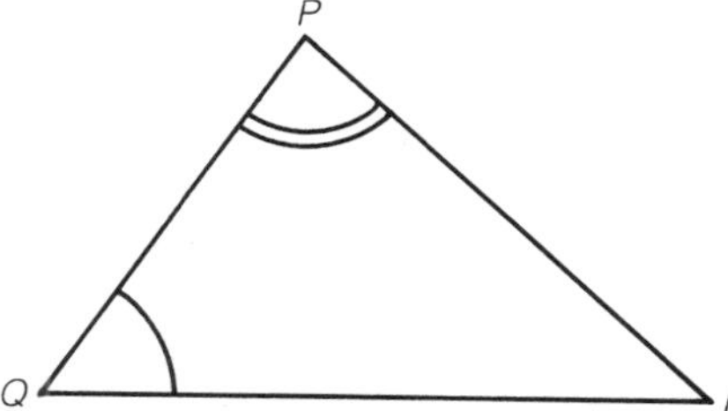

Fig. 31.1

In the similar triangles ABC and PQR shown in Fig. 31.1,

$\angle A = \angle P$, $\angle B = \angle Q$ and hence, $\angle C = \angle R$

And so, $\dfrac{AB}{PQ} = \dfrac{BC}{QR} = \dfrac{AC}{PR}$

Example 1 The two triangles, in Fig. 31.2, are similar (A.A.A.). Find the unknown marked lengths (x cm and y cm).

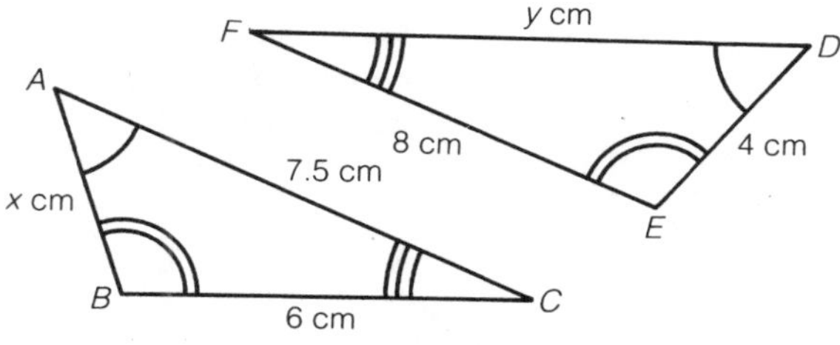

Fig. 31.2

Since $\angle A = \angle D$, $\angle B = \angle E$ and $\angle C = \angle F$

then, $\dfrac{AB}{DE} = \dfrac{BC}{EF} = \dfrac{AC}{DF}$

Hence, $\dfrac{x}{4} = \dfrac{6}{8} = \dfrac{7.5}{y}$

So, $8x = 24$ and $6y = 60$

$\therefore x = 3$ and $y = 10$

Example 2 Find the length QR in Fig. 31.3.

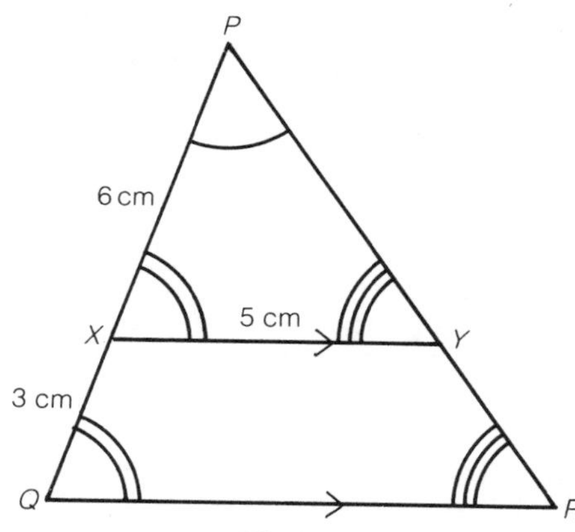

Fig. 31.3

$\triangle PXY$ is similar to $\triangle PQR$ since $\angle P$ is common to both triangles.

$\angle PXY = \angle PQR$ and $\angle PYX = \angle PRQ$ (corresponding angles)

Hence, the sides are in the ratio

$$\frac{PX}{PQ} = \frac{PY}{PR} = \frac{XY}{QR}$$

And so, $\dfrac{6}{9} = \dfrac{5}{QR}$

$6QR = 45$; $QR = \dfrac{45}{6}$

$\therefore QR = 7\frac{1}{2}$ cm

Activities

The drawings, below, are **not** to scale.

1 The following questions refer to Fig. 31.4.

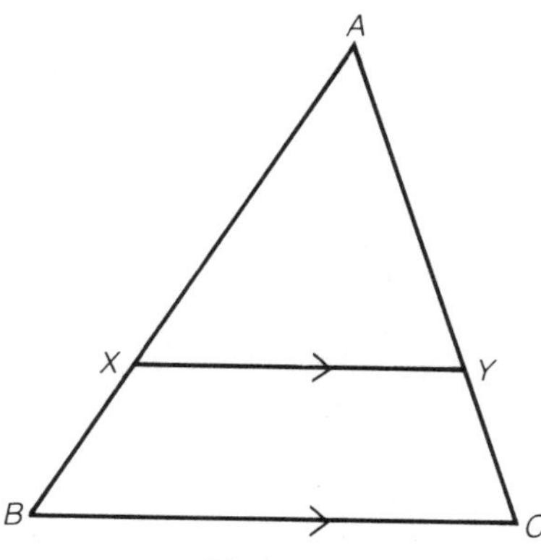

Fig. 31.4

(a) $AB = 8$ cm, $AX = 6$ cm, $AC = 12$ cm. Find AY.

(b) $AX = 12$ cm, $AY = 9$ cm, $AC = 15$ cm. Find AB.

(c) $AY = 2.4$ cm, $YC = 1.8$ cm, $XB = 2.4$ cm. Find AX.

2

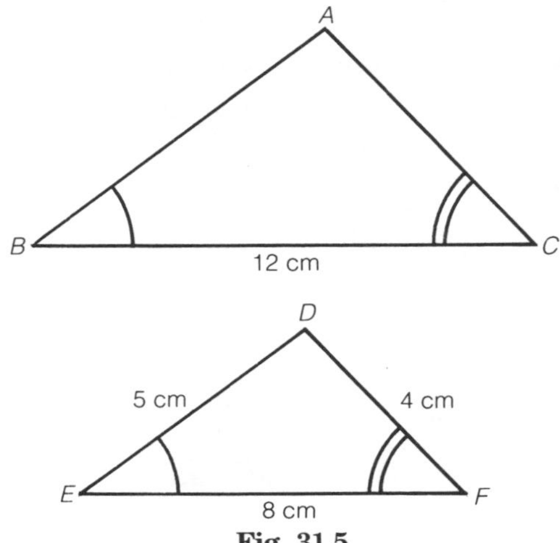

Fig. 31.5

In Fig. 31.5, if ABC and DEF are two similar triangles, then calculate,

(a) lengths AB and AC

(b) the ratio of the area of triangle ABC to the area of triangle DEF

3

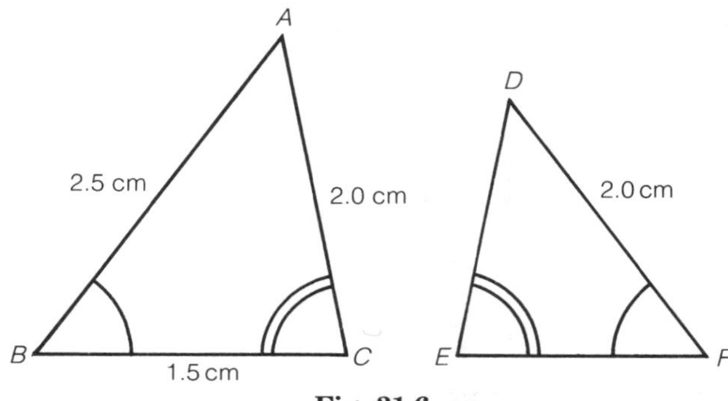

Fig. 31.6

In Fig. 31.6, if ABC and DEF are two similar triangles, then calculate,

(a) the lengths DE and EF

(b) the ratio of the area of triangle DEF to the area of triangle ABC

4

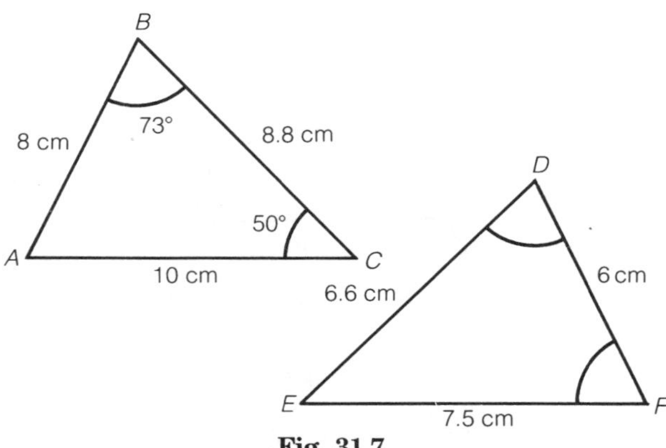

Fig. 31.7

In Fig. 31.7, state the size of,

(a) angle D **(b)** angle E **(c)** angle F

Unit 32

Angle properties of a circle

There are a few angle properties of a circle that we should be aware of at this stage of our studies, but there are more, of a slightly advanced nature, which will not be dealt with in this section.

1 The angle subtended at the centre of a circle is twice the angle subtended at the circumference by the same chord (or arc). (See Fig. 32.1.)

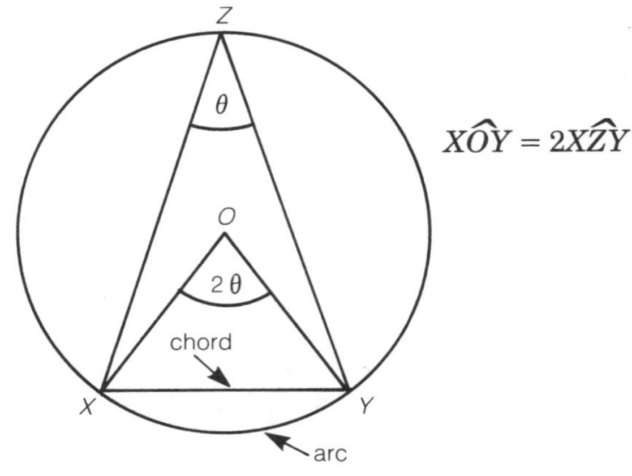

Fig. 32.1

$X\widehat{O}Y = 2X\widehat{Z}Y$

2 Angles subtended at the circumference of a circle, by the same chord (or arc), are equal. (See Fig. 32.2.)

$A\widehat{X}B = A\widehat{Y}B = A\widehat{Z}B = \theta°$

The angles $\widehat{X}$, $\widehat{Y}$ and $\widehat{Z}$ are subtended by the chord AB and the minor arc AB.

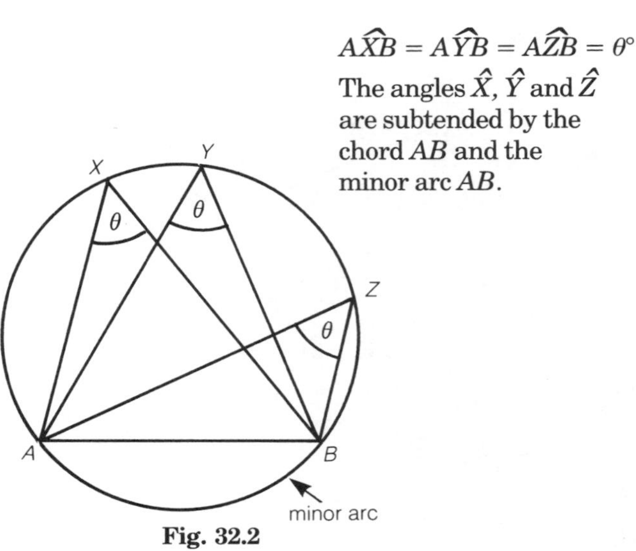

Fig. 32.2

3 The angles subtended at the circumference of a circle, by a diameter, are right angles. (See Fig. 32.3.)

$X\widehat{L}Y = X\widehat{M}Y = 90°$
XY is a diameter of the circle.

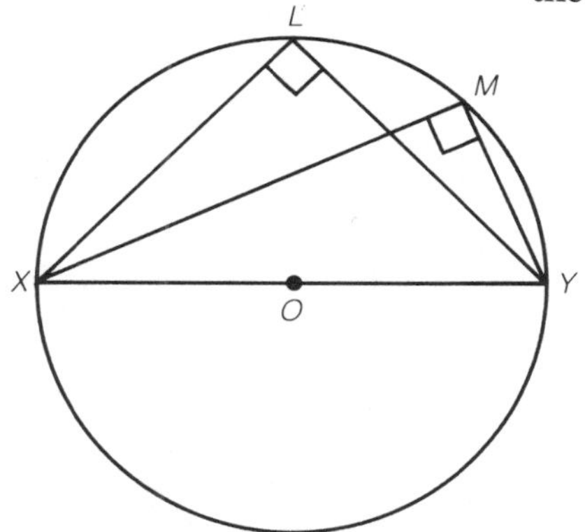

Fig. 32.3

4 Opposite angles of a cyclic quadrilateral (a quadrilateral with all four vertices on the circumference of a circle), are supplementary. (See Fig. 32.4.)

$\widehat{\alpha} + \widehat{\beta} = 180°$

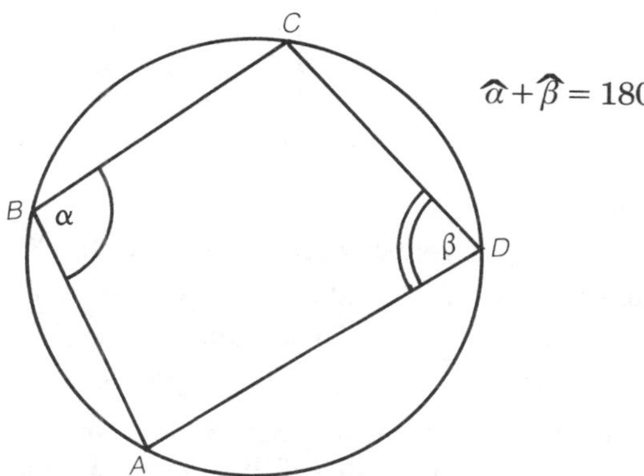

Fig. 32.4

5 A tangent is always at right angles to a radius of the circle, at the point of contact. (See Fig. 32.5.)

$O\widehat{P}Q = 90°$

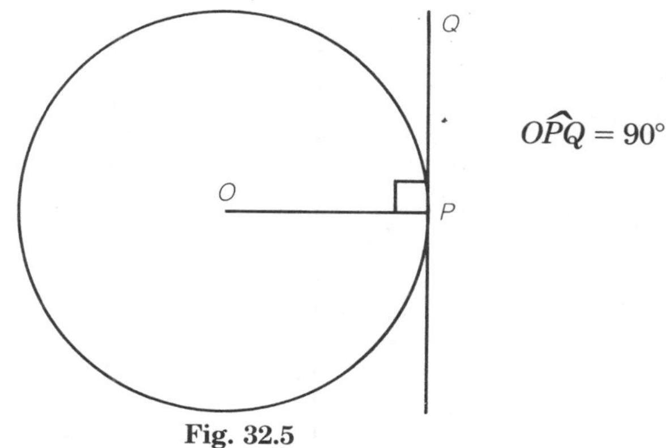

Fig. 32.5

Activities

1 Find the sizes of the angles marked by letters, in Fig. 32.6 (not drawn to scale). O is the centre of each circle.

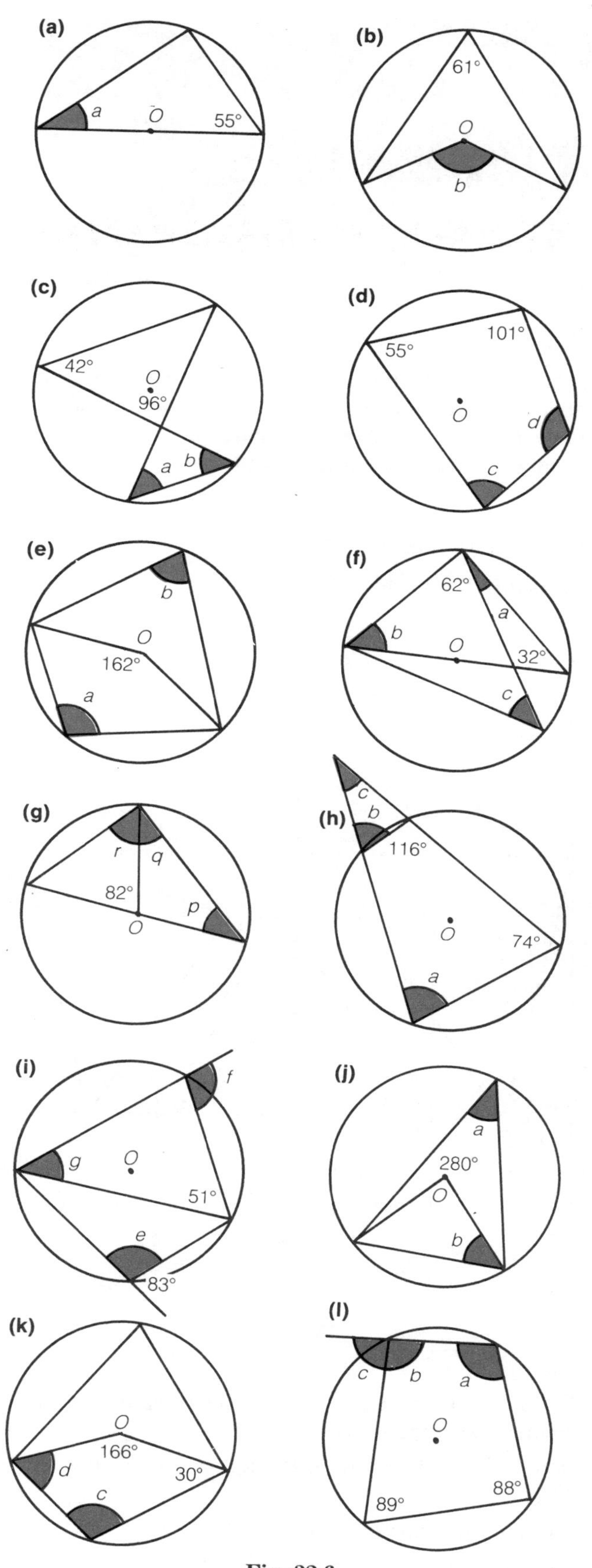

Fig. 32.6

2 A, B, C, D are four points on the circumference of a circle. $A\widehat{B}D = 44°$ and AB is parallel to DC. Find,

(a) $A\widehat{C}D$ **(b)** $B\widehat{D}C$ **(c)** $B\widehat{A}C$

3 The chord AB in a circle is parallel to a diameter CD. If $C\widehat{A}B = 110°$, find $C\widehat{D}B$, $D\widehat{C}B$, and $C\widehat{B}A$.

Unit 33

Geometric transformations

33.1 Introduction

A **transformation** is simply a change. Those that we are concerned with are simple transformations of plane figures, i.e. **reflections, rotations, enlargements** and **translations**.

33.2 Reflections

Example 1 See Fig. 33.1

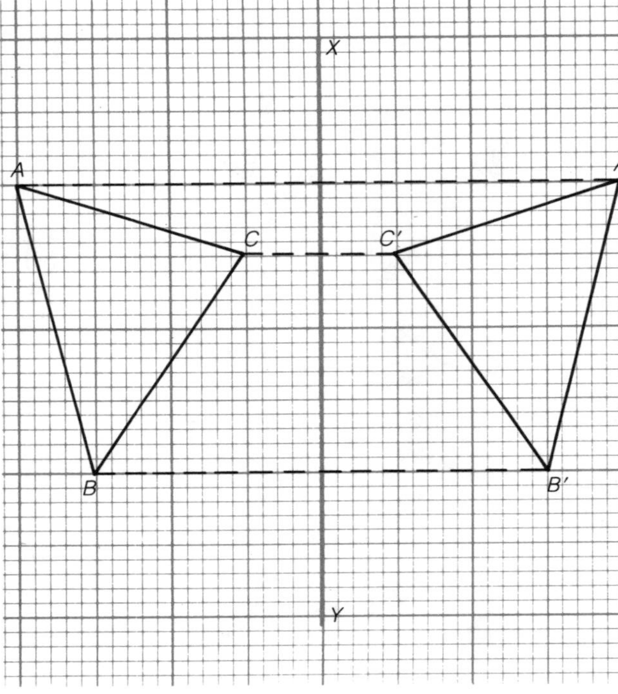

Fig. 33.1

Triangle ABC, when reflected in the **mirror** line XY, produces an image $A'B'C'$

Hence, $\triangle A'B'C'$ is the **reflection** of $\triangle ABC$ in line XY.

It is important to note that,

(a) size and shape are unchanged.

(b) the order of points is reversed.

(c) lines joining points to their image points are perpendicular to the mirror line XY, and are also bisected by the mirror line.

(d) the equation (position) of the mirror line must be given.

Example 2 Using graph paper find the co-ordinates of the point (3,2), after reflection in,

(a) the x-axis ($y = 0$) **(c)** the line $y = x$
(b) the y-axis ($x = 0$) **(d)** the line $y = -x$

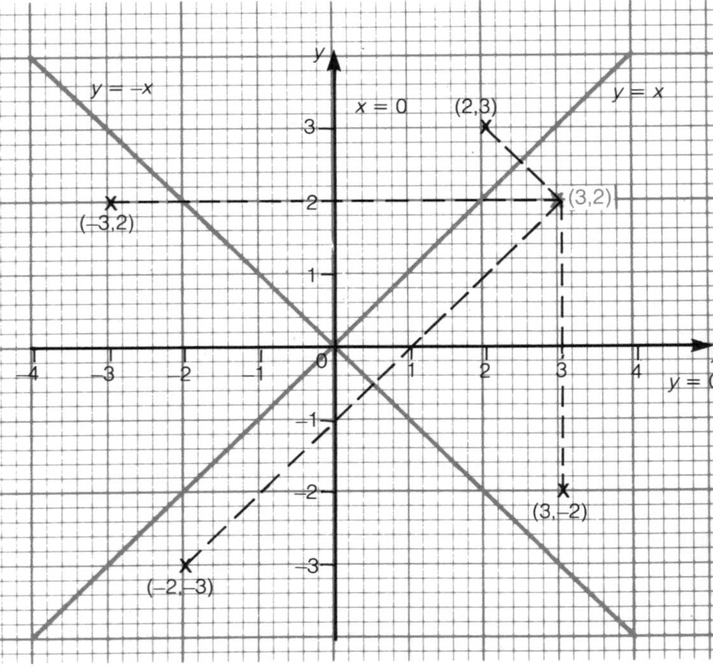

Fig. 33.2

See Fig. 33.2.

(a) image of (3,2) reflected in the x-axis is (3,−2)
(b) image of (3,2) reflected in the y-axis is (−3,2)
(c) image of (3,2) reflected in the line $y = x$ is (2,3)
(d) image of (3,2) reflected in the line $y = -x$ is (−2,−3)

Note With a little care and practice, it is possible to write down the co-ordinates of the images without having to draw the graph.

Activities

1 Reflect the shapes, in Figs. 33.3 and 33.4, in the lines AB.

(a)

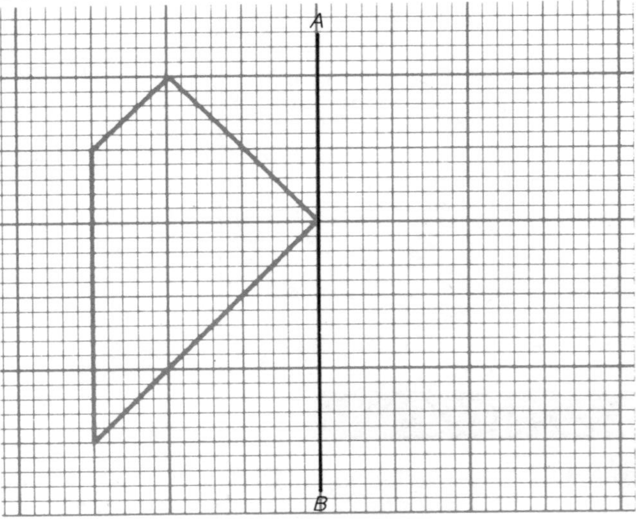

Fig. 33.3

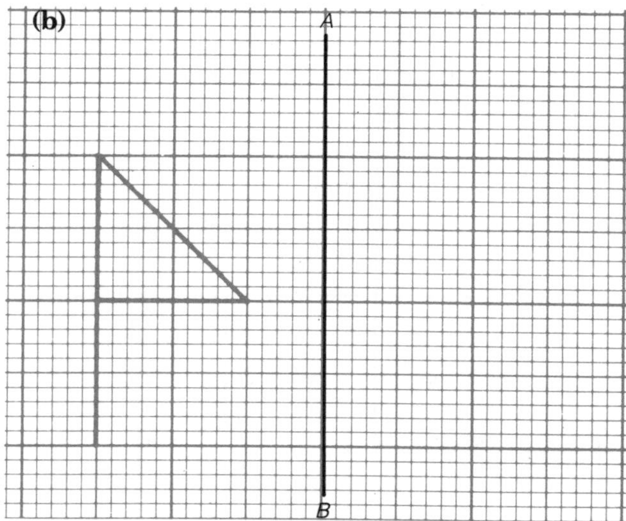

Fig. 33.4

2 Reflect the shapes, in Figs. 33.5 and 33.6, in the lines AB. Then, for each, reflect the whole shape in the line CD.

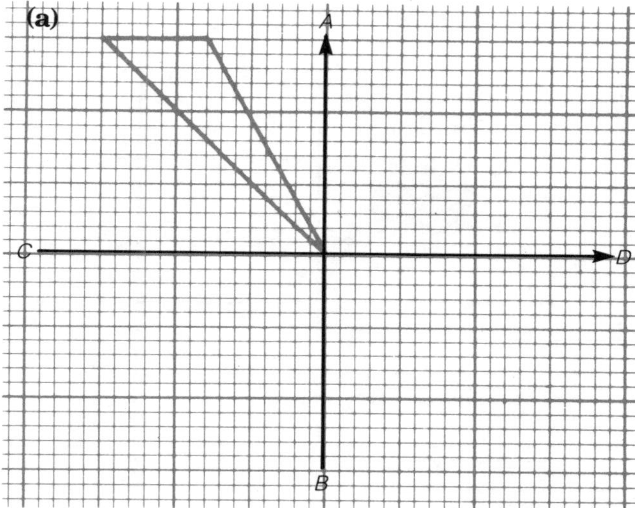

Fig. 33.5

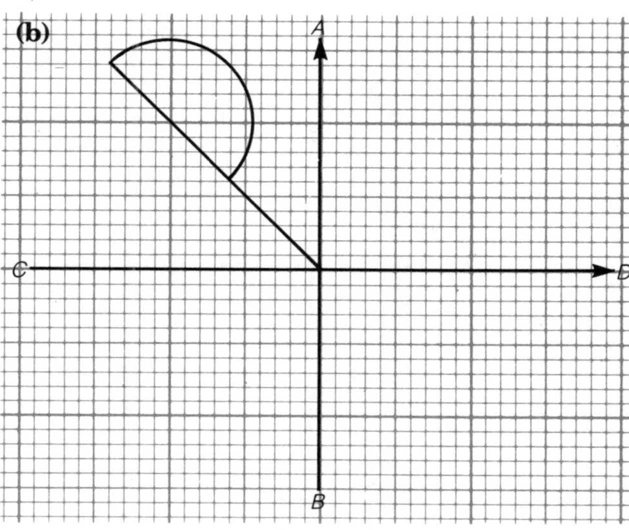

Fig. 33.6

3 Using graph paper, plot the points $A(2,5)$, $B(4,2)$, $C(2,0)$, $D(4,-2)$, $E(2,-5)$. Using the line $x = 0$ as the mirror line, plot A', B', C', D' and E', the images of A, B, C, D and E. Join up $ABCDE$and $A'B'C'D'E'$.

4 Using graph paper, plot the points $A(-2,-1)$, $B(-2,3)$, $C(0,-1)$, $D(0,3)$. Join up $ABDC$. Now draw its mirror image in the line $x = 1$, and write down the co-ordinates of the images A', B', C' and D'.

5 Write down the images of these points after reflection in the line $y = 0$.

(a) (2,3) **(b)** (−5,6) **(c)** (3,−4) **(d)** (0,7)

6 Without drawing a diagram, write down the images of the following points after reflection in $y = x$.

(a) (−1,2) **(b)** (0,4) **(c)** (6,0) **(d)** (3,−1)

33.3 Rotations

Example 1 In Fig. 33.7, the triangle XYZ has been rotated through 90° clockwise (−90°) about the **centre of rotation**, O.

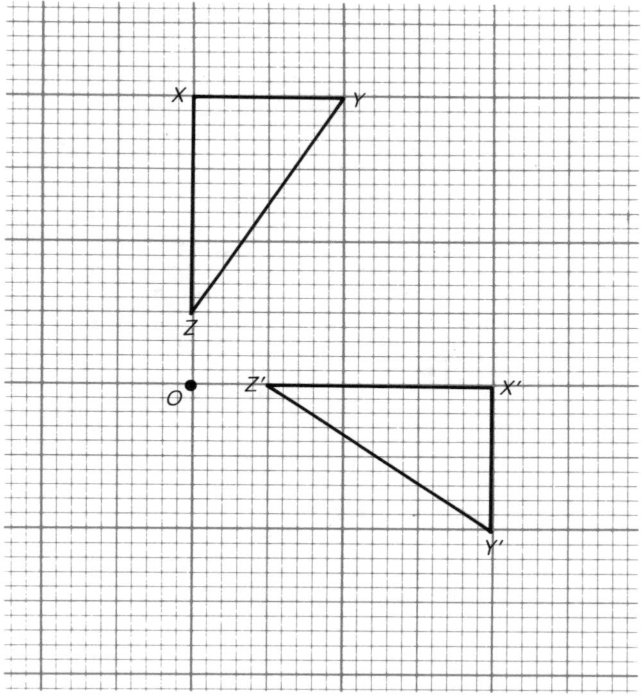

Fig. 33.7

The image of $\triangle XYZ$ is $\triangle X'Y'Z'$

It is important to note the following.

(a) Size and shape are, again, unchanged.

(b) The centre of rotation, O, must remain static.

(c) The angle between the line joining a point to the centre of rotation, and the line joining the corresponding image point to the centre of rotation, is called the **angle of rotation**.

(d) We say that an anticlockwise rotation is positive and a clockwise rotation is negative.

(e) The centre of rotation, the angle and direction of rotation, must be given.

Example 2 Using graph paper, find the co-ordinates of the point (3,1) after an anticlockwise rotation of 90° about

(a) (1,0) **(b)** (1,2) **(c)** (−1,0) **(d)** (2,−2)

See Figs. 33.8, 33.9, 33.10 and 33.11.

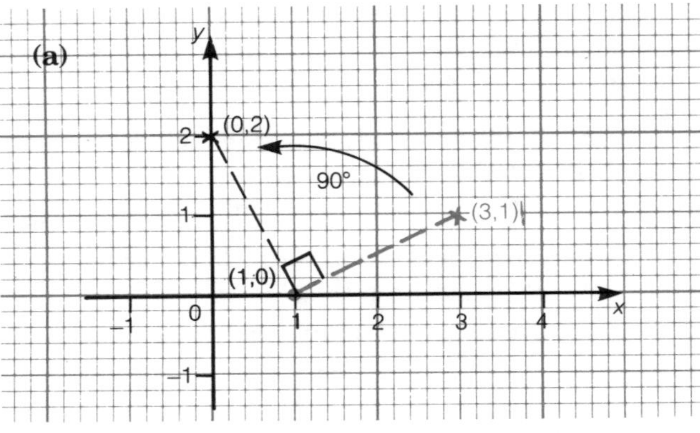

(3,1)→(0,2)

Fig. 33.8

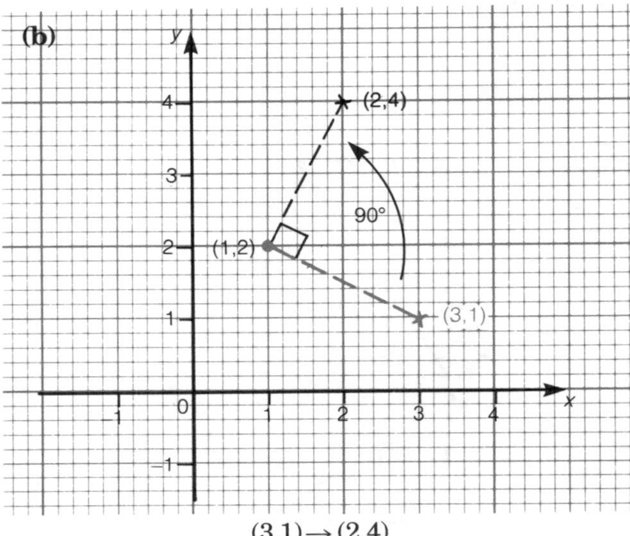

(3,1)→(2,4)

Fig. 33.9

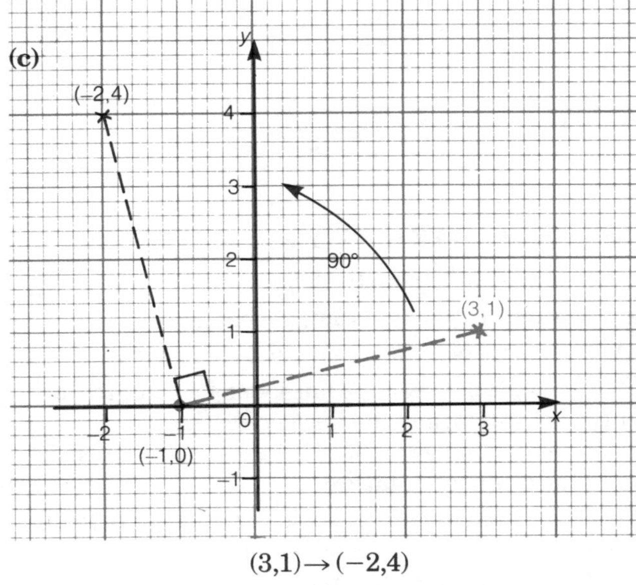

(3,1)→(−2,4)

Fig. 33.10

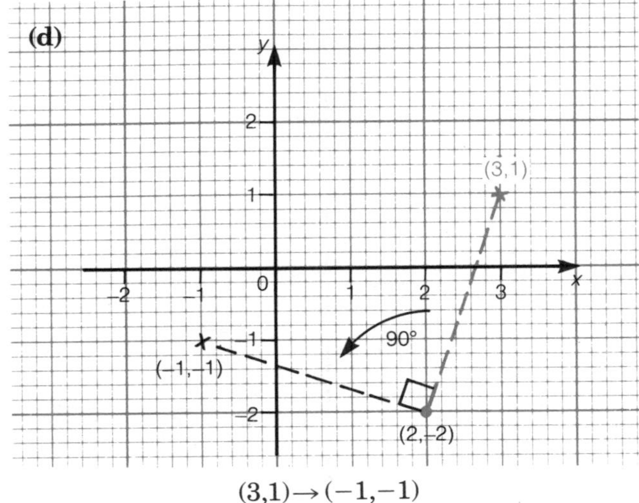

(3,1)→(−1,−1)

Fig. 33.11

Activities

1 See Figs. 33.12 and 33.13. Rotate each shape through 90° about the origin, *O*, and keep on rotating until you reach the start position.

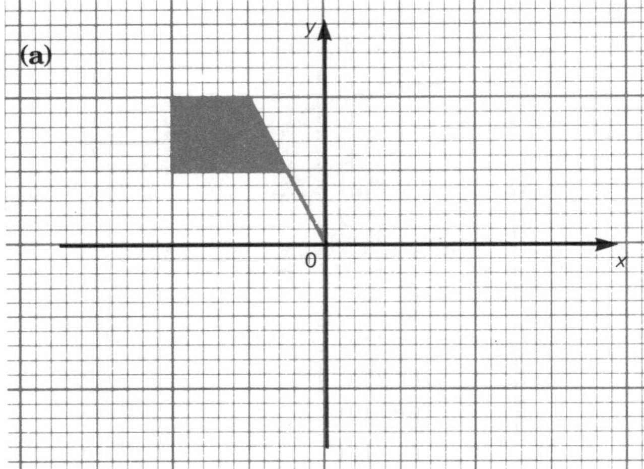

Fig. 33.12

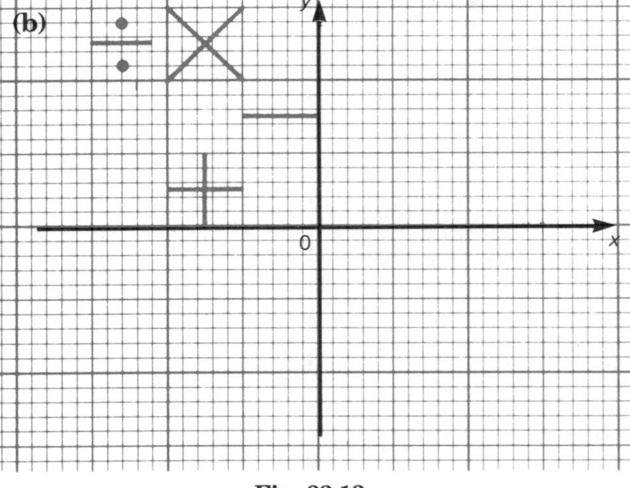

Fig. 33.13

2 Copy triangle ABC, in Figure 33.14, and rotate it about A through 60° in a clockwise direction. Through what angle has AB turned? Now repeat the rotation, but this time rotate the triangle about B.

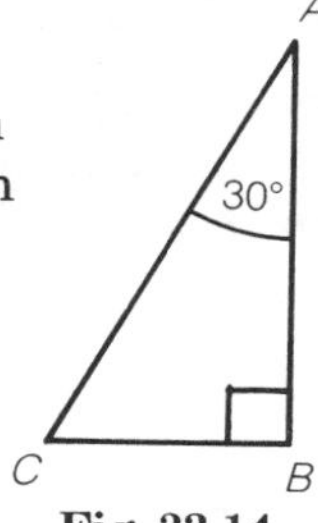

Fig. 33.14

3 On graph paper, draw triangle ABC, by joining the points $A(1,0)$, $B(3,0)$, $C(3,3)$.

Mark the positions after it has been rotated about the origin through, **(i)** 90°, **(ii)** 180°, **(iii)** 270°.

Call these triangles T_1, T_2 and T_3.

(a) Describe the transformation that maps T_2 onto T_3

(b) Describe the transformation that maps T_3 onto T_2

4 On graph paper, draw the square S, formed by joining the points $A(-1,0)$, $B(-1,2)$, $C(1,2)$, $D(1,0)$.

Draw the square S_1, formed when S is rotated clockwise through 90° about A.

Write down the co-ordinates of A', B', C' and D'.

S_2 has vertices $A''(1,-2)$, $B''(1,-4)$, $C''(-1,-4)$, $D''(-1,-2)$. Find the point of rotation and the angle of rotation, for S_1 moving to S_2.

33.4 Enlargements

Example See Fig. 33.15.

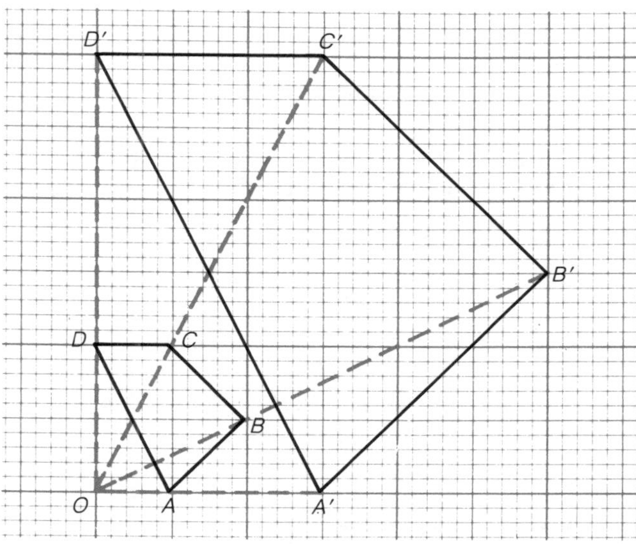

Fig. 33.15

The quadrilateral $ABCD$, in Fig. 33.15, has been **enlarged** by a scale factor of 3, with the centre of enlargement the point O. The image of $ABCD$ is $A'B'C'D'$.

It is important to note the following.

(a) The shape is unchanged.

(b) Straight lines can be drawn from the centre of enlargement, O, through each point and its image, e.g. OCC', OAA' etc.

(c) The centre of enlargement, O, is a static point.

(d) The ratios, $\frac{OD'}{OD} = \frac{OC'}{OC} = \frac{OB'}{OB} = \frac{OA'}{OA} = 3$

This is known as the **scale factor**. Hence, $A'B'C'D'$ is a quadrilateral, three times the size of the quadrilateral $ABCD$.

(e) In order to make an enlargement, we need to know the scale factor and also the centre of enlargement.

(f) Scale factors may be fractional (producing a reduced image) or even negative (producing an inverted image).

Activities

1 Use graph paper to draw the original shape, as shown in Fig. 33.16. Then, enlarge the shape as follows,

(a) by a scale factor of 2

(b) by a scale factor of 3

(c) by a scale factor of $\frac{1}{2}$

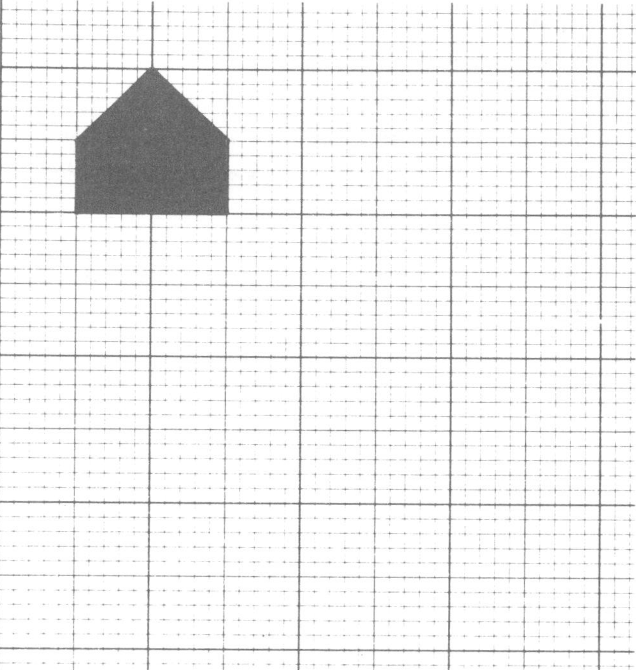

Fig. 33.16

2 Draw axes for x and y from 1 to 10. For each example, below, plot the shape given and then the image, using the given centre of enlargement.

(a) Plot triangle ABC with $A(3,3)$, $B(6,2)$, $C(5,6)$. Centre of enlargement (5,4) and scale factor 2.

(b) Plot triangle PQR with $P(1,1)$, $Q(3,1)$, $R(1,5)$. Centre of enlargement (0,0) and scale factor 2.

(c) Plot triangle EFG with $E(1,2)$, $F(4,4)$, $G(2,1)$. Centre of enlargement (1,1) and scale factor 3.

33.5 Translations

A **translation** is a movement of a figure from one position to another (its image).

Example See Fig. 33.17.

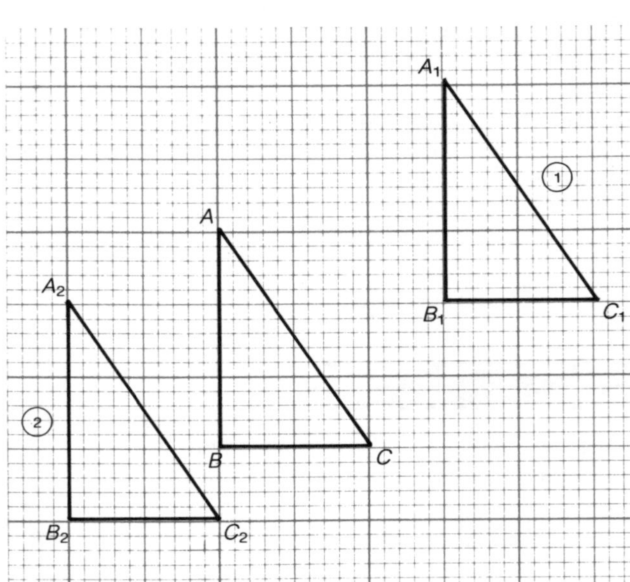

Fig. 33.17

Translation ① $\triangle ABC$ is moved (translated) to $A_1B_1C_1$ by an 'x' shift of +3 and a 'y' shift of +2.

Translation ② $\triangle ABC$ is moved to $A_2B_2C_2$ by an 'x' shift of −2 and a 'y' shift of −1.

It is important to note the following.

(a) Size and shape are unchanged.

(b) All lines joining points to images are parallel for each translation.

(c) Every point moves.

(d) The 'x' and 'y' shifts need to be given, usually as a (2 × 1) matrix, which is known as a **column vector**. In the example, above,

$$\text{Translation ①} = \begin{pmatrix} 3 \\ 2 \end{pmatrix} \quad \text{Translation ②} = \begin{pmatrix} -2 \\ -1 \end{pmatrix}$$

Activities

1 Show on graph paper what the given shape, in Fig. 33.18, becomes after translation by the following column vectors.

(a) $\begin{pmatrix} 2 \\ 3 \end{pmatrix}$ **(b)** $\begin{pmatrix} 3 \\ 0 \end{pmatrix}$ **(c)** $\begin{pmatrix} -2 \\ 5 \end{pmatrix}$ **(d)** $\begin{pmatrix} 0 \\ 4 \end{pmatrix}$

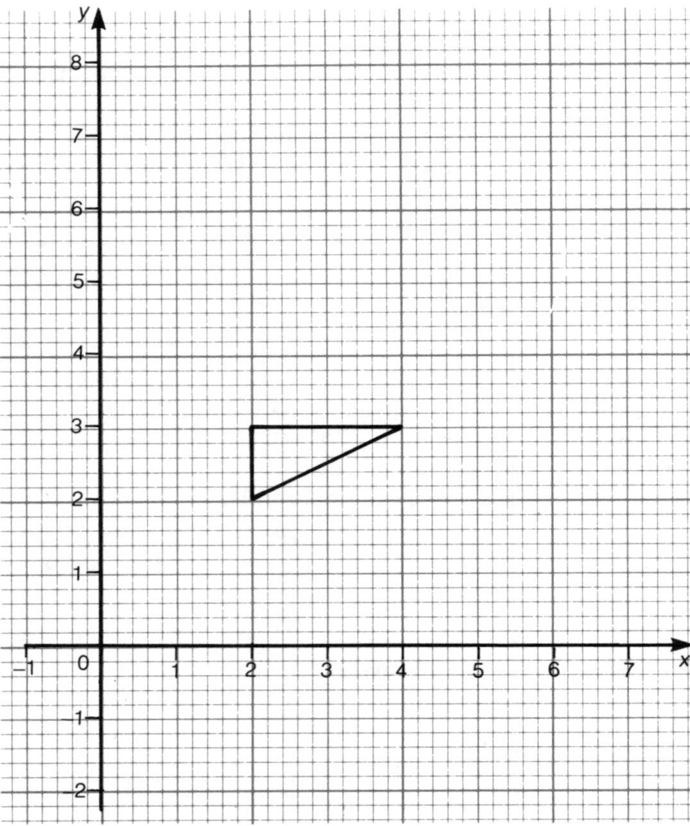

Fig. 33.18

2 Triangle ABC has co-ordinates A(1,2), B(3,3), C(2,5). Find the co-ordinates of its image, $A'B'C'$ after translation by the column vector $\begin{pmatrix} -3 \\ 2 \end{pmatrix}$.

3 Triangle $A'B'C'$ is the image of triangle ABC after translation by the column vector $\begin{pmatrix} 5 \\ -1 \end{pmatrix}$.

If the co-ordinates are $A'(5,3)$, $B'(3,1)$, and $C'(4,2)$, find the co-ordinates of A, B and C.

Unit 34

Transformation matrices

There is a close connection between many of the geometrical transformations we considered in the previous Unit, and certain matrices.

We can regard the matrix as operating on the co-ordinates (expressed in column form) of all points in the plane, thus producing a geometrical transformation.

Suppose we operate, by the following matrices, on a general point (a,b) and then describe the corresponding transformation.

(a,b) is written in column form $\begin{pmatrix} a \\ b \end{pmatrix}$.

Example 1 $\begin{pmatrix} 1 & 0 \\ 0 & 1 \end{pmatrix}\begin{pmatrix} a \\ b \end{pmatrix} = \begin{pmatrix} a \\ b \end{pmatrix}$ Identity matrix – no change

Example 2 $\begin{pmatrix} -1 & 0 \\ 0 & -1 \end{pmatrix}\begin{pmatrix} a \\ b \end{pmatrix} = \begin{pmatrix} -a \\ -b \end{pmatrix}$ Represents a rotation of 180°

Example 3 $\begin{pmatrix} 1 & 0 \\ 0 & -1 \end{pmatrix}\begin{pmatrix} a \\ b \end{pmatrix} = \begin{pmatrix} a \\ -b \end{pmatrix}$ Represents a reflection in the x-axis

Example 4 $\begin{pmatrix} -1 & 0 \\ 0 & 1 \end{pmatrix}\begin{pmatrix} a \\ b \end{pmatrix} = \begin{pmatrix} -a \\ b \end{pmatrix}$ Represents a reflection in the y-axis

Example 5 $\begin{pmatrix} 0 & 1 \\ 1 & 0 \end{pmatrix}\begin{pmatrix} a \\ b \end{pmatrix} = \begin{pmatrix} b \\ a \end{pmatrix}$ Represents a reflection in the line $y = x$

Example 6 $\begin{pmatrix} 0 & -1 \\ -1 & 0 \end{pmatrix}\begin{pmatrix} a \\ b \end{pmatrix} = \begin{pmatrix} -b \\ -a \end{pmatrix}$ Represents a reflection in the line $y = -x$

Example 7 $\begin{pmatrix} 0 & -1 \\ 1 & 0 \end{pmatrix}\begin{pmatrix} a \\ b \end{pmatrix} = \begin{pmatrix} -b \\ a \end{pmatrix}$ Represents an anticlockwise rotation of 90° about origin 0

Example 8 $\begin{pmatrix} 0 & 1 \\ -1 & 0 \end{pmatrix}\begin{pmatrix} a \\ b \end{pmatrix} = \begin{pmatrix} b \\ -a \end{pmatrix}$ Represents a clockwise rotation of 90° about origin 0

Example 9 $\begin{pmatrix} k & 0 \\ 0 & k \end{pmatrix}\begin{pmatrix} a \\ b \end{pmatrix} = \begin{pmatrix} ka \\ kb \end{pmatrix}$ Represents an enlargement of scale factor k

where k can be +ve or −ve

Let us now operate on a particular point, as an exercise in producing geometric transformations. Consider the point (3,2) under the transformations

(a) $\begin{pmatrix} 1 & 0 \\ 0 & -1 \end{pmatrix}$ and **(b)** $\begin{pmatrix} 0 & 1 \\ -1 & 0 \end{pmatrix}$

(a) $\begin{pmatrix} 1 & 0 \\ 0 & -1 \end{pmatrix}\begin{pmatrix} 3 \\ 2 \end{pmatrix} = \begin{pmatrix} 3 \\ -2 \end{pmatrix}$

Hence, $(3,2) \rightarrow (3,-2)$ which is, of course, a reflection in the x-axis.

(b) $\begin{pmatrix} 0 & 1 \\ -1 & 0 \end{pmatrix}\begin{pmatrix} 3 \\ 2 \end{pmatrix} = \begin{pmatrix} 2 \\ -3 \end{pmatrix}$

Hence, $(3,2) \rightarrow (2,-3)$ which is, of course, a clockwise rotation of the point (3,2) through 90° about the origin.

Activities

1 The line AB joins $A(2,3)$ and $B(3,5)$. Use the geometric transformation $\begin{pmatrix} 1 & 0 \\ 0 & -1 \end{pmatrix}$ on the line and find the image of AB.

By sketching, or otherwise, describe the transformation in geometric terms.

2 The line PQ joins $P(1,3)$ and $Q(5,2)$. Use the matrix transformation $\begin{pmatrix} -1 & 0 \\ 0 & 1 \end{pmatrix}$ on the line and find the image of PQ.

By sketching, or otherwise, describe the transformation in geometric terms.

3 The line FG joins $F(2,3)$ and $G(4,1)$. Use the matrix transformation $\begin{pmatrix} 0 & -1 \\ 1 & 0 \end{pmatrix}$ on the line and find the image of FG.

By sketching, or otherwise, describe the transformation in geometric terms.

4 Find the image of the unit square $O(0,0)$ $A(1,0)$ $B(1,1)$ and $C(0,1)$ under the transformation given by each of the following matrices.

(a) $\begin{pmatrix} 3 & 0 \\ 0 & 3 \end{pmatrix}$ **(b)** $\begin{pmatrix} -2 & 0 \\ 0 & -2 \end{pmatrix}$ **(c)** $\begin{pmatrix} 2 & 1 \\ 1 & 2 \end{pmatrix}$

Sketch each image.

5 Look at your answer to Question **4(a)** and describe in geometrical terms the following matrix transformations.

(a) $\begin{pmatrix} 2 & 0 \\ 0 & 2 \end{pmatrix}$ **(b)** $\begin{pmatrix} 5 & 0 \\ 0 & 5 \end{pmatrix}$ **(c)** $\begin{pmatrix} \frac{1}{2} & 0 \\ 0 & \frac{1}{2} \end{pmatrix}$

6 Triangle ABC has vertices $A(-2,1)$ $B(4,2)$ and $C(-1,4)$. Find the co-ordinates of the image of triangle ABC, after the matrix transformation given by $\begin{pmatrix} 4 & 2 \\ 2 & 1 \end{pmatrix}$.

7 Use the matrix $\begin{pmatrix} 0 & -2 \\ 2 & 0 \end{pmatrix}$ to transform the square with vertices $P(2,1)$, $Q(4,1)$, $R(4,3)$ and $S(2,3)$. Plot the points on a diagram and label the image square $P_1Q_1R_1S_1$.

8 Show that the matrix transformation $\begin{pmatrix} 0 & -2 \\ 2 & 0 \end{pmatrix}$ as used in Question **7**, is a composite transformation made up from,

$$\begin{pmatrix} 2 & 0 \\ 0 & 2 \end{pmatrix} \text{ and then } \begin{pmatrix} 0 & -1 \\ 1 & 0 \end{pmatrix}$$

Since matrix multiplication is generally non-commutative, does it make any difference in this case, in which order the transformations are performed?

Also, describe both the transformations which make up the composite transformation.

9 *OABC* is a parallelogram where *O* is (0,0), *A* is (2,0), *B* is (4,4) and *C* is (2,4). Using the appropriate transformation matrix, find the following.

(a) The co-ordinates of the points O_1, A_1, B_1, C_1, when *OABC* is reflected in the *y*-axis.

(b) The co-ordinates of the points O_2, A_2, B_2, C_2, when *OABC* is reflected in the line $y = -x$.

10 *OAB* is an isoceles triangle with *O*(0,0), *A*(4,0) and *B*(2,6). Using the appropriate transformation matrix, find the co-ordinates of the points O_1, A_1, B_1, when $\triangle OAB$ is rotated through 90° clockwise (i.e. −90°), about *O*.

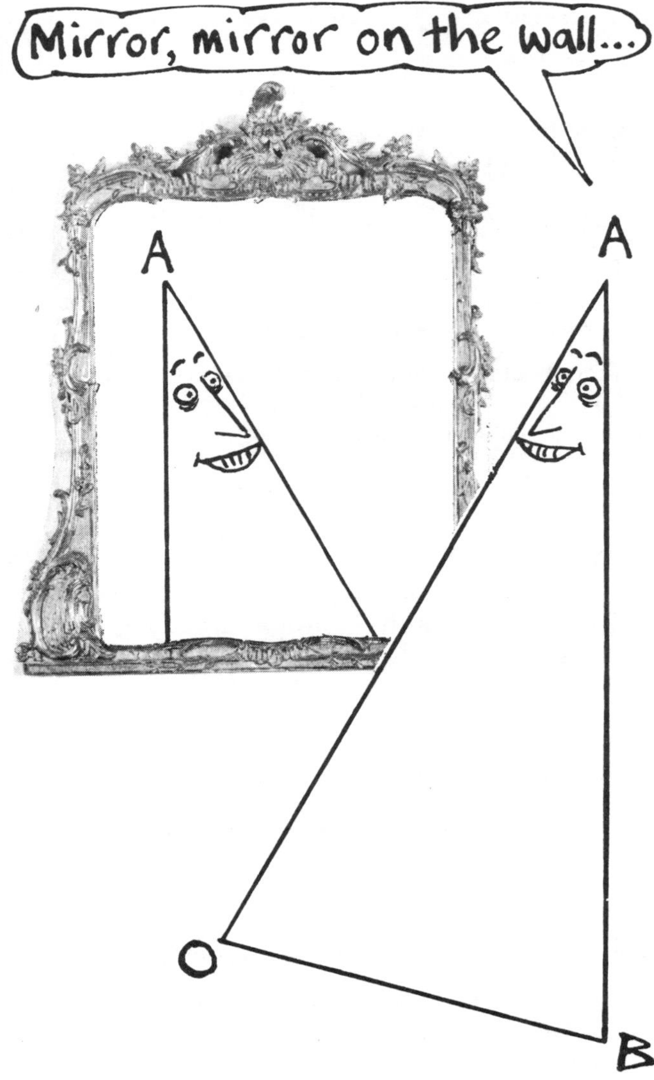

STATISTICS/ PROBABILITY

Unit 35

Cumulative frequency

35.1 Cumulative frequency tables

It is very useful to know how many pupils have scored more than a certain mark in an examination, or how many people are less than a certain height in a group of people. An easy way to find these facts is by making use of a **cumulative frequency** table.

We can easily convert a frequency table into a cumulative frequency table, by adding each frequency to the total of the previous frequencies.

Example The marks (out of 10) of 50 pupils in an examination, are shown in the frequency distribution table, Table 35.1.

Mark	0–9	10–19	20–29	30–39	40–49	50
Frequency	0	1	2	5	10	

cont.

Mark	60–69	70–79	80–89	90–99
Frequency	9	5	2	1

Table 35.1

We always draw the cumulative frequency in vertical column form, as in Table 35.2.

Marks (less than)	Cumulative Frequency
9.5	0
19.5	1 (0 + 1)
29.5	3 (1 + 2)
39.5	8 (3 + 5)
49.5	18 (8 + 10)
59.5	33 (18 + 15)
69.5	42 (33 + 9)
79.5	47 (42 + 5)
89.5	49 (47 + 2)
99.5	50 (49 + 1)

Table 35.2

From this cumulative frequency table, it is very easy to answer typical questions of the following type.

(a) How many pupils scored less than 50 marks?

Answer — 18 pupils

(b) How many pupils scored more than 69 marks?

Answer——8 pupils (i.e. 50 – 42)

(c) If the pass mark was 40, how many pupils were successful in the Examination?

Answer——42 pupils (i.e. 50 – 8) passed the Examination

Activities

1 Table 35.3 shows the heights of 30 children, correct to the nearest cm.

Height	145	146	147	148	149	150	151	152	153	154
Number of children	2	1	3	5	7	4	3	2	0	3

Table 35.3

Convert this frequency table into a cumulative frequency table, taking the first value as 'less than 145.5 cm', etc.

2 In a competition, 80 people estimated the mass of a cake, to the nearest 100 g. The results are shown in the frequency table, Table 35.4.

Mass (g)	600	700	800	900	1000	1100	1200
Frequency	3	10	24	22	13	6	2

Table 35.4

Draw up a cumulative frequency table for the above information taking the first value as 'less than 650 g'.

3 The marks obtained in a Maths test (marked out of 10) by 130 students, are shown in the frequency distribution table, Table 35.5.

Mark	1	2	3	4	5	6	7	8	9
Number of students	1	2	7	21	35	35	21	7	1

Table 35.5

Draw up a cumulative frequency table for the above information taking the first value as 'less than 1.5'.

4 The scores of 10 golfers, over 4 rounds each in a tournament, are shown in Table 35.6.

71	65	69	70	70	68	68	67	68	66
73	75	67	69	73	70	74	72	70	69
68	72	74	70	68	75	68	71	69	70
69	71	71	71	68	66	69	68	69	70

Table 35.6

(a) Draw a frequency distribution table for the scores.

(b) Convert the frequency distribution table into a cumulative frequency table.

(c) Use the cumulative frequency table to determine how many rounds of less than 71 were scored.

(d) Use the cumulative frequency table to find how many rounds of more than 72 were scored.

5 The timings for 100 telephone calls are shown in the frequency distribution table, Table 35.7.

Time (seconds)	Frequency
0–20	1
21–40	2
41–60	3
61–80	6
81–100	9
101–120	25
121–140	21
141–160	15
161–180	9
181–200	7
201–220	2

Table 35.7

(a) Form a cumulative frequency table for the above frequency distribution.

(b) How many calls lasted for a minute or less?

(c) How many calls lasted for 2 minutes or more?

(d) What percentage of calls lasted for 100 seconds or less?

(e) What percentage of calls lasted for 80 seconds or more?

6 In a survey 200 people were asked to state the total time (to the nearest hour) that they had spent watching TV in the previous week. The results are shown in Table 35.8.

Number of hours	0–2	3–5	6–8	9–11	12–14	15–17
Number of people	34	44	58	36	18	10

Table 35.8

Draw a cumulative frequency table of the above results and calculate the percentage number of people who watched TV for 9 hours or more.

35.2 Cumulative frequency curves (ogives)

We are now in a position to draw a graph of a cumulative frequency distribution (known as a **cumulative frequency curve** or **ogive**).

It is interesting to note that all cumulative frequency curves have the same characteristic shape, as we can see in the next Example and in the Activities, following.

In order to draw an ogive we need to follow this basic outline.

(a) Turn the given frequency distribution into a cumulative frequency distribution (as shown in Unit 35.1).

(b) Draw a horizontal and a vertical axis on graph paper.

(c) Mark off the vertical axis scale as cumulative frequencies.

(d) Mark off the horizontal axis scale in the units of the 'less than' column.

(e) Plot each 'less than' value against its cumulative frequency, marking the position with a cross.

(f) Join the crosses on the graph with a smooth curve.

Note It is very important to note that the **vertical axis** must always show the **cumulative frequency**.

Example The frequency distribution, in Table 35.9, gives the masses of 160 people, measured to the nearest kg.

Mass (kg)	40–43	44–47	48–51	52–55	56–59	60–63	64–67	68–71
Frequency	2	12	28	42	37	23	11	5

Table 35.9

Table 35.10 is the cumulative frequency table.

Mass (kg) (less than)	Cumulative Frequency
43.5	2
47.5	14
51.5	42
55.5	84
59.5	121
63.5	144
67.5	155
71.5	160

Table 35.10

The cumulative frequency curve (ogive) is then constructed using this data, as in Fig. 35.1.

Fig. 35.1

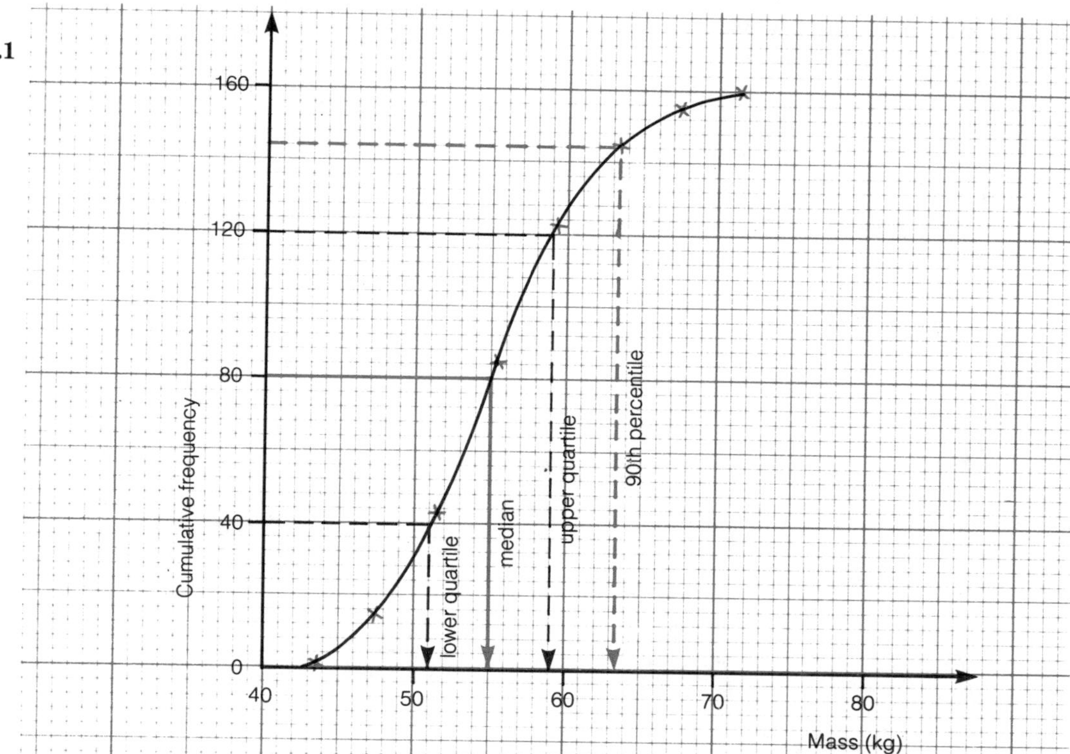

35.3 Finding the median from a cumulative frequency curve

It is possible to find the **median** from a cumulative frequency curve by the following.

(a) Find the mid-value on the cumulative frequency axis (80, in the ogive in Fig. 35.1).

(b) Draw a horizontal line from this point, to the curve.

(c) Draw a vertical line from the curve to the horizontal axis.

(d) Read off the horizontal scale for the value of the median. (In Fig. 35.1, this is 55 kg. Hence, half of the people (80) have masses of under 55 kg.)

The median is also known as the **50th percentile**.

35.4 Further measures of dispersion

In Volume 2, Unit 32, we considered range, mean deviation and standard deviation as measures of dispersion.

We are now in a position to consider a further measure of dispersion, namely, the **semi-interquartile range**, and for this we shall again refer to Fig. 35.1.

We need to know that a **quartile** divides the information into quarters and that a **percentile** divides the information into one hundredths. This explains the median being known as the 50th percentile.

Now, a quarter of the people (40) have masses of under 51 kg. This mass is known as the **lower quartile** (or the 25th percentile).

Similarly, three-quarters of the people (120) have masses of under 59 kg. This mass is known as the **upper quartile** (or the 75th percentile).

The **semi-interquartile range** is half of the difference between the upper and lower quartiles. Hence, the semi-interquartile range (dispersion) of the above distribution will be $\frac{1}{2}(59-51)$ kg, i.e. 4 kg.

Also marked on the ogive in Fig. 35.1 is the 90th percentile, showing that 90 per cent of the people (144) have masses of less than 64 kg. Hence, the 90th percentile is 64 kg.

Any other percentiles, such as the 10th or 30th percentile, can easily be found in a similar manner.

Further Example Plot an ogive of the frequency distribution in Table 35.11. showing the weekly pocket money of 120 pupils, and estimate,

(a) the median amount of pocket money,
(b) the semi-interquartile range.

Money (pence)	0–19	20–39	40–59
Number of pupils	6	32	44

continued

Money (pence)	60–79	80–99	100–119
Number of pupils	26	10	2

Table 35.11

Table 35.12 is the cumulative frequency table.

Money (pence) (less than)	Cumulative Frequency
20	6
40	38
60	82
80	108
100	118
120	120

Table 35.12

From the graph in Fig. 35.2, we can see that,

(a) the median (50th percentile) is 50p,

(b) the lower quartile (L.Q.) is 36p, and the upper quartile (U.Q.) is 64p.

Hence, the semi-interquartile range $= \frac{1}{2}(64 - 36)\text{p}$
$= 14\text{p}$

Note Drawing accuracy and suitable scales play important parts in the estimation of medians and other percentiles.

Fig. 35.2

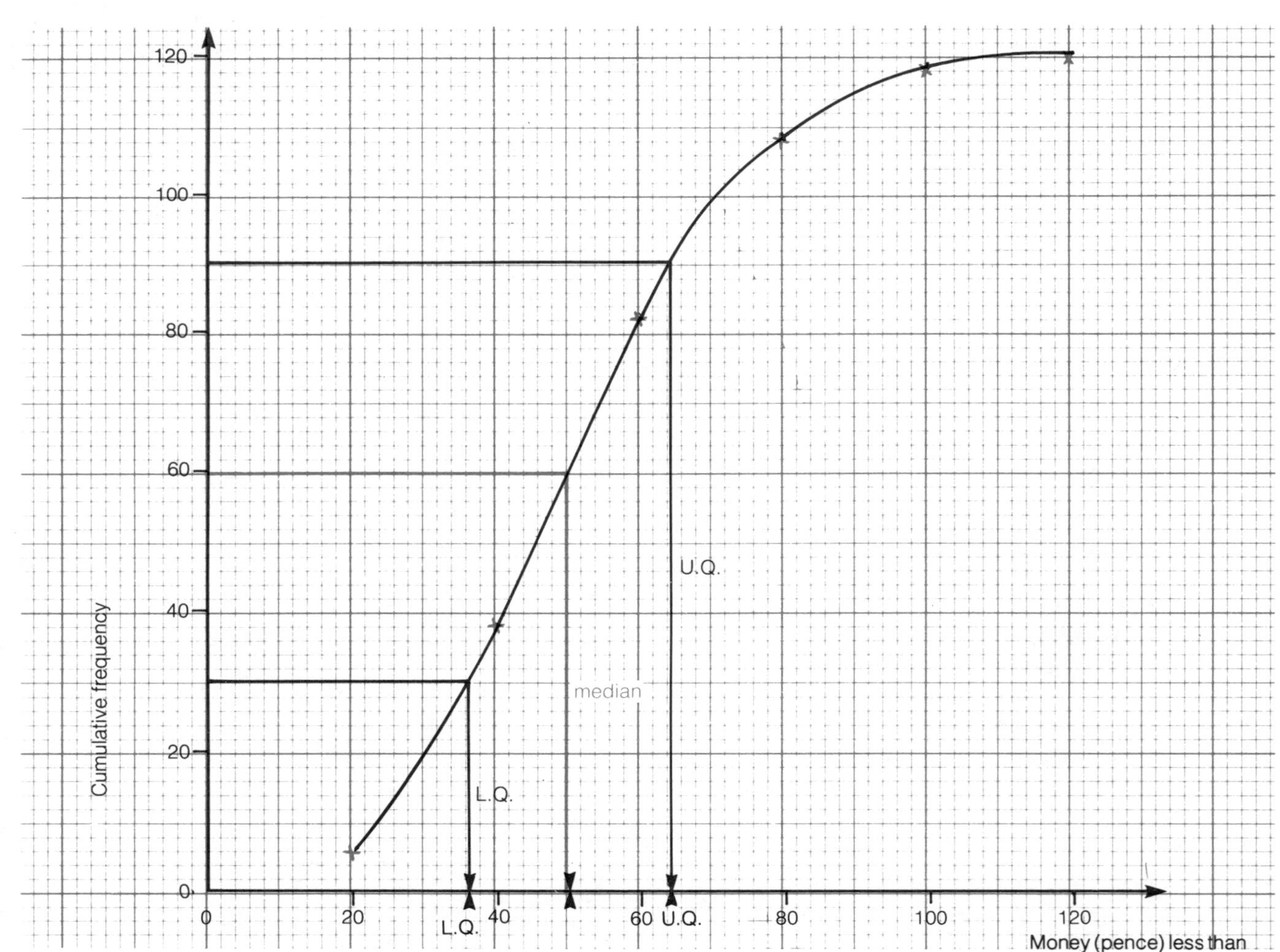

Activities

1 The cumulative frequency table for the masses of 120 pupils is given in Table 35.13.

Mass (kg) (less than)	Cumulative Frequency
35	1
40	3
45	11
50	27
55	54
60	92
65	112
70	118
75	120

Table 35.13

(a) How many of the pupils had masses of at least 60 kg?

(b) How many had masses of at least 65 kg but less than 70 kg?

(c) On graph paper, plot the ogive and use it to estimate the median mass.

2 The masses of a sample of packets of soap powder were recorded, and the results grouped as shown in the frequency distribution table, Table 35.14.

Mass (g)	1480–	1490–	1500–	1510–	1520–1530
Number of packets	6	20	34	40	20

Table 35.14

(a) Convert to a cumulative frequency table of the above, using < 1490 g as the first result.
(b) Use graph paper to plot the cumulative frequency curve of the above information.
(c) Use your curve to estimate the median mass of the soap powder packets.
(d) Estimate, from your curve, the number of packets having a mass greater than 1495 g.
(e) Use your curve to estimate the greatest mass which was exceeded by $\frac{1}{2}$ of the packets.

3 The cumulative frequency table of 180 candidates in an Examination is shown in Table 35.15.

Marks (less than)	Cumulative Frequency
10	1
20	6
30	14
40	31
50	58
60	96
70	139
80	167
90	177
100	180

Table 35.15

(a) Draw the ogive of the above cumulative frequency table, on graph paper.
(b) Use your curve to estimate the median mark.
(c) The pass mark was fixed at 45. Use your curve to estimate the number who failed the Examination.
(d) Estimate the mark exceeded by 30 % of the candidates.
(e) Find the semi-interquartile range.

4 To test the petrol consumption of a particular type of car, 100 drivers were asked to record the distances they travelled on 10 litres of petrol. The results were grouped and shown in Table 35.16, the cumulative frequency table.

Distances (km) (less than)	Cumulative Frequency
110	0
115	2
120	8
125	25
130	47
135	79
140	94
145	97
150	100

Table 35.16

(a) Draw a cumulative frequency curve, on graph paper.
(b) Estimate the median.
(c) Find the semi-interquartile range.
(d) Estimate, from your graph, the 90th percentile distance.

Unit 36

Probability

36.1 Introduction

In probability, we measure the chances (or likelihood) of an event happening. The scale of measurement of probability of an event, ranges from zero to one, and is measured either in fractional or decimal form, i.e. $\frac{1}{4}$ or 0.25, etc.

zero represents **impossibility**
and **one** represents **certainty**

Hence, $0 \leqslant P \leqslant 1$

Suppose we consider the probabilities of the following events.

A 'It will go dark before tomorrow morning.'
B 'Next year will be AD 1900.'
C 'One of my Premium Bonds will win £100 000 one day.'
D 'A tossed coin will land tails.'

Events such as **A** are **certain** to happen

so, $P(\mathbf{A}) = 1$

Events such as **B** are **absolutely impossible**

so, $P(\mathbf{B}) = 0$

Events such as **C** have a probability between 0 and 1. In fact, the more likely the event, then the higher the probability will be.

In the case of Event **D**, we can easily see that,

$P(\text{tail}) = \frac{1}{2}$ or 0.5

since the coin is equally likely to land heads.

36.2 Finding probabilities

If we consider Event **D** (above), i.e. 'a tossed coin will land tails', there are two ways of finding the probability of this event.

1 by experiment **2** by calculation

36.3 Probability by experiment

By repeating the experiment (i.e. tossing the coin many times) the fraction, below, may be calculated.

$$\frac{\text{number of times event occurred during experiment}}{\text{total number of trials performed in experiment}}$$

The fraction, in this case, will be

$$\frac{\text{number of tails recorded}}{\text{total number of tosses}}$$

and will give us a value known as the **experimental probability**.

Typical results are shown below, but you can obtain your own set of results for this experiment by working through that described in the Activities following.

$$\text{After 10 throws, } P(\text{tail}) = \frac{4}{10} = 0.4$$

$$\text{After 100 throws, } P(\text{tail}) = \frac{54}{100} = 0.54$$

$$\text{After 1000 throws, } P(\text{tail}) = \frac{491}{1000} = 0.491$$

$$\text{After 10 000 throws, } P(\text{tail}) = \frac{5032}{10\,000} = 0.5032$$

We must remember, of course, that the probability of an event worked out by experiment is only an estimate of the actual probability of that event.

If an experiment consists of a large number of trials, then the chances of the experiment producing good estimates of the actual probabilities is far greater.

In fact, the larger the number of trials, the better the estimates will become, as is shown in our typical result above.

Activities

Experiment 1 Tossing a coin

For this experiment you need a coin to toss, and paper and pencil to note the results. Remember, also, to spin the coin in the air before it falls.

Record the number of heads and tails obtained in a tally table as shown in Table 36.1.

(a) Number of tosses = 100

	Tally	Total
Heads		
Tails		

Table 36.1

Compare your experimental results with the expected result.

We would expect that, in 100 tosses, the number of tails $= \frac{1}{2} \times 100 = 50$ and, similarly, the number of heads $= \frac{1}{2} \times 100 = 50$.
How close are your results to the expected results?

(b) Number of tosses = 200
Repeat the above experiment, tossing the coin 200 times. Record the results in the same way and compare the experimental results with the expected results.

(c) Ask other members of the family to do the experiment (the more the better) for 200 tosses. Then collect all the results together. If 5 people have taken part, then you will have 1000 tosses in the experiment. Once again compare the results with the expected results.

(d) What do you notice about the experimental results in **(a)**, **(b)** and **(c)** above?

Experiment 2 Throwing a die

This is a similar experiment to the coin tossing. You need a 6-sided die and a shaker, and paper and pencil to record the results.

(a) Throw the die 120 times and record the results on a tally table similar to the one in Table 36.2.

	Tally	Total
1		
2		
3		
4		
5		
6		

Table 36.2

The expected number of '1's in 120 throws would be $\frac{1}{6} \times 120 = 20$; similarly, we would expect the same result for '2's, '3's etc.

(b) Repeat the experiment, throwing the die 240 times and recording the results in a table, as before. Once again, compare the experimental results with the expected results.

(c) Ask other members of the family to do the experiment for 240 throws. Collect all the results together. If 5 people have taken part, then you will have 1200 throws in the experiment. Once again, compare the results of the experiment with the expected results.

(d) What do you notice about the experimental results in **(a)**, **(b)** and **(c)** above?

Note For further experiments, dice with 4, 8, 10, 12 and 20 sides can be used, in a similar way to the 6-sided die.

If you have no 6-sided die, you could make a 'spinner' from a piece of hexagonal card and a match-stick. A roulette wheel would be useful for such probability experiments.

36.4 Probability by calculation (expected probability)

When all the possible results are equally likely, we can calculate the **expected probability** that an event will occur from the formula,

$$P(\text{event}) = \frac{\text{number of outcomes favourable to the event}}{\text{total number of possible outcomes}}$$

In the case of Event **D** in Unit 36.1,

$$\frac{\text{the number of tails}}{\text{total number possible (head or tail)}} = \tfrac{1}{2} \text{ or } 0.5$$

Hence, $P(\text{tail})$ is expected to be $\frac{1}{2}$ or 0.5 when a coin is tossed.

We can now consider the likelihood of certain other events taking place.

Example 1 What is the probability of drawing an Ace from a pack of cards?

Number of favourable outcomes
i.e. (number of Aces in pack) = 4

Total number of possible outcomes
i.e. (total number of cards in pack) = 52

and so, $P(\text{Ace}) = \frac{4}{52} = \frac{1}{13}$

Example 2 What is the probability of throwing a 5, with a normal six-sided die?

Number of favourable outcomes = 1
Total number of possible outcomes = 6

and so, $P(5) = \frac{1}{6}$

Example 3 A box contains 10 black, 15 yellow and 5 red balls. Find the probability of pulling out a yellow ball at the first attempt.

Number of yellow balls = 15
Total number of balls = 30

and so, $P(\text{yellow ball}) = \frac{15}{30} = \frac{1}{2}$

Activities

1 Consider a normal pack of playing cards (i.e. 52 cards in the pack). What is the probability of drawing,

- **(a)** an eight
- **(b)** the eight of diamonds
- **(c)** a spade
- **(d)** a picture card (excluding aces)
- **(e)** a joker?

2 If a letter is taken at random from the word 'PROBABILITY', what is the probability that

- **(a)** it is a vowel
- **(b)** it is a 'B'?

3 If a number is chosen at random from the numbers 1 to 20 inclusive, what is the probability of drawing,

- **(a)** a prime number
- **(b)** a square number
- **(c)** a multiple of 3
- **(d)** a factor of 20?

4 A bag contains 50 marbles, 40 yellow ones and 10 green. What is the probability of drawing,

- **(a)** a green marble
- **(b)** a yellow marble
- **(c)** a red marble?

5 There are 24 beads in a box, some black and some white. For taking out one bead at random, $P(\text{black}) = \frac{1}{4}$. How many of each colour are there in the box?

6 A bag contains 8 green, 7 red and 5 yellow sweets. One is taken out at random. Find,

- **(a)** $P(\text{red})$
- **(b)** $P(\text{green})$
- **(c)** $P(\text{yellow})$

Unit 37

Complementary events

Here, we consider the **probability** of an event **not happening**.

Since we know that an event will either take place or not take place, the sum of the probabilities must be 1, i.e.

$$P(\mathbf{A}) + P(\text{not } \mathbf{A}) = 1$$

and, rearranging $P(\text{not } \mathbf{A}) = 1 - P(\mathbf{A})$

Hence, in order to find the probability of an event not happening, it is quite often best to find the probability that the event will happen and subtract this answer from 1.

Example 1 What is the probability of **not** throwing a 5 with a normal six-sided die?

Since the probability of throwing a 5 is

$$P(5) = \tfrac{1}{6}$$

then, $P(\text{not } 5) = 1 - \tfrac{1}{6} = \tfrac{5}{6}$

Example 2 What is the probability of **not** drawing a picture card from a pack of cards? (We shall not call aces picture cards.)

$$P(\text{picture card}) = \tfrac{12}{52} = \tfrac{3}{13}$$

then, $P(\text{not a picture card}) = 1 - \tfrac{3}{13} = \tfrac{10}{13}$

Example 3 A bag contains 5 red sweets, 3 green sweets and 2 yellow sweets. What is the probability of **not** taking out a yellow sweet at the first attempt?

$$P(\text{yellow sweet}) = \tfrac{2}{10} = \tfrac{1}{5}$$

then, $P(\text{not a yellow sweet}) = 1 - \tfrac{1}{5} = \tfrac{4}{5}$

Activities

1 When a die is thrown, what is $P(6)$? And what is $P(\text{not } 6)$?

2 The probability that Jane will miss the school bus is $\tfrac{1}{8}$. What is the probability that she will **not** miss the bus?

3 An egg tray contains $2\tfrac{1}{2}$ dozen eggs, of which 27 are perfect, the rest are cracked. What is the probability of picking out, at random, a cracked egg?

4 The probability of a horse winning a race is 0.6. What is the probability of the horse losing the race?

5 A box contains 36 pencils of which 9 have broken points. What is the probability of picking out one which does **not** have a broken point?

6 If the letters of the word 'STATISTICS' are each written on a piece of paper and dropped into a bag, what is the probability of drawing out a piece of paper which does **not** have the letter 'S' on it?

7 A card is drawn from a pack of playing cards. What is the probability of

- **(a)** **not** picking a picture card? (Aces not called picture cards.)
- **(b)** picking a card other than a heart?

8 A box contains 5 white, 3 yellow and 2 blue coloured pencils. One is taken out at random. Find,

- **(a)** $P(\text{not white})$
- **(b)** $P(\text{not blue})$
- **(c)** $P(\text{not yellow})$
- **(d)** $P(\text{not red})$

Unit 38

Sample spaces and combined events

38.1 Sample spaces

A list or table of all of the possible outcomes which follow from a particular course of action is called a **sample space**.

Example
The sample space when a normal six-sided die is tossed is

1 2 3 4 5 6

The sample space when a coin is tossed is,

head tail

P(event occurring)

$$= \frac{\text{number of favourable outcomes to the event in the sample space}}{\text{total number of possible outcomes in the sample space}}$$

Example 1 Find the probability of throwing an odd number, with a normal six-sided die.

The sample space is, ① 2 ③ 4 ⑤ 6

Hence, $P(\text{odd}) = \frac{3}{6} = \frac{1}{2}$

Example 2 If counters, numbered 1 to 24 inclusive, are placed in a box, what is the probability that a counter pulled out of the box has a number on it which is,

(a) a multiple of 4
(b) a multiple of 6
(c) a multiple of both 4 and 6
(d) a multiple of either 4 or 6?

The sample space is shown in Table 38.1.

1	2	3	(4)	5	[6]	7	(8)
9	10	11	[(12)]	13	14	15	(16)
17	[18]	19	(20)	21	22	23	[(24)]

Table 38.1

Hence,

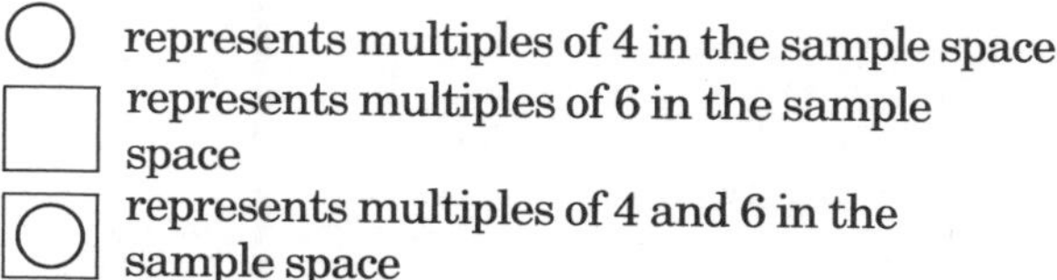

○ represents multiples of 4 in the sample space
□ represents multiples of 6 in the sample space
◻○ represents multiples of 4 and 6 in the sample space

So, (a) $P(\text{multiple of } 4) = \frac{6}{24} = \frac{1}{4}$

(b) $P(\text{multiple of } 6) = \frac{4}{24} = \frac{1}{6}$

(c) $P(\text{multiple of both 4 and 6}) = \frac{2}{24} = \frac{1}{12}$

(d) $P(\text{multiple of either 4 or 6}) = \frac{8}{24} = \frac{1}{3}$

Note The sample space makes the problem much easier to visualize, and helps us considerably.

38.2 Combined events

Sample spaces are particularly useful when the probabilities of events which result from a combination of the outcomes of two (or more) separate happenings, are required.

A **composite** sample space is formed, by combining the sample spaces for each separate happening.

Consider, for example, the composite sample space (Table 38.2) for the total scores of two dice, being thrown at the same time.

		die 2					
	+	1	2	3	4	5	6
die 1	1	2	3	4	5	6	7
	2	3	4	5	6	7	8
	3	4	5	6	7	8	9
	4	5	6	7	8	9	10
	5	6	7	8	9	10	11
	6	7	8	9	10	11	12

Table 38.2

We can then use the composite sample space to find the probabilities of the following.

(a) a score of 9
(b) a score greater than 10
(c) a score less than or equal to 5
(d) a score of not 7
(e) a score of 13

Since there are 36 possible outcomes in the sample space,

(a) $P(\text{score of } 9) = \frac{4}{36} = \frac{1}{9}$

(b) $P(\text{score} > 10) = \frac{3}{36} = \frac{1}{12}$

(c) $P(\text{score} \leqslant 5) = \frac{10}{36} = \frac{5}{18}$

(d) $P(\text{score} \neq 7) = 1 - P(\text{score of } 7)$
$= 1 - \frac{6}{36} = \frac{30}{36} = \frac{5}{6}$

(e) $P(\text{score of } 13) = 0$ (since 13 does not appear in the composite sample space)

Note Providing the events are separate happenings, then the sample spaces and resulting composite sample space, makes the calculation quite easy.

Activities

Sample spaces and combined events

1 Two coins are tossed together. What is the probability of two tails showing? Draw a sample space to help you to solve the problem.

2 Draw a sample space of the results when a coin and a die are thrown together. What is the probability of,

(a) a head and a 4 showing
(b) a tail and a 3 showing
(c) a head and a 7 showing?

3 Two normal dice (both numbered 1–6), one black and one white, are thrown together. Draw a composite sample space diagram to represent the sum of the dice and then use it to find the following.

(a) P(a total score of 5)
(b) P(a total score of < 8)
(c) P(a total score of $\geqslant 10$)
(d) What is the most likely sum?

4 Draw up a composite sample space showing the sums which can be obtained by taking one number from each of the sets $\{2, 4, 6, 8, 10\}$ and $\{5, 7, 9\}$.

If a number is chosen at random from each set, what is the probability that the sum of the two numbers is,

(a) 9 (b) >9 (c) even total (d) a multiple of 3

5 Two special dice, each bearing the numbers 1, 1, 2, 3, 3, 4, are thrown together and the results added. Draw the composite sample space for the event and use it to find the following.

(a) P(total of 4) (b) P(total of 5)
(c) P(even number)

In the following questions, you may draw a composite sample space diagram, if it will help to solve the problem.

6 When throwing two dice, a double is obtained when the two numbers shown are the same. Find,

(a) P(double) (b) P(not a double)

7 A spinner having four sides numbered 1–4 inclusive, is spun twice and the two numbers are multiplied together. Find,

(a) P(a product of 2)
(b) P(a product of 4)
(c) P(an even product)
(d) P(an odd product)
(e) P(not a product of 18)

8 Jane draws a card from one pack of playing cards and Elizabeth draws a card from another pack. Find the probability that both of the cards are hearts.

9 A bag contains one black and three white balls; a second bag contains one white and two black balls. One ball is drawn at random from each bag. Find,

(a) P(two black) (b) P(two white)
(c) P(one of each colour)

Hint A sample space diagram may be very helpful.

10 Three dice are thrown together and the scores are added. Write down in the form, $1 + 2 + 3$, the ways in which the total can be 6. What is P(total of 6)?

11 A number p is chosen at random from the set $\{1, 2, 3, 4, 5\}$ and a number q is chosen at random from the set $\{6, 7, 8, 9, 10\}$. Find the probability of each of the following events taking place.

(a) q is prime (b) pq is odd (c) $p + q$ is even

Hint Again, a sample space diagram may be useful.

Unit 39

Combining probabilities

39.1 Mutually exclusive events

Two or more events are said to be **mutually exclusive** if they cannot happen at the same time.

For such an 'either/or' situation, we have the **addition rule** for the probability, of one event **or** another taking place. This says that,

$$P(\mathbf{A} \text{ or } \mathbf{B}) = P(\mathbf{A}) + P(\mathbf{B})$$

Example 1 When a die is thrown, what is the probability of scoring either a 2 or a 5?

Since we have mutually exclusive events (i.e. if 2 is scored then 5 cannot be scored, and vice versa) then,

$$P(2 \text{ or } 5) = P(2) + P(5) = \tfrac{1}{6} + \tfrac{1}{6} = \tfrac{2}{6} = \tfrac{1}{3}$$

Example 2 A bag contains 20 black, 10 white and 20 yellow beads. A bead is drawn at random from the bag. What is the probability of drawing a black or a white bead from the bag?

$$P(b \text{ or } w) = P(b) + P(w) = \tfrac{20}{50} + \tfrac{10}{50} = \tfrac{30}{50} = \tfrac{3}{5}$$

We do however have to be careful when applying the rule. Consider the following example.

Example 3 What is the probability of drawing an Ace or a Heart from a pack of playing cards?

In this case, it would **not** be true to say that,

$$P(A \text{ or } H) = P(A) + P(H)$$

since one of the Aces is the Ace of Hearts

Hence, $P(\text{Ace or Heart}) = \frac{4}{52} + \frac{(13-1)}{52}$

the Ace being counted in the Hearts

$$= \tfrac{16}{52} = \tfrac{4}{13}$$

Activities

1 Find the probability that when a die is thrown, the result will be either a 1 or a 6.

2 Find the probability of drawing either a diamond or a club from a pack of playing cards, at the first attempt.

3 Find the probability of drawing a King or a Queen or a Jack from a pack of playing cards, at the first attempt.

4 Use a sample space diagram to help you to show that for the sum of two thrown dice,

$$P(4 \text{ or } 9) = P(4) + P(9)$$

5 Again, using a sample space diagram to help you, show that for the sum of two thrown dice,

(a) $P(8 \text{ or a double}) \neq P(8) + P(\text{double})$, and explain why this is the case

(b) $P(9 \text{ or a double}) = P(9) + P(\text{double})$

6 Show, for two thrown dice that,

$P(\text{total} > 10 \text{ or total} < 4) = P(\text{total} > 10) + P(\text{total} < 4)$

7 The probability of Horse A winning a race is $\frac{2}{5}$ and the probability of Horse B winning is $\frac{3}{10}$. What is the probability of either Horse A or Horse B winning the race? (They cannot tie for first place.)

8 A box contains 5 cans of coke, 6 cans of orangeade and 4 cans of limeade. What is the probability, when picking out of the box at random, of getting,

(a) a coke or an orangeade

(b) a coke or a limeade

(c) an orangeade or a limeade?

39.2 Independent events

Events are said to be **independent** if they do not affect each other in any way.

For such an 'and' situation we have the **multiplication rule** for the probability, of one event **and** another taking place. This says that,

$$P(\mathbf{A} \text{ and } \mathbf{B}) = P(\mathbf{A}) \times P(\mathbf{B})$$

Example 1 If a die and a coin are tossed together, then,

$$P(\text{tail and a } 5) = P(\text{tail}) \times P(5) = \tfrac{1}{2} \times \tfrac{1}{6} = \tfrac{1}{12}$$

and,

$$P(\text{head and an even number}) = P(\text{head}) \times P(\text{even}) = \tfrac{1}{2} \times \tfrac{3}{6} = \tfrac{1}{4}$$

Example 2 Suppose we have a bag containing 7 red balls and 3 white balls. If a ball is picked out and its colour noted and then replaced, and another ball is then picked out and its colour noted, find,

(a) $P(r \text{ and } r)$

(b) $P(w \text{ and } w)$

The two events are quite independent and the first ball is replaced, so

(a) $P(r \text{ and } r)$ (with replacement) $= P(r)$ (1st withdrawal) $\times P(r)$ (2nd withdrawal)

$$= \tfrac{7}{10} \times \tfrac{7}{10} = \tfrac{49}{100}$$

(b) $P(w \text{ and } w)$ (with replacement) $= P(w) \times P(w)$

$$= \tfrac{3}{10} \times \tfrac{3}{10} = \tfrac{9}{100}$$

Example 3 Now consider the same problem, except that the first ball is **not replaced**. The events will still be independent but, in this instance, there will only be 9 balls to choose from on the 2nd withdrawal.

Hence, $P(r \text{ and } r)$ (without replacement) $= P(r) \times P(r) = \tfrac{7}{10} \times \tfrac{6}{9} = \tfrac{7}{15}$

And, $P(w \text{ and } w)$ (without replacement) $= P(w) \times P(w) = \tfrac{3}{10} \times \tfrac{2}{9} = \tfrac{1}{15}$

Activities

1 A die is thrown and a playing card is drawn from a pack. Find,

(a) $P(5 \text{ and a diamond})$ (b) $P(6 \text{ and a black card})$

2 One playing card is drawn from each of two separate packs. Find,

(a) $P(\text{two spades})$ (b) $P(\text{Jack and a King})$ in that order

3 A box contains 3 yellow and 5 blue counters. One is drawn out and replaced and a second draw is then made. Find,

(a) $P(\text{yellow first and yellow second})$

(b) $P(\text{yellow first and then blue})$

(c) $P(\text{blue first and then yellow})$

(d) $P(\text{blue first and blue second})$

Why do the answers to the above add up to 1?

4 A die is thrown three times. Find,

(a) $P(\text{three fives})$ (b) $P(\text{three odd numbers})$

5 Four coins are tossed together. What is the probability of obtaining 4 tails?

6 The probability of a man taking sandwiches for lunch is $\frac{1}{5}$. The probability of going to work by bus rather than by car is $\frac{4}{5}$. The probability of him finishing work at 5 p.m. is $\frac{3}{10}$. Find,

(a) $P(\text{all three events taking place on one day})$

(b) $P(\text{none of the events taking place on one day})$

7 The probability of a particular footballer scoring a goal is $\frac{1}{6}$. The probability that he is 'booked' in any match is $\frac{1}{7}$. The probability of his team winning is $\frac{2}{3}$. Find,

(a) $P(\text{he does not score, gets 'booked' and is on the winning side})$

(b) $P(\text{he scores, does not get 'booked' and does not win})$

Unit 40

Probability tree diagrams

A very useful method of illustrating independent events is by drawing a **probability tree**. With such a picture before us, the situation is much clearer.

Suppose we now represent Example **3**, from Unit 39.2, concerning the 7 red balls and 3 white balls (without replacement). It will look as in Fig. 40.1.

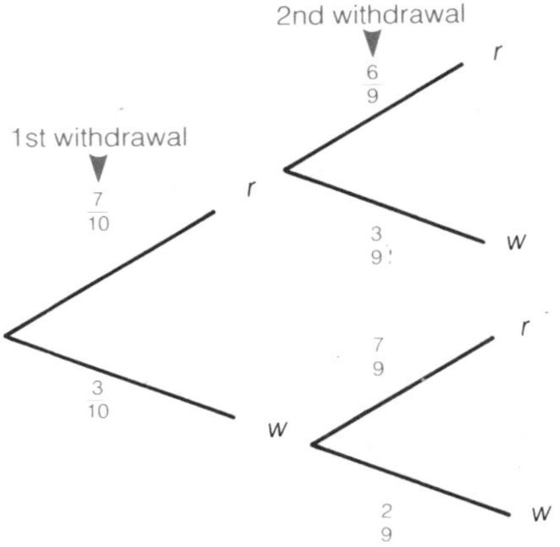

Fig. 40.1

We can see immediately from this diagram that,

$P(r \text{ and } r) = \frac{7}{10} \times \frac{6}{9} = \frac{7}{15}$ $\quad P(r \text{ and } w) = \frac{7}{10} \times \frac{3}{9} = \frac{7}{30}$

$P(w \text{ and } r) = \frac{3}{10} \times \frac{7}{9} = \frac{7}{30}$ $\quad P(w \text{ and } w) = \frac{3}{10} \times \frac{2}{9} = \frac{1}{15}$

Note The probabilities of all these happenings when added, totals 1 (i.e. certainty). It is also worth noting that probabilities on adjacent branches of the tree always total 1 (which is useful as a check for errors).

If we were asked for the probability of a red and a white ball (in any order), then we would have to account for either $P(r$ and $w)$ or $P(w$ and $r)$, i.e. mutually exclusive events, (Addition Rule).

Hence, $P(r \text{ and } w) \text{ or } P(w \text{ and } r) = \frac{7}{30} + \frac{7}{30} = \frac{7}{15}$

We can, of course, extend the tree for further withdrawals, for instance, the tree for 3 withdrawals in the above example would look as in Fig. 40.2.

From the tree we can immediately see, for instance, that,

$$P(r \text{ and } r \text{ and } r) = \frac{7}{10} \times \frac{6}{9} \times \frac{5}{8} = \frac{7}{24}$$

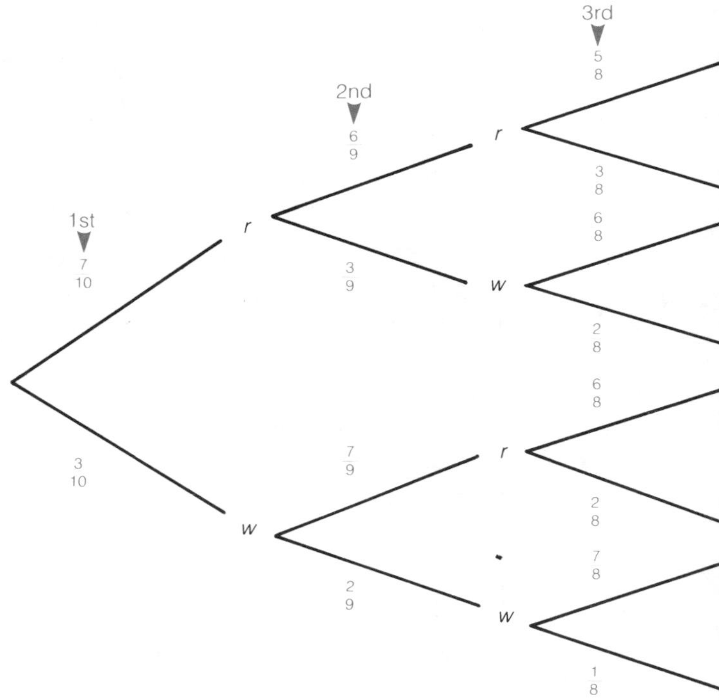

Fig. 40.2

Activities

1 A coin is spun twice. Draw a tree diagram to show the possible outcomes, and state the probability of each.

2 A box contains 3 white and 5 black beads. One is drawn out at random and replaced. A second draw is then made. Draw a tree diagram and use it to calculate the probability of,

(a) both white **(b)** both black
(c) one of each colour

Note P(one of each colour) $= P(w$ and $b)$ or $P(b$ and $w)$.

3 Repeat Question **2**, but without replacement.

4 A bag contains 2 white, 3 red and 5 green fruitdrops. Two are taken out. Find the probability that,

(a) both are white **(b)** both are green
(c) both are red
(d) one is green and the other is red
(e) one is white and the other is green

Hint Draw the probability tree diagram.

5 Repeat Question **4**, but with three sweets being taken out. Start by drawing a probability tree diagram for three withdrawals. Find,

(a) P(3 white) **(c)** P(3 red)
(b) P(3 green) **(d)** P(one of each colour)

6 A drawer contains 2 grey and 4 black socks. Two are drawn out at random, one after the other. Draw a tree diagram to show the possible outcomes. What is the probability of,

(a) two of the same colour
(b) two of different colours

7 Draw a probability tree diagram showing the possible outcomes and their respective probabilities, for a spade being drawn from a pack of playing cards and a 3 being thrown with a die.

ANSWERS

Unit 1 The use of a calculator

Order of operations (page 9)

1 (a) 18, 14 (b) 19, 15 (c) 6, −8
(d) 16, 1 (e) 20, $1\frac{1}{4}$ (f) 1, 9
2 (a) 16 (b) 18 (c) 20 (d) 6 (e) 2 (f) 6
3 (a) $(7+2)\times 3 = 27$ (b) $15-(4-2)=13$
(c) $(12+9)\div 3 = 7$ (d) $8\times(5-2)=24$
(e) $(16\div 8)-2=0$ (f) $(24-16)\div 2 = 4$
4 (a) 67 (b) 125 (c) 510 (d) 40 (e) 24.6
(f) 5 (g) 9 (h) 21 (i) 91 (j) 17

Calculator work (page 9)

1 (a) 48.4 (b) 102.07 (c) 4.3
(d) 2 (e) 51.8 (f) 7.2
2 (a) 27.04 (b) 625 (c) 45.5625
(d) 60 025 (e) 0.4489 (f) 55 225
3 (a) 7.9 (b) 55.4 (c) 5.5
(d) 44 (e) 322 (f) 78
4 (a) 38.44 (b) 5.1 (c) 153.76
(d) 62.4 (e) 179.2 (f) 93.5089
5 (a) 8 (b) 0.006 451 6 (c) 0.307 692 3
(d) 0.16 (e) 0.040 322 5 (f) 25
6 (a) 0.469 471 5 (b) 2.475 086 9 (c) 0.819 152
(d) 0.955 278 3 (e) 0.671 972 1 (f) 0.481 753 6
7 (a) 43° (b) 70° (c) 61°
(d) 66.2° (e) 66.7° (f) 22.3°
8 (a) 2.836 956 7 (b) 1.414 639 1 (c) −1.340 844 7
(d) 4.661 074 (e) 2.091 103 9 (f) 5.965 201 7
9 (a) 1.751 862 4 (b) 6058.9867 (c) 84.004 006
(d) 0.184 416 6 (e) 0.036 041 2 (f) 108.817 81
10 (a) 3375 (b) 10 793.861 (c) 25.628 906
(d) 3450.2525

11 [1] [2] [9] [6] [2ndF] [$\sqrt[x]{y}$] [3] [=]
(a) 13 (b) 21 (c) 3

Unit 2 Standard form

Simple examples; the use of standard form (page 12)

1 (a) 1000 (b) 100 000 (c) 100 (d) 1 000 000
(e) 10 (f) 0.1 (g) 1 (h) 0.01
(i) 0.000 1 (j) 10 000
2 (a) 15 (b) 27 (c) 12.5 (d) 320
(e) 6875 (f) 120 (g) 27 000 (h) 1 600 000
(i) 990 (j) 7250
3 (b) $4.4\times 100 = 440$ (c) $3.62\times 10\,000 = 36\,200$
(d) $5.95\times 1\,000\,000 = 5\,950\,000$ (e) $7.03\times 10 = 70.3$
(f) $8.36\times 1000 = 8360$
4 (a) 6870 (b) 368.9 (c) 504 000
(d) 45.8 (e) 70 800
5 (a) 0.075 (b) 0.006 75 (c) 0.457
(d) 0.000 48 (e) 0.003 98 (f) 0.06
6 (a) $4.95\times 10^{-3} = 4.95\times\frac{1}{10^3} = 0.00495 = 4.95\div 10^3$
(b) $9.6\times 10^{-1} = 9.6\times\frac{1}{10^1} = 0.96 = 9.6\div 10^1$
(c) $3.21\times 10^{-5} = 3.21\times\frac{1}{10^5} = 0.000\,032\,1 = 3.21\div 10^5$
7 (a) 2780 (b) 3 160 000 (c) 0.07
(d) 0.0055 (e) 33 (f) 0.0876
8 (a) $2800 = 2.8\times 1000 = 2.8\times 10^3$
(b) $2090 = 2.09\times 1000 = 2.09\times 10^3$
(c) $460\,000 = 4.6\times 100\,000 = 4.6\times 10^5$
(d) $500 = 5\times 100 = 5\times 10^2$
(e) $4\,750\,000 = 4.75\times 1\,000\,000 = 4.75\times 10^6$
9 (a) $0.0063 = 6.3\div 1000 = 6.3\times 10^{-3}$
(b) $0.071 = 7.1\div 100 = 7.1\times 10^{-2}$
(c) $0.000\,047\,2 = 4.72\div 100\,000 = 4.72\times 10^{-5}$

Multiplication and division, in standard form (page 13)

1 (a) 255 000 000 000 (b) 46 750 000
(c) 0.000 000 003 3 (d) 0.000 006 78
2 (a) 8.95 −08 (b) 5.56 10
(c) 6.82 −13 (d) 2.38 13
3 (a) 1.155×10^{10} (b) 2.1505×10^{13}
(c) 1.25×10^{-8} (d) 1.25×10^{-8}
4 (a) 7.5×10^5 (b) 1.26×10^8 (c) 1.1×10^4
(d) 1.44×10^{-3} (e) 2×10^5 (f) 6.875×10^{-2}
(g) $3.378\,378\times 10^9$ (h) $1.111\,111\,1\times 10^{-11}$
5 (a) 5.2×10^1 (b) 5.2×10^8 (c) 5.2×10^4

Further examples, using standard form (page 14)

1 (a) 6.2×10^4 (b) 1.12×10^8 (c) 1.25×10^{-4}
(d) 9.22×10^5 (e) 7.56×10^{-2} (f) 3.5×10^2
(g) 6.7×10^6 (h) 3.674×10^{-3}
2 (a) 1.482×10^6 (b) 5.96×10^3 (c) 5.44×10^3
(d) 3.249×10^7
3 (a) 2.88×10^{-5} (b) 5×10^0 (c) 9.6×10^{-3}
(d) 1.44×10^{-4}
4 (a) 2.5×10^8 (b) 2.5×10^2 (c) 2.5×10^4
(d) 2.5×10^{-4}
5 (a) 1×10^{-6} (b) 2.777×10^{-4} (c) 2×10^7
(d) 5.555×10^1 (e) 1×10^8

Problem solving in standard form (page 15)

1 1.275×10^7 m²
2 (a) 1.8×10^4 km/h (b) 8.33×10^3 hours
3 (a) 5×10^6 g (b) 5×10^3 kg
4 (a) 2.32×10^{11} (b) 13:120 (c) 20:13
5 (a) 1.08×10^9 (b) 1.5×10^8 km (c) 0.138 888 hours

Unit 3 Powers/indices

Examples of indices (page 16)

1 (a) 5 (b) 2 (c) 3 (d) 4
(e) 125 (f) $\frac{1}{49}$ (g) $\frac{1}{125}$ (h) $\frac{1}{2}$
(i) 1 (j) $\frac{1}{10\,000}$ (k) 343 (l) 1
(m) 125 (n) $\frac{1}{8}$ (o) 1 (p) $\frac{1}{2}$
(q) 5 (r) $\frac{1}{256}$ (s) 1 (t) 64
(u) 1 000 000 (v) $\frac{1}{25}$
2 (a) $6a^5$ (b) $10a^3b^5$ (c) c^6 (d) x^3
(e) x^8 (f) e (g) x^8 (h) $g^{\frac{7}{2}}$
(i) $a^{\frac{5}{6}}$ (j) $a^{\frac{5}{4}}$ (k) $a^{\frac{1}{4}}$ (l) $2x^{\frac{2}{3}}$
(m) $\frac{1}{25x^2}$ (n) $\frac{1}{9x^{\frac{2}{3}}}$ (o) $x^{\frac{1}{2}}$ (p) 1
(q) $6x^{-1}$ (r) $125x^2$ (s) $\frac{1}{a^6}$ (t) $p^{\frac{3}{2}}$
(u) $p^{\frac{4}{3}}$ (v) $x^{-\frac{1}{4}}$
3 (a) 64 (b) 6 (c) $\frac{x^6}{1000}$

Unit 4 Logarithms

Logarithm work (page 18)

1 (a) 2 (b) 6 (c) 5
(d) −2 (e) −5 (f) −6

2 (a) 0.69897 (b) 1.69897 (c) 3.69897
(d) −0.30103 (e) −1.30103 (f) −3.30103
3 (a) 1.9031 (b) 2.9031 (c) 4.9031
(d) −0.0969 (e) −1.0969 (f) −2.0969
4 (a) 1.875; $75 = 10^{1.875}$ (b) 2.6021; $400 = 10^{2.6021}$
(c) 0.3979; $2.5 = 10^{0.3979}$
5 (a) $5 \times 6 = 10^{0.6990} \times 10^{0.7782} = 10^{1.4772} = 30$
(b) $7 \times 9 = 10^{0.8451} \times 10^{0.9542} = 10^{1.7993} = 63$
(c) $2 \times 8 = 10^{0.3010} \times 10^{0.9031} = 10^{1.2041} = 16$
(d) $3.3 \times 6.2 = 10^{0.5185} \times 10^{0.7924} = 10^{1.3109} = 20.46$
(e) $4.7 \times 8.2 = 10^{0.6721} \times 10^{0.9138} = 10^{1.5859} = 38.54$
6 (a) $\log_{10}12$ (b) $\log_{10}15$ (c) $\log_{10}28$ (d) $\log_{10}20$
(e) $\log_{10}75$
7 (a) 0.7781 (b) 0.6020 (c) 0.9542
(d) 1.0091 (e) 1.2552 (f) 0.9030
8 (a) 1.0000 (b) 1.1761 (c) 1.4771
(d) 1.3980 (e) 1.6990 (f) 1.6532
9 (a) 1.5441 (b) 1.7404 (c) 1.8865
(d) 1.6902 (e) 2.0828 (f) 2.0970
10 (a) 2.159 (b) 3715 (c) 0.090 22
(d) 23 130 (e) 121 100 (f) 4.624
11 (a) $\log_{10}8$ (b) $\log_{10}4$ (c) $\log_{10}6$ (d) $\log_{10}4$
(e) $\log_{10}3$
12 (a) 0.9031 (b) 0.6021
13 (a) 1.0792 (b) 0.6021
14 (a) 507.5 (b) 77.14 (c) 30.17 (d) 12.37
15 (a) $\log_{10}100$ (b) $\log_{10}5$ (c) $\log_{10}60$
(d) $\log_{10}10$ (e) $\log_{10}1000$ (f) $\log_{10}10$
16 (a) $3\log_{10}a$ (b) $2\log_{10}m$ (c) $4\log_{10}5$
(d) $5\log_{10}2$ (e) $\frac{1}{2}\log_{10}h$ (f) $\frac{1}{3}\log_{10}9$
(g) $\frac{2}{3}\log_{10}f$ (h) $\frac{3}{4}\log_{10}4$
17 (a) 482.6 (b) 85 360 (c) 540.4 (d) 2.274
(e) 21.63 (f) 3.416 (g) 11.12 (h) 245.6
18 (a) 0.30105 (b) 1.2042 (c) 1.8063
(d) 0.90315 (e) 1.50525
19 (a) 1.398 (b) 2.097 (c) 2.796
20 (a) true (b) true (c) false
(d) false (e) false

Unit 5 Square roots

Examples of square roots (page 20)

1 (a) 4 (b) 6 (c) 10 (d) 3
(e) 1 (f) 5 (g) 12 (h) 9
(i) 2.846 (j) 0.8 (k) 20 (l) 50
(m) 0.2 (n) 500 (o) 0.1 (p) 100
2 (a) 0.3 (b) 0.4 (c) 800
(d) 0.006 (e) 3000 (f) 0.03
3 (a) 50 (b) 158.11 (c) 0.05 (d) 0.158 11
4 (a) 0.3162 (b) 0.031 62 (c) 31.62 (d) 1000
5 (a) 1.2 (b) 0.3795 (c) 37.95 (d) 120
(e) 0.012 (f) 1200
6 (a) $\sqrt{81 \times 100 \times 100 \times 100} = 9 \times 10 \times 10 \times 10 = 9000$
(b) $\sqrt{49 \times 100 \times 100} = 7 \times 10 \times 10 = 700$
(c) $\sqrt{9 \times 100 \times 100 \times 100} = 3 \times 10 \times 10 \times 10 = 3000$

Square roots and standard form (page 21)

1 (a) 10 (b) 100 (c) 1000 (d) 10 000
(e) 100 000 (f) 0.1 (g) 0.01 (h) 0.001
(i) 0.0001
2 (a) 500 (b) 9000 (c) 150
(d) 1200 (e) 1000 (f) 1100
3 (a) 600 (b) 70 (c) 200
(d) 130 (e) 90 (f) 4000
4 (a) 0.004 (b) 0.06 (c) 0.007
(d) 0.08 (e) 0.0009 (f) 0.0011
5 (a) 70 (b) 0.009 (c) 0.03
(d) 1000 (e) 0.01 (f) 2000

Unit 6 Modulo arithmetic

Calculating in modulo arithmetic (page 22)

1 (a) 2 (b) 4 (c) 2 (d) 0 (e) 1 (f) 3
2 (a) 3 (b) 6 (c) 6 (d) 1 (e) 1 (f) 5
3 (a) 5 (b) 9 (c) 8 (d) 7 (e) 3 (f) 8
4 (a) 1 (b) 0 (c) 3
5 (a) 1 (b) 3 (c) 2
6 (a) 2 (b) 3 (c) 4 (d) 4 (e) 2
7 (a) 3 (b) 4 (c) 4 (d) 2
8 (a) 3 (b) 0 (c) 1 (d) 2
9 (a) 6 (b) 7 (c) 4 (d) 0
10 (a) 6 (b) 1 (c) 3 (d) 1
11 (a) 2 (b) 3 (c) 2 (d) 4
12 (a) 2 (b) 3 (c) 3 (d) 4
13 (a) 7 (b) 7 (c) 4 (d) 2
14 (a) 4 (b) 4 (c) 3 (d) 5
15 (a) 4 (b) 1 (c) 0

Solving equations in modulo arithmetic (page 24)

1 (a) 4 (b) 4 (c) 4 (d) 3 (e) 4 (f) 3
2 (a) 3 (b) 1 (c) 2 (d) 3 (e) 4 (f) 4
3 (a) 4 (b) 3 (c) 3 (d) 3 (e) 2; 5 (f) 0; 2; 4
4 (a) 1 (b) 4 (c) 1; 5 (d) 2; 3 (e) 3
5 (a) 2 (b) 1 (c) 1
6 (a) 6 (b) 6 (c) 2; 6

Unit 7 Area – revision (page 25)

1 (a) 28.09 cm² (b) 21.17 cm² (c) 14 cm²
(d) 11.28 cm² (e) 80 cm² (f) 34.56 cm²
(g) 28 cm² (h) 21.78 cm² (i) 616 cm²
(j) 128.7 cm²
2 306.25 cm² **3** 135.02 cm² **4** 7.28 cm²
5 4.615 cm **6** (a) 10.2 cm (b) 6.8 cm
7 112 cm² **8** (a) 10 cm (b) 48 cm **9** (a) 616 mm²
(b) 1780.24 cm² (c) 2464 m² **10** 1.4 cm

Unit 8 Area of a triangle (2)

The trigonometric method (page 28)

1 (a) 17.61 cm² (b) 19.7 cm² (c) 19.39 cm²
(d) 5.2 cm² (e) 4.46 cm² (f) 11.28 cm²
(g) 20.55 cm² (h) 8.0 cm² (i) 536.8 cm²
(j) 6.45 cm²

Hero's method (page 30)

1 (a) 6.50 cm² (b) 85.45 cm² (c) 1833 m²
(d) 5.33 cm² (e) 56.13 cm² (f) 71.78 cm²
2 (a) 6.615 cm² (b) 27.77 cm² (c) 21.03 cm²
(d) 43.86 cm² (e) 20.25 cm² (f) 199.0 cm²

Unit 9 Area of a parallelogram (2)

Areas of parallelograms (page 32)

1 (a) 28.53 cm² (b) 27.32 cm² (c) 29.06 cm²
(d) 21.24 cm²
2 (a) 34.31 cm² (b) 62.05 cm² (c) 11.04 cm²
(d) 32.73 cm²

Areas of triangles and parallelograms (page 33)

1 6.86 cm **2** 14 cm **3** 7.22 cm **4** 6.85 cm
5 2.25 cm **6** 3 cm **7** 11.74 cm²
8 14.30 cm² **9** 13.07 cm² **10** 9.8 cm²
11 4391 m² **12** 53.43 cm² **13** 43° and 137°

Unit 10 Circular area

Areas of rings or washers (page 34)

1 22 cm² **2** 267.9 cm² **3** 43.99 cm²
4 (a) 15 386 m² (b) 10 048 m² **5** 78.45 mm²

6 (a) 3.14 cm^2 (b) 25.12 cm^2 (c) 50.24 cm^2 (d) 75.36 cm^2 7 1178.6 mm^2

Arc lengths and sector angles (page 36)

1 (a) $\frac{1}{15}$ (b) $\frac{1}{12}$ (c) $\frac{1}{10}$ (d) $\frac{1}{9}$ (e) $\frac{3}{10}$ (f) $\frac{2}{5}$ (g) $\frac{3}{8}$ (h) $\frac{7}{12}$ (i) $\frac{3}{4}$ (j) $\frac{5}{6}$
2 (a) 30 cm (b) 25 mm (c) 80 cm (d) 10 cm (e) 25 mm
3 (a) 4.71 cm (b) 6.28 cm (c) 9.42 mm (d) 7.85 cm (e) 31.4 cm
4 (a) 72° (b) 300° (c) 210° (d) 144° (e) 225°
5 (a) 45° (b) 120°

Longitude, and distances between places (page 38)

1 (a) 6158 km (b) 8248 km (c) 8798 km (d) 9237 km (e) 5938 km
2 (a) 3299 km (b) 1650 km (c) 990 km (d) 4949 km (e) 1320 km

Sector area problems (page 38)

1 (a) 14 cm^2 (b) 15 mm^2 (c) 35 cm^2 (d) 12 cm^2 (e) 30 mm^2
2 (a) 108° (b) 24° (c) 210° (d) 30° (e) 150°
3 (a) 3080 mm^2 (b) 154 cm^2 (c) 77 cm^2 (d) 154 cm^2 (e) 231 cm^2
4 (a) 4.713 mm^2 (b) 9.426 cm^2 (c) 3.142 cm^2 (d) 18.852 cm^2 (e) 1.571 mm^2
5 15.4 cm^2

Arc length and sector area problems (page 39)

1 (a) 59.23 cm (b) 84.834 cm^2
2 (a) 78.55 cm (b) 54.985 cm (c) 1178.25 cm^2 (d) 824.775 cm^2
3 103° 4 42.63 cm 5 85.9°
6 6.284 cm^2 7 167.6 cm^2 8 25.46 cm

Unit 11 The cylinder

Volumes and surface areas of cylinders (page 42)

1 (a) 3080 mm^3 (b) 880 mm^2
2 (a) 461.58 cm^3 (b) 302.225 cm^2
3 (a) 226.224 cm^3 (b) 251.36 cm^2
4 3179.25 cm^3 5 14.58 cm
6 44 m^3 7 84.57 cm^2 8 77 000 mm^3
9 25 308 mm^2 10 (a) 2010.88 m^3 (b) 703.81 m^2

Unit 12 Volume, density and mass (page 43)

1 450 kg 2 5650 g 3 26.18 kg
4 (a) 0.2463 m^3 (b) 505 kg 5 103.68 kg

Unit 13 The cone and the pyramid

Cones and pyramids, volume and surface area (page 44)

1 66 cm^3 2 25 136 mm^3
3 (a) 13 cm (b) 204.1 cm^2 (c) 282.6 cm^2 (d) 314 cm^3
4 98.4 cm^3 5 (a) 384 cm^3 (b) 384 cm^2
6 193.375 cm^3 7 (a) 25.136 cm^3 (b) 52.31 cm^2

Unit 14 The sphere

Spheres and hemispheres, volume and surface area (page 45)

1 (a) 11 498 cm^3 (b) 4190 cm^3 (c) 33.52 cm^3 (d) 268.2 cm^3 (e) 91 989 cm^3
2 (a) 154 cm^2 (b) 616 cm^2 (c) 1386 cm^2 (d) 50.29 cm^2 (e) 240.6 cm^2
3 (a) 407.5 cm^3 (b) 265.8 cm^2
4 (a) 5748 cm^3 (b) 1847.5 cm^2
5 348 cm^3

Volume and surface area – more examples (page 46)

1 357.3 cm^2 2 890.2 cm^3
3 (a) 817.1 cm^3 (b) 6.37 kg
4 (a) 1316.4 cm^3 (b) 16.19 kg 5 40 cm

Unit 15 Distance, speed and time (page 47)

1 (a) 60 km (b) 40 km (c) 24 km (d) 1 km (e) 270 km
2 90 km/h 3 $\frac{2}{3}$ cm/second 4 $2\frac{1}{2}$ hours
5 65 km/h 6 (a) 186 km (b) 62 km/h
7 (a) 265 km (b) 53 km/h
8 (a) 10 m/s (b) 126 km/h

Unit 16 Algebraic fractions

Examples of algebraic fractions (page 49)

1 (a) $\frac{3a}{5}$ (b) $\frac{5b}{6}$ (c) $\frac{3}{4y}$ (d) $\frac{2m}{5n}$ (e) $\frac{2}{5m}$ (f) $\frac{4u}{5v}$ (g) $\frac{2x}{5y}$ (h) $\frac{5}{3q}$ (i) $4b$ (j) $\frac{3x}{5y}$

2 (a) $\frac{x}{4}=\frac{2x}{8}$ (b) $\frac{3x}{15}$ (c) $\frac{3x}{3y}$ (d) $\frac{4a}{3}$ (e) $\frac{20}{4x}$ (f) $\frac{3c}{4}$ (g) $\frac{3}{2}$ (h) $\frac{1}{6}$ (i) $\frac{5}{8m}$ (j) $\frac{3}{4}$

3 (a) $\frac{a}{b}$ (b) $\frac{5u}{6v}$ (c) $\frac{b}{4c}$ (d) $\frac{2q}{3r}$ (e) $\frac{8}{21q}$ (f) $\frac{y}{5z}$ (g) $\frac{3x^2}{4y^2}$ (h) $\frac{5r}{6q}$ (i) $\frac{5b^2}{8c^2}$ (j) $\frac{7z^2}{12y^2}$

4 (a) $\frac{a}{b}=\frac{3a}{3b}=\frac{a^2}{ab}=\frac{am}{bm}$
(b) $\frac{m}{n}=\frac{5m}{5n}=\frac{m^2}{nm}=\frac{mn}{n^2}$
(c) $\frac{2p}{3q}=\frac{8p}{12q}=\frac{2px}{3qx}=\frac{6p^2}{9pq}$

5 (a) $\frac{a+b}{2}$ (b) $\frac{x-y}{2}$ (c) $\frac{a+2b}{4}$ (d) $\frac{3p-2}{4}$ (e) $\frac{6x-y}{4}$ (f) $\frac{8x+9y}{12}$ (g) $\frac{2x}{3}$ (h) $\frac{11x}{15}$ (i) $\frac{2a}{3b}$ (j) $\frac{8m}{3n}$ (k) $\frac{10p}{3}$ (l) $\frac{8m^2}{9n^2}$ (m) $\frac{a^2}{d^2}$ (n) $\frac{8m^2}{3n^3}$ (o) 1 (p) $9b^3$

6 (a) $\frac{33a}{20}$ (b) $\frac{10a+13}{12}$ (c) $\frac{7a+10}{6}$ (d) $\frac{11x+17}{15}$ (e) $\frac{13a+2}{18}$ (f) $\frac{11}{2a}$ (g) $\frac{5a+10}{12}$ (h) $\frac{a-31}{15}$ (i) $\frac{4}{5c}$ (j) $\frac{8}{x}$

Algebraic equations (page 50)

1 (a) 10 (b) 20 (c) 8 (d) 25 (e) $\frac{4}{5}$ (f) 9 (g) 45 (h) 21 (i) 7 (j) $4\frac{1}{5}$
2 (a) $4\frac{8}{13}$ (b) $-1\frac{3}{5}$ (c) -12 (d) $\frac{1}{3}$ (e) $\frac{7}{10}$ (f) 14 (g) $3\frac{11}{14}$ (h) $\frac{29}{55}$ (i) $-2\frac{1}{3}$ (j) 40 (k) $-4\frac{1}{6}$ (l) 18

Unit 17 Simple algebraic problems (page 51)

1 £35 **2 (a)** 70 m **(b)** 9800 m^2 **3** £7 **4** £14
5 £28 **6** 30 tiles **7 (a)** $\frac{7}{5}x + 33 = 180$ **(b)** 105°
8 17 litres **9** 180 kg

Unit 18 Inequalities

Solution of inequalities (page 52)

1 (a) $x > 3$ **(b)** $x < 5$ **(c)** $x \geqslant 5$ **(d)** $x \leqslant 3$
(e) $x \geqslant -4$ **(f)** $x < -5$ **(g)** $x > 5$ **(h)** $x < 4$
(i) $x \geqslant 4$ **(j)** $x \leqslant 9$ **(k)** $x \leqslant -6$
2 (a) 2, 3, 4, 5, 6 **(b)** −1, 0 **(c)** −7, −6
(d) −1, 0, 1, 2, 3 **(e)** −1, 0, 1, 2 **(f)** 0, 1, 2, 3
(g) 3, 4, 5 **(h)** 4, 5
3 (a) $x \geqslant 2\frac{1}{2}$ **(b)** $x \geqslant \frac{2}{3}$ **(c)** $x > 5\frac{1}{2}$
(d) $x > 0$ **(e)** $x < 10\frac{1}{2}$ **(f)** $x < 1$
4 (a) $-1 > x$ **(b)** $-2\frac{2}{3} < x$ **(c)** $-3 < x$ **(d)** $-3 \geqslant x$
(e) $8\frac{1}{2} < x$ **(f)** $2 \geqslant x$ **(g)** $3 > x$ **(h)** $-2 \geqslant x$
(i) $1\frac{2}{5} > x$ **(j)** $x > -2\frac{1}{4}$
5 (a) 2, 3, 4 **(b)** 0, 1, 2, 3 **(c)** 4, 5, 6
(d) −3, −2 **(e)** φ

Solution sets for inequalities (page 52)

1 (a) $\{x{:}x > 2\}$ **(b)** $\{x{:}x < 3\}$ **(c)** $\{x{:}x \geqslant 5\}$
(d) $\{x{:}x \leqslant 4\}$ **(e)** $\{x{:}3 < x\}$ **(f)** $\{x{:}x > 2\}$
(g) $\{x{:}x \geqslant 6\}$ **(h)** $\{x{:}x \geqslant 4\}$ **(i)** $\{x{:}x \leqslant -1\}$
(j) $\{x{:}x > -\frac{1}{2}\}$
2 (a) $\{x{:}x > 12\frac{2}{3}\}$ **(b)** $\{x{:}x \geqslant 1\}$ **(c)** $\{x{:}x > -1\}$
(d) $\{x{:}12\frac{1}{2} \leqslant x\}$ **(e)** $\{x{:}x \geqslant 3\frac{2}{3}\}$ **(f)** $\{x{:}x > 12\}$
(g) $\{x{:}x \geqslant -14\}$ **(h)** $\{x{:}x < 81\}$
3 (a) $\{4 < x < 5\}$ **(b)** $\{2 \leqslant x < 7\frac{1}{5}\}$ **(c)** $\{-5 < x \leqslant 1\}$
(d) $\{-1 < x \leqslant 3\}$ **(e)** $\{6 < x \leqslant 8\}$ **(f)** φ
(g) $\{8 < x \leqslant 12\}$ **(h)** φ
4 (a) φ **(b)** {2, 3, 4, 5, 6, 7} **(c)** {−4, −3, −2, −1, 0, 1}
(d) {0, 1, 2, 3} **(e)** {7, 8} **(f)** φ **(g)** {9, 10, 11, 12}
(h) φ

Unit 19 Solution of simultaneous equations (page 54)

1 (a) $x = 4$ $y = 1$ **(b)** $x = 3$ $y = 2$
(c) $x = 2$ $y = 3$ **(d)** $x = -2$ $y = 5$
(e) $x = 5$ $y = 1$ **(f)** $x = 1$ $y = \frac{1}{2}$
(g) $x = 0$ $y = 2$ **(h)** $x = \frac{1}{2}$ $y = -\frac{1}{3}$
2 (a) $x = 3$ $y = 1$ **(b)** $x = 1$ $y = 3$
(c) $x = 2$ $y = 5$ **(d)** $x = 6$ $y = 1$
(e) $x = 0$ $y = 3$ **(f)** $x = -1$ $y = 3$
(g) $x = 1$ $y = -4$ **(h)** $x = -1$ $y = 3$
3 (a) $x = 1$ $y = 2$ **(b)** $x = 4$ $y = 0$
(c) $x = 2$ $y = 1$ **(d)** $x = 2$ $y = 5$
4 (a) $x = 3$ $y = 3$ **(b)** $x = 5$ $y = 3$
(c) $x = 2$ $y = 2$ **(d)** $x = -1$ $y = 4$
(e) $x = 5$ $y = \frac{1}{5}$ **(f)** $x = \frac{1}{2}$ $y = \frac{1}{2}$
5 (a) $x = 2$ $y = 3$ **(b)** $x = 3$ $y = 1$
(c) $x = 4$ $y = 0$ **(d)** $x = 2$ $y = 5$
(e) $x = 5$ $y = 1$ **(f)** $x = 1$ $y = 2$
(g) $x = 3$ $y = 3$ **(h)** $x = 2$ $y = -1$
(i) $x = -1$ $y = 2$ **(j)** $x = \frac{1}{2}$ $y = \frac{1}{2}$
6 (a) $x = 2$ $y = 2$ **(b)** $x = 1$ $y = 3$
(c) $x = 5$ $y = 4$ **(d)** $x = 1$ $y = 7$
(e) $x = 3$ $y = 1$ **(f)** $x = 3$ $y = 0$
(g) $x = 2$ $y = 6$ **(h)** $x = -1$ $y = 4$
(i) $x = 1$ $y = -1$ **(j)** $x = -1$ $y = -2$
7 (a) $x = 2$ $y = 3$ **(b)** $x = 2$ $y = 2$
(c) $x = 4$ $y = 6$ **(d)** $x = 5$ $y = 3$

Unit 20 Quadratic functions

Factorizing quadratic functions (page 56)

1 (a) $(x+1)(x+3)$ **(b)** $(x+8)(x+1)$
(c) $(x+4)(x+1)$ **(d)** $(x+10)(x+1)$
(e) $(x+3)(x+5)$ **(f)** $(x+2)(x+10)$
(g) $(x+2)(x+9)$ **(h)** $(x+7)(x-1)$
(i) $(x+5)(x-1)$ **(j)** $(x+8)(x-1)$
(k) $(x+3)(x+7)$ **(l)** $(x-7)(x+1)$
(m) $(x-5)(x+3)$ **(n)** $(x-4)(x+2)$
(o) $(x-8)(x+2)$ **(p)** $(x-5)(x+4)$
(q) $(x-2)(x-11)$ **(r)** $(x-7)(x+5)$
(s) $(x-6)(x+2)$ **(t)** $(x-3)(x-10)$
2 (a) $(2x+1)(x+1)$ **(b)** $(2x+3)(x+1)$
(c) $(2x+1)(x+3)$ **(d)** $(3x+1)(x+3)$
(e) $(3x+3)(x+1)$ **(f)** $(5x+2)(x+1)$
(g) $(5x+1)(x+3)$ **(h)** $(5x+3)(x+1)$
(i) $(7x-3)(x+1)$ **(j)** $(7x+3)(x-1)$
(k) $(5x+2)(x-1)$ **(l)** $(11x-3)(x+1)$
(m) $(7x+5)(x-1)$ **(n)** $(5x-1)(x+7)$
(o) $(2x-1)(2x-1)$ **(p)** $(4x+15)(x-1)$
(q) $(2x-10)(3x-1)$ **(r)** $(2x-1)(3x-10)$
(s) $(6x+5)(x-2)$ **(t)** $(3x-10)(2x+1)$
3 (a) $x(x-8)$ **(b)** $x(2x-11)$
(c) $3x(x-3)$ **(d)** $2x(x+4)$
(e) $3x(2x+5)$ **(f)** $6x(3x+2)$
(g) $7x(2x-3)$ **(h)** $x(5x+4)$

Difference between two squares (page 56)

1 (a) $x^2 - 9$ **(f)** $4x^2 - 49$
(b) $x^2 - 25$ **(g)** $9x^2 - 16$
(c) $x^2 - y^2$ **(h)** $25x^2 - 81$
(d) $a^2 - 4b^2$ **(i)** $a^2 - 1$
(e) $4x^2 - y^2$ **(j)** $9a^2 - 64$
2 (a) $(x+10)(x-10)$ **(f)** $(2x+y)(2x-y)$
(b) $(x+8)(x-8)$ **(g)** $(a+6)(a-6)$
(c) $(x+1)(x-1)$ **(h)** $(3a+11)(3a-11)$
(d) $(x+12)(x-12)$ **(i)** $(6x+13)(6x-13)$
(e) $(x+15)(x-15)$ **(j)** $(5x+9)(5x-9)$
3 (a) 2400 **(b)** 7600 **(c)** 2900 **(d)** 600
(e) 9800 **(f)** 200 **(g)** 2600 **(h)** 631 800
(i) 1 236 400 **(j)** 58 800
4 (a) 12.6 **(b)** 11 **(c)** 30 **(d)** 6900
(e) 4.04 **(f)** $7\frac{1}{2}$ **(g)** 20 **(h)** 50
(i) 21.6 **(j)** 45

Solution of quadratics (page 58)

1 (a) 2, −3 **(b)** −3, −5 **(c)** 4, 7
(d) $\frac{1}{2}, -2$ **(e)** $\frac{2}{3}, -2\frac{1}{2}$
2 (a) −1, −3 **(b)** −1, −8 **(c)** −1, −9 **(d)** −1, −4
(e) 1, −7 **(f)** 3, −5 **(g)** 3, −6 **(h)** 4, −5
(i) 1, 14 **(j)** 2 **(k)** 5, −3 **(l)** 8, −1
(m) 1, 8 **(n)** 4, 5 **(o)** 3, 4 **(p)** 9, −8
3 (a) ±5 **(b)** ±10 **(c)** ±2 **(d)** ±4
(e) ±9 **(f)** $\pm\frac{1}{2}$ **(g)** ±3 **(h)** $\pm 2\frac{1}{2}$
(i) $\pm 2\frac{1}{3}$ **(j)** ±3
4 (a) 7, −1 **(b)** 1, 21 **(c)** 9, −3
(d) 2, 11 **(e)** 3, −4 **(f)** 3, 11

Graphical solution to quadratics (page 58)

1 $x = 1, x = 3$ **2** $x = 1, x = -4$
3 $x = 1, x = 6$ **4** $x = 2, x = 5$ **5** $x = -2.56, x = 1.56$

More difficult quadratic equations (page 59)

1 (a) $1, -\frac{1}{2}$ **(f)** $1, 1\frac{2}{5}$
(b) $\frac{1}{5}, -1$ **(g)** $1, 1\frac{2}{3}$
(c) $\frac{2}{7}, -4$ **(h)** $-\frac{3}{4}, -2\frac{1}{2}$
(d) $3\frac{3}{4}, -1$ **(i)** $\frac{1}{2}$
(e) $1, -1\frac{1}{8}$ **(j)** $1\frac{1}{2}, -\frac{4}{5}$

2 (a) 5, 2 (b) −7.62, −1.38 (c) −9.72, +2.72 (d) −3.45, +1.45 (e) −6.70, −0.30 (f) −2.59, 0.26 (g) 2.35, −0.85 (h) 1.36, 0.44 (i) −5.21, −0.29 (j) −1.40, 0.90

3 (a) $x = 3$ cm (b) $x = 9$ cm (c) 8 metres (d) 10 metres (e) $1\frac{1}{2}$ metres

Unit 21 Algebraic manipulation

Algebraic manipulation and substitution (page 61)

1 (a) $x = b - a$ (b) $x = \dfrac{1}{a+b}$ (c) $x = a + b$ (d) $x = -(a + b)$ (e) $x = \dfrac{ab}{a+b}$ (f) $x = a - 2b$ (g) $x = \dfrac{5a}{b-a}$ (h) $x = \sqrt{a^2 - b^2}$ (i) $x = a + b$ (j) $x = \dfrac{m-n}{an - bm}$

2 (a) (i) (1,−2) (ii) (−2,−11) (iii) $(5\frac{2}{3},12)$ (iv) (−5,−20)
(b) (i) (2,11) (ii) (−3,1) (iii) (−2,3) (iv) (5,17)
(c) (i) (5,−2) (ii) (−3,2) (iii) (9,−4) (iv) $(2,-\frac{1}{2})$
(d) (i) (4,−2) (ii) (−2,−5) (iii) (10,1) (iv) (−4,−6)

3 (a) $x = \dfrac{10}{2a + 5b}$ (b) $x = 4ab$ (c) $x = \dfrac{6b}{a}$ (d) $x = \dfrac{17}{3y}$ (e) $x = 3a^2$ (f) $x = \dfrac{a+5}{3}$ (g) $x = \dfrac{ab + 5b - 3a}{a+b}$ (h) $x = 5 - 3a$

Unit 22 Transformation of formulae

Change of subject (page 62)

1 (a) $r = \dfrac{C}{2\pi}$ (b) $m = \dfrac{y}{x}$ (c) $L = \dfrac{A}{B}$ (d) $R = \dfrac{100I}{PT}$ (e) $h = \dfrac{2A}{b}$ (f) $h = \dfrac{V}{\pi r^2}$ (g) $T = \dfrac{S}{V}$ (h) $x = \dfrac{y^2}{4a}$

2 (a) $x = \dfrac{S - 2y}{2}$ (b) $x = 2s - y - z$ (c) $x = \dfrac{v^2 - u^2}{2a}$ (d) $x = \dfrac{y - c}{m}$ (e) $x = 90 - C$ (f) $x = \dfrac{3y - 2a}{4}$ (g) $x = \dfrac{-By - c}{A}$ (h) $x = \dfrac{E}{v^2 - u^2}$

3 (a) $x = \dfrac{V}{a + 2b}$ (b) $x = \dfrac{Y}{3 - 2a}$ (c) $x = \dfrac{T}{g - a}$ (d) $x = \dfrac{a}{1 - a}$ (e) $x = \dfrac{C}{a - b}$ (f) $x = \dfrac{b}{a - 1}$ (g) $x = \dfrac{Pa}{P - 1}$ (h) $x = \dfrac{yf}{y - f}$

4 (a) $x = \dfrac{a}{b - 1}$ (b) $x = \dfrac{y - a^2}{a^2}$ (c) $x = \dfrac{h}{a}$ (d) $x = \sqrt{\dfrac{A}{\pi}}$ (e) $x = y^2$ (f) $x = \sqrt{c^2y}$ (g) $x = \sqrt{\dfrac{c^2}{y}}$ (h) $x = y^2 - a$ (i) $x = \dfrac{P^2}{2gm^2}$ (j) $x = \dfrac{P^2 - 1}{P^2 + 1}$

Evaluating formulae (page 63)

1 (a) $A = 35$ (b) $L = 4$ (c) $B = 8$
2 (a) $I = 120$ (b) $P = 600$ (c) $T = 10$
3 (a) $V = 24$ (b) $U = 13$ (c) $T = 10$
4 (a) $v = 7$ (b) $u = 10$ (c) $a = 6$
5 (a) $A = 78.5$ (b) $r = 3.5$
6 (a) $V = 1570$ (b) $h = 35$ (c) $r = 5.75$
7 (a) $y = 13$ (b) $m = 2$ (c) $c = 6$
8 (a) $y = 20$ (b) $x = 9$ (c) $a = 20$

Various exercises (page 63)

1 (a) $\dfrac{53x}{30}$ (b) $\dfrac{17x - 11}{12}$
2 (a) $x = 3$ (b) $x = 58$
3 (a) $x > 3$ (b) $4 < x$ (c) $x \geqslant 4$ (d) $x \leqslant 20$
4 (a) $x = 3, y = 1$ (b) $x = 8, y = -9$
5 (a) $x = 2, y = 3$ (b) $x = 2, y = 3$
6 (a) $5p(p - 4)$ (b) $(q + 5)(q - 5)$ (c) $(x + 1)(x - 5)$
7 (a) $x = 8$ or -6 (b) $x = -1$ or -3
8 (a) $x = \dfrac{V}{lw}$ (b) $x = \dfrac{3V}{r^2}$ (c) $x = \dfrac{P - 2y}{2}$
9 newspaper 18p magazine 28p
10 choc ice 22p lollipop 15p

Unit 23 Matrix algebra

Addition of matrices (page 64)

1 (a) 2×3 (b) 3×2 (c) 1×3 (d) 3×1 (e) 2×2 (f) 3×3

2 (a) $\begin{pmatrix} 5 \\ 11 \end{pmatrix}$ (b) $\begin{pmatrix} 5 & 5 \end{pmatrix}$ (c) $\begin{pmatrix} 4 & -1 \end{pmatrix}$ (d) $\begin{pmatrix} 1 \\ 3 \end{pmatrix}$
(e) $\begin{pmatrix} 4a & -c \end{pmatrix}$ (f) $\begin{pmatrix} c + d \\ e + b \end{pmatrix}$ (g) $\begin{pmatrix} 7 & 11 \\ 5 & 2 \end{pmatrix}$
(h) $\begin{pmatrix} 1 & 9 \\ 1 & 6 \end{pmatrix}$ (i) $\begin{pmatrix} 4 & 2 \\ 2 & 5\frac{1}{2} \end{pmatrix}$ (j) $\begin{pmatrix} 1\frac{1}{4} & -1\frac{1}{4} \\ 1 & -1 \end{pmatrix}$
(k) $\begin{pmatrix} 4a & c \\ 7a & -c \end{pmatrix}$ (l) $\begin{pmatrix} 2x & 2y \\ 2x & y \end{pmatrix}$

3 (a) $\begin{pmatrix} 2 & -3 \\ 12 & 5 \end{pmatrix}$ (b) $\begin{pmatrix} -2 & 0 \\ 12 & 1 \end{pmatrix}$ (c) $\begin{pmatrix} 2 & -3 \\ 12 & 5 \end{pmatrix}$
(d) $\begin{pmatrix} 2 & 0 \\ 17 & 4 \end{pmatrix}$

4 (a) $\begin{pmatrix} -3 & -1 \\ -3 & 3 \end{pmatrix}$ (b) $\begin{pmatrix} 1 & -1 \\ -7 & 5 \end{pmatrix}$ (c) $\begin{pmatrix} 2 & 0 \\ 0 & 8 \end{pmatrix}$
(d) $\begin{pmatrix} 0 & -1 \\ -5 & 8 \end{pmatrix}$ (e) $\begin{pmatrix} 0 & -1 \\ -5 & 8 \end{pmatrix}$ Commutative Law

Subtraction of matrices (page 65)

1 (a) $\begin{pmatrix} 4 \\ 2 \end{pmatrix}$ (b) $\begin{pmatrix} -3 \\ -6 \end{pmatrix}$ (c) $\begin{pmatrix} 2 \\ 6 \end{pmatrix}$ (d) $\begin{pmatrix} 5 \\ 8 \end{pmatrix}$ (e) $\begin{pmatrix} -2 \\ -6 \end{pmatrix}$

2 (a) $\begin{pmatrix} 4 & 2 \\ 2 & 2 \end{pmatrix}$ (b) $\begin{pmatrix} 4 & 0 \\ 8 & 8 \end{pmatrix}$ (c) $\begin{pmatrix} -3 & 4 \\ 1 & -2 \end{pmatrix}$
(d) $\begin{pmatrix} 1 & 3 \\ 5 & 2 \end{pmatrix}$ (e) $\begin{pmatrix} x & -2y \\ 2x & 3y \end{pmatrix}$ (f) $\begin{pmatrix} -g & 2h \\ 2g & 2h \end{pmatrix}$

3 (a) $\begin{pmatrix} -2 & 6 \\ 4 & 4 \end{pmatrix}$ (b) $\begin{pmatrix} 5 & 3 \\ 2 & 6 \end{pmatrix}$ (c) $\begin{pmatrix} 4 & -2 \\ 2 & 4 \end{pmatrix}$
(d) $\begin{pmatrix} 7 & -3 \\ -2 & 2 \end{pmatrix}$ (e) $\begin{pmatrix} -7 & 3 \\ 2 & -2 \end{pmatrix}$

4 (a) $\begin{pmatrix} 3 & 1 \\ 3 & 0 \end{pmatrix}$ (b) $\begin{pmatrix} -2 & 2 \\ -4 & 2 \end{pmatrix}$ (c) $\begin{pmatrix} -5 & 0 \\ 2 & 3 \end{pmatrix}$
(d) $\begin{pmatrix} 4 & 11 \\ 8 & 2 \end{pmatrix}$

Multiplying a matrix by a scalar (page 66)

1 (a) $\begin{pmatrix} 4 \\ 8 \end{pmatrix}$ (b) $\begin{pmatrix} 12 \\ 6 \\ 3 \end{pmatrix}$ (c) $\begin{pmatrix} 2 & 6 & 10 \end{pmatrix}$
(d) $\begin{pmatrix} 6 & 15 \\ 9 & 3 \end{pmatrix}$ (e) $\begin{pmatrix} 1 & 2 \\ 3 & 4 \end{pmatrix}$ (f) $\begin{pmatrix} -2 & 4 \\ -6 & -2 \end{pmatrix}$

2 (a) $\begin{pmatrix} 4 & 10 \\ 2 & 6 \end{pmatrix}$ (b) $\begin{pmatrix} 6 & 15 \\ 3 & 9 \end{pmatrix}$ (c) $\begin{pmatrix} 10 & 25 \\ 5 & 15 \end{pmatrix}$
(d) $\begin{pmatrix} -4 & -10 \\ -2 & -6 \end{pmatrix}$

3 (a) $\begin{pmatrix}-10 & 15\\ 5 & 10\end{pmatrix}$ (b) $\begin{pmatrix}2 & -3\\ -1 & -2\end{pmatrix}$ (c) $\begin{pmatrix}-8 & 12\\ 4 & 8\end{pmatrix}$

(d) yes

4 (a) $\begin{pmatrix}4 & -6\\ 8 & 0\end{pmatrix}$ (b) $\begin{pmatrix}-6 & 8\\ 4 & -2\end{pmatrix}$ (c) $\begin{pmatrix}6 & -9\\ 12 & 0\end{pmatrix}$

(d) $\begin{pmatrix}-1 & 1\\ 6 & -1\end{pmatrix}$ (e) $\begin{pmatrix}-2 & 2\\ 12 & -2\end{pmatrix}$ (f) $\begin{pmatrix}-2 & 2\\ 12 & -2\end{pmatrix}$

(g) $\begin{pmatrix}5 & -7\\ 2 & 1\end{pmatrix}$ (h) $\begin{pmatrix}10 & -14\\ 4 & 2\end{pmatrix}$ (i) $\begin{pmatrix}10 & -14\\ 4 & 2\end{pmatrix}$

(j) distributive law

5 (a) $\begin{pmatrix}4\\ -3\\ -2\end{pmatrix}$ (b) $\begin{pmatrix}2\\ -2\\ 1\end{pmatrix}$ (c) $\begin{pmatrix}2 & 5\\ -1 & 3\end{pmatrix}$

(d) $\begin{pmatrix}3 & 2\\ -1 & 3\end{pmatrix}$ (e) $\begin{pmatrix}2 & 2\frac{1}{2}\\ -\frac{1}{2} & 1\frac{1}{2}\end{pmatrix}$

Multiplication of two matrices (page 67)

1 (a) (10) (b) (22) (c) (2) (d) (−4)

(e) $\begin{pmatrix}11\\ 4\end{pmatrix}$ (f) $\begin{pmatrix}12\\ 7\end{pmatrix}$ (g) $\begin{pmatrix}-9\\ 4\end{pmatrix}$

(h) $\begin{pmatrix}-7\\ 8\end{pmatrix}$ (i) $\begin{pmatrix}-11\\ -10\end{pmatrix}$ (j) $\begin{pmatrix}0\\ 6\end{pmatrix}$

2 (a) $\begin{pmatrix}3 & 10\\ 3 & 9\end{pmatrix}$ (b) $\begin{pmatrix}19 & 6\\ 15 & 15\end{pmatrix}$ (c) $\begin{pmatrix}10 & 20\\ 3 & 7\end{pmatrix}$

(d) $\begin{pmatrix}8 & 39\\ 2 & 6\end{pmatrix}$ (e) $\begin{pmatrix}22 & -5\\ 2 & 20\end{pmatrix}$ (f) $\begin{pmatrix}9 & -11\\ 0 & -17\end{pmatrix}$

(g) $\begin{pmatrix}-4 & 6\\ 10 & 0\end{pmatrix}$ (h) $\begin{pmatrix}1 & 4\\ 0 & 9\end{pmatrix}$

3 (a) $\begin{pmatrix}0 & 24\\ -13 & 10\end{pmatrix}$ (b) $\begin{pmatrix}-4 & -23\\ 16 & 14\end{pmatrix}$

4 (a) $\begin{pmatrix}-2 & -6\\ -1 & 17\end{pmatrix}$ (b) $\begin{pmatrix}13 & -6\\ -11 & 2\end{pmatrix}$ (c) $\begin{pmatrix}4 & -12\\ -18 & 30\end{pmatrix}$

(d) $\begin{pmatrix}10 & 6\\ -10 & 18\end{pmatrix}$ (e) $\begin{pmatrix}2 & -18\\ -19 & 47\end{pmatrix}$ (f) $\begin{pmatrix}2 & -18\\ -19 & 47\end{pmatrix}$

5 (a) $\begin{pmatrix}14 & 3\\ -7 & -2\end{pmatrix}$ (b) $\begin{pmatrix}0 & 6\\ 0 & 2\end{pmatrix}$

The identity matrix (page 68)

1 (a) $\begin{pmatrix}2 & 3\\ 1 & 5\end{pmatrix}$ (b) $\begin{pmatrix}-2 & 3\\ 3 & -2\end{pmatrix}$ (c) $\begin{pmatrix}-2 & 5\\ 3 & 1\end{pmatrix}$

(d) $\begin{pmatrix}2 & a\\ a & 5\end{pmatrix}$

2 (a) $\begin{pmatrix}2 & 4\\ 5 & 2\end{pmatrix}\begin{pmatrix}1 & 0\\ 0 & 1\end{pmatrix} = \begin{pmatrix}2 & 4\\ 5 & 2\end{pmatrix}$

(b) $\begin{pmatrix}1 & 0\\ 0 & 1\end{pmatrix}\begin{pmatrix}-2 & 5\\ 2 & 3\end{pmatrix} = \begin{pmatrix}-2 & 5\\ 2 & 3\end{pmatrix}$

3 (a) $\begin{pmatrix}1 & 0\\ 0 & 1\end{pmatrix}$ (b) $\begin{pmatrix}1 & 0\\ 0 & 1\end{pmatrix}$ (c) $\begin{pmatrix}1 & 0\\ 0 & 1\end{pmatrix}$ (d) $\begin{pmatrix}1 & 0\\ 0 & 1\end{pmatrix}$

4 (a) $\begin{pmatrix}1 & -1\\ -1 & 2\end{pmatrix}$ (b) $\begin{pmatrix}5 & -3\\ -3 & 2\end{pmatrix}$ (c) $\begin{pmatrix}7 & -3\\ -9 & 4\end{pmatrix}$

The inverse of a matrix (page 69)

1 (a) 1 (b) 2 (c) 4 (d) −10 (e) 10 (f) 17

2 (a) $\begin{pmatrix}3 & -4\\ -2 & 3\end{pmatrix}$ (b) $\begin{pmatrix}\frac{3}{2} & -\frac{1}{2}\\ -2 & 1\end{pmatrix}$ (c) $\begin{pmatrix}\frac{1}{2} & -\frac{1}{2}\\ -\frac{1}{4} & \frac{3}{4}\end{pmatrix}$

(d) $\begin{pmatrix}\frac{1}{5} & -\frac{3}{10}\\ -\frac{1}{5} & -\frac{1}{5}\end{pmatrix}$ (e) $\begin{pmatrix}\frac{1}{10} & \frac{1}{10}\\ -\frac{3}{5} & \frac{2}{5}\end{pmatrix}$ (f) $\begin{pmatrix}\frac{4}{17} & \frac{3}{17}\\ -\frac{3}{17} & \frac{2}{17}\end{pmatrix}$

3 (a) $\begin{pmatrix}-1 & 0\\ 0 & 1\end{pmatrix}\begin{pmatrix}-1 & 0\\ 0 & 1\end{pmatrix} = \begin{pmatrix}1 & 0\\ 0 & 1\end{pmatrix}$

(b) $\begin{pmatrix}1 & 0\\ 0 & -1\end{pmatrix}\begin{pmatrix}1 & 0\\ 0 & -1\end{pmatrix} = \begin{pmatrix}1 & 0\\ 0 & 1\end{pmatrix}$

(c) $\begin{pmatrix}0 & -1\\ -1 & 0\end{pmatrix}\begin{pmatrix}0 & -1\\ -1 & 0\end{pmatrix} = \begin{pmatrix}1 & 0\\ 0 & 1\end{pmatrix}$

4 (a) $\begin{pmatrix}7 & 24\\ 4 & 14\end{pmatrix}$ (b) $\begin{pmatrix}4 & 11\\ 6 & 17\end{pmatrix}$ (c) $\begin{pmatrix}3 & -5\\ -1 & 2\end{pmatrix}$

(d) $\begin{pmatrix}2 & -1\\ -\frac{1}{2} & \frac{1}{2}\end{pmatrix}$ (e) $\begin{pmatrix}7 & -12\\ -2 & \frac{7}{2}\end{pmatrix}$ (f) $\begin{pmatrix}8\frac{1}{2} & -5\frac{1}{2}\\ -3 & 2\end{pmatrix}$

5 (a) $\begin{pmatrix}6 & 17\\ 8 & 22\end{pmatrix}$ (b) $\begin{pmatrix}2 & -8\\ -7 & 26\end{pmatrix}$ (c) $\begin{pmatrix}-4 & 3\\ -1 & 1\end{pmatrix}$

(d) $\begin{pmatrix}\frac{5}{4} & \frac{1}{2}\\ -\frac{1}{2} & 0\end{pmatrix}$ (e) $\begin{pmatrix}-\frac{11}{2} & \frac{17}{4}\\ 2 & -\frac{3}{2}\end{pmatrix}$ (f) $\begin{pmatrix}-6\frac{1}{2} & -2\\ -1\frac{3}{4} & -\frac{1}{2}\end{pmatrix}$

6 Determinant is zero

7 $A^2 = \begin{pmatrix}-1 & 0\\ 0 & -1\end{pmatrix}$ $A^3 = \begin{pmatrix}0 & 1\\ -1 & 0\end{pmatrix}$

$(A^2)^{-1} = \begin{pmatrix}-1 & 0\\ 0 & -1\end{pmatrix}$ $(A^3)^{-1} = \begin{pmatrix}0 & -1\\ 1 & 0\end{pmatrix}$

Matrix solutions to simultaneous equations (page 70)

1 (a) $2x + y = 11$
$x + y = 7$ (b) $\begin{pmatrix}4\\ 3\end{pmatrix}$

2 (a) $\begin{pmatrix}3 & 2\\ 1 & 1\end{pmatrix}\begin{pmatrix}x\\ y\end{pmatrix} = \begin{pmatrix}9\\ 4\end{pmatrix}$ (b) $x = 1, y = 3$

3 (a) $x = 0, y = 1$ (b) $x = 2, y = -1$
(c) $x = 3, y = 4$ (d) $x = -9, y = 20$

4 (a) $x = 3, y = 5$ (b) $x = 0, y = 1$
(c) $x = 0, y = -1$ (d) $x = 1\frac{2}{5}, y = \frac{4}{5}$

5 (a) $x = 4, y = 1$ (b) $x = 2, y = 0$

Unit 24 Mappings

Relations and mappings (page 71)

1

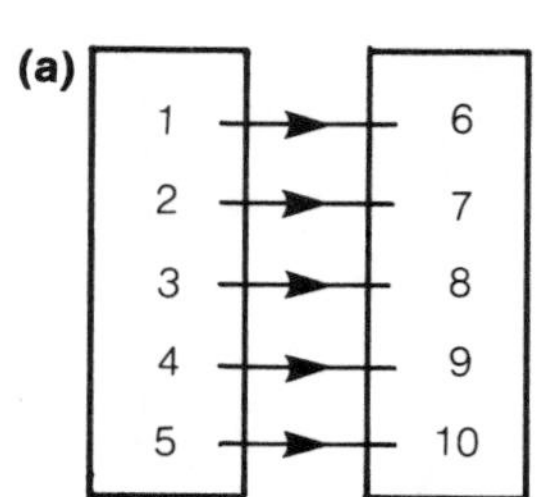

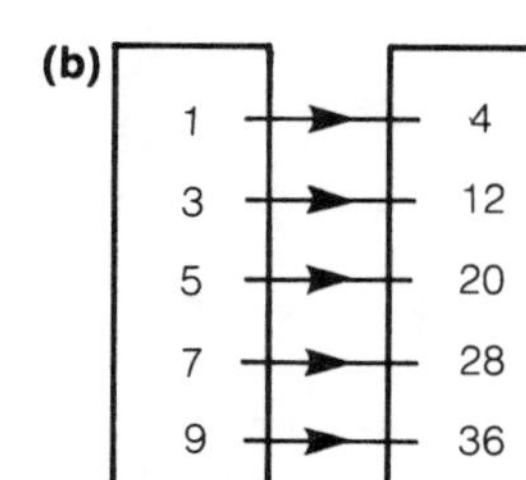

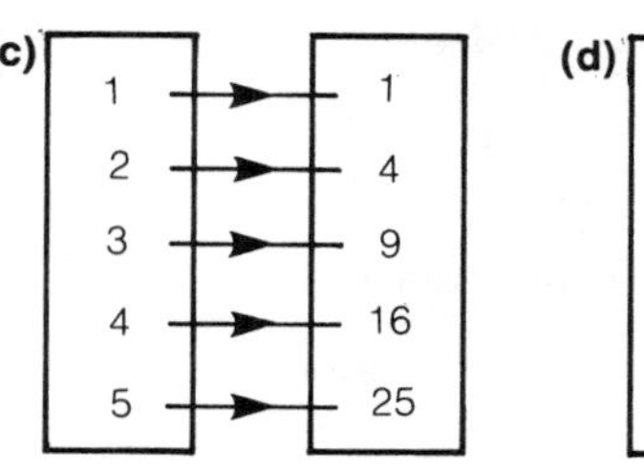

(d)

¼	0.25
½	0.5
¾	0.75
1½	1.5

Fig. A24.1

2

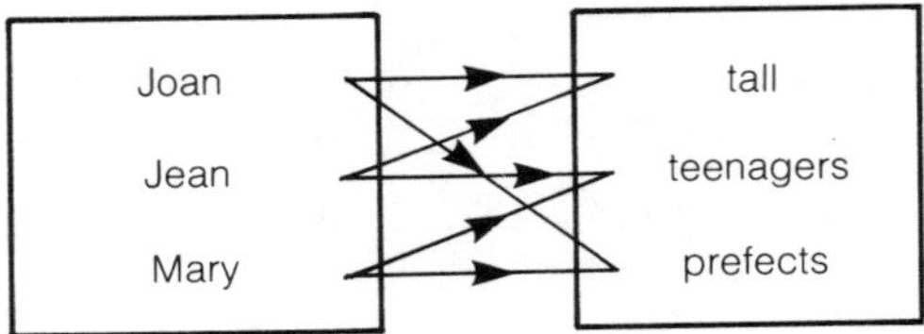

Fig. A24.2

3

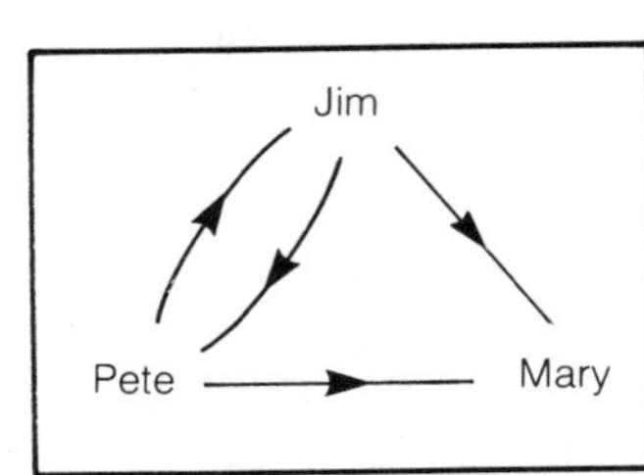

Fig. A24.3

4 (a) A 'is the square' of B
(b) A 'is one quarter' of B
(c) A 'is 5 times' B

5 (a) One-to-one mapping
(b) Many-to-one mapping
(c) Not a mapping

Functions (page 71)

1 (a) $\{3, 6, 9, 12, 15\}$ (b) $\{4, 5, 6, 7, 8\}$
(c) $\{3, 5, 7, 9, 11\}$ (d) $\{1, 4, 7, 10, 13\}$

2 (a) $\{2, 6, 10, 14\}$ (b) $\{-3, -1, 1, 3\}$
(c) $\{2, 12, 22, 32\}$ (d) $\{-9, -3, 3, 9\}$

3 (a) $\{-8, -4, 0, 4, 8\}$ (b) $\{-7, -5, -3, -1, 1\}$
(c) $\{-2, 0, 2, 4, 6,\}$ (d) $\{9, 8, 7, 6, 5\}$

4 (a) $x \rightarrow 3x + 1$ (b) $x \rightarrow 2x - 3$ (c) $x \rightarrow \frac{1}{2}x + 1$

5

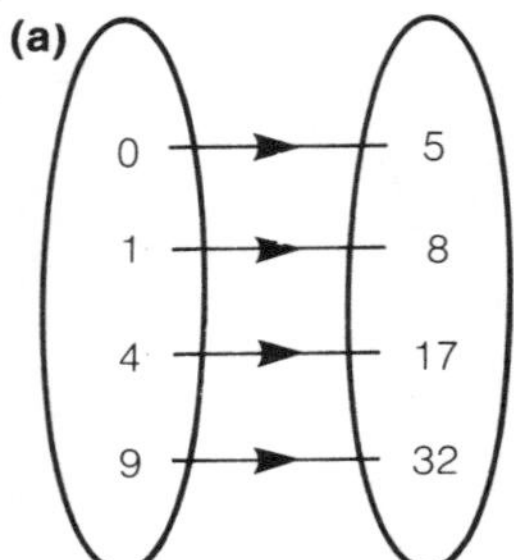

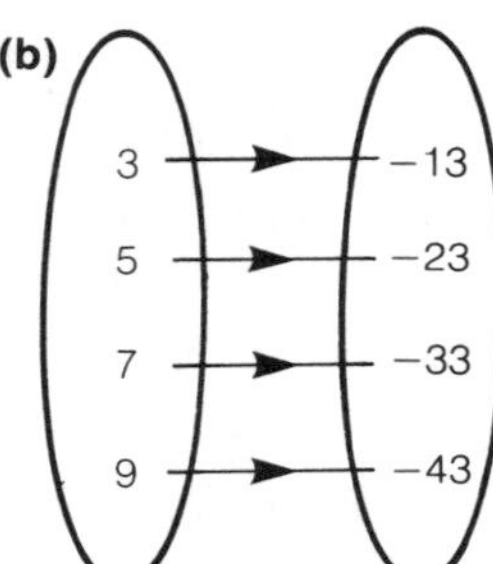

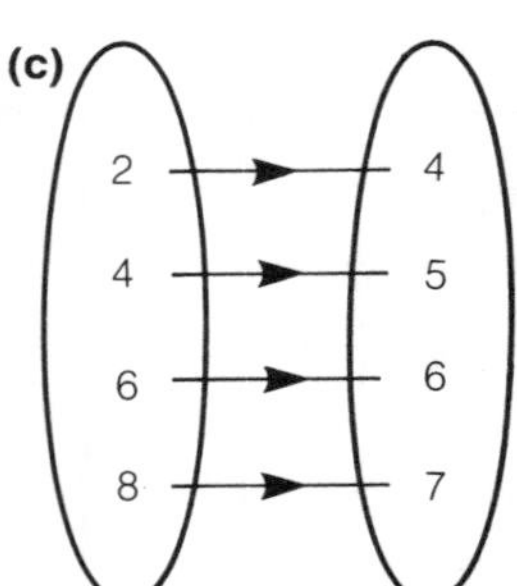

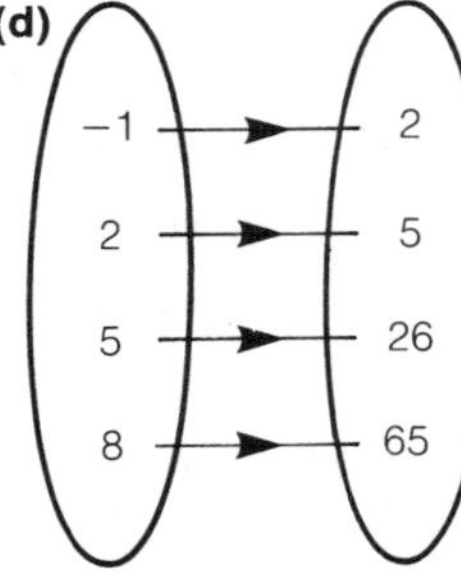

Fig. A24.4

6 (a) 11 (b) 17 (c) 7 (d) 1

7 (a) $x = 2$ (b) $x = -3$

Functions and inverse functions (page 72)

1 (a) $x \rightarrow \dfrac{x-2}{5}$ (b) $x \rightarrow \dfrac{x+1}{4}$ (c) $x \rightarrow 2(x+3)$

2 (a) $x \rightarrow \dfrac{x+9}{3}$ (b) -3 (c) $3\frac{2}{3}$

3 (a) $x \rightarrow \dfrac{x}{3} + 3$ (b) -6 (c) $3\frac{1}{3}$

4 (a) 7 (b) 35 (c) 5

5 (a) 5 (b) 25 (c) 18

6 (a) $-\frac{1}{5}$ (b) -1 (c) 8

7 (a) -1 (b) $-4\frac{3}{4}$ (c) 7

8 (a) 1 (b) $-2\frac{1}{2}$ (c) $-\frac{1}{2}$

9 (a) 4 (b) -2 (c) $x = 0$ or 3

Composite functions (page 73)

1

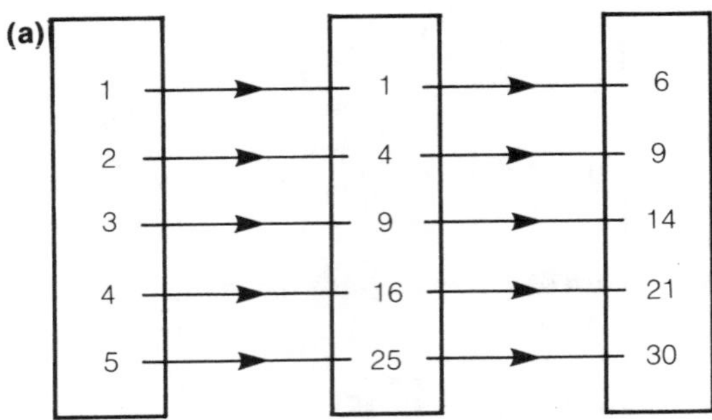

Fig. A24.5

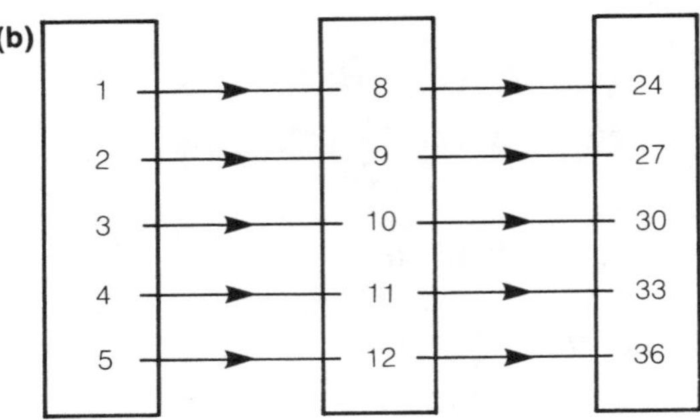

Fig. A24.6

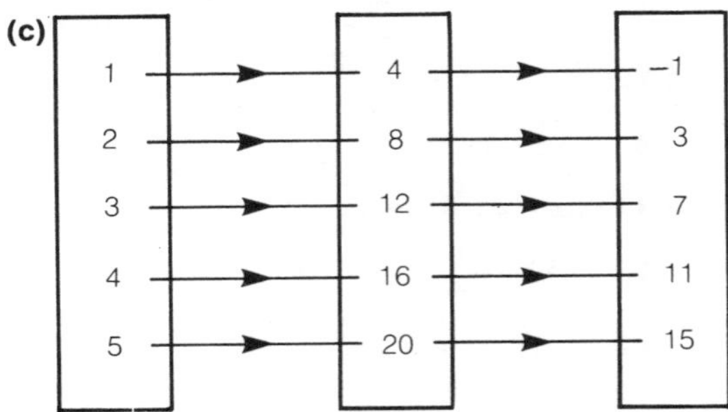

Fig. A24.7

2 (a) $x \rightarrow 14x - 35$
(b) $x \rightarrow 5 - 5x$
(c) $x \rightarrow x^2 - 6x + 9$
(d) $x \rightarrow \dfrac{1}{6x-5}$

3 (a) 10 (b) 25 (c) 28 (d) 100 (e) 76
(f) 256

4 (a) 28 (b) -10 (c) 3 (d) -28

5 (a) 17 (b) 81 (c) 16 (d) 37

6 (a) 3 (b) -1 (c) $1\frac{2}{5}$ (d) $-\frac{1}{5}$

7 (a) $x = 3$ (b) $x = 5$ 8 (a) $x = 4$ (b) $x = 2$

Unit 25 Set problems – algebraic solutions

Problems with sets (page 74)

1 5 2 19 3 (a) $58 - x = 39; x = 19$ (b) 3 (c) 17

4 (a)

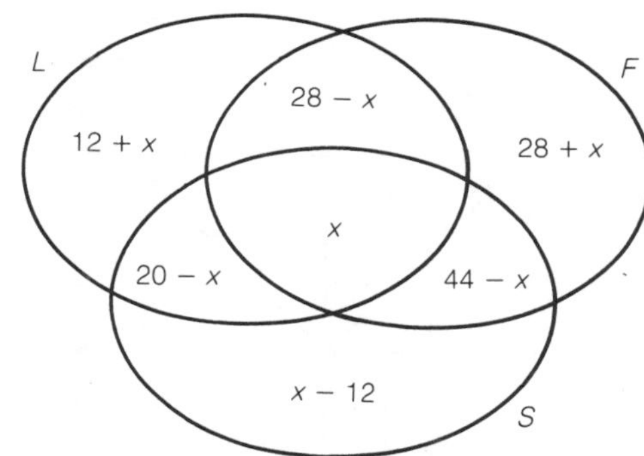

Fig. A25.1

(a) $(12+x)+(28-x)+(28+x)+x+(20-x)+(44-x)+(x-12)=136; x=16$

(b) 12 (c) 28 (d) 4

5 (a) 6 (b) 65 (c) 57 (d) 57 (e) 13 (f) 11 (g) 9

6 (a) 84 (b) 47 (c) 42 (d) 142

7 $(x-18)+(22-x)+(x-17)+x+(36-x)+(26-x)+(x-13)=58; x=22$

(a) 18 (b) 4 (c) 5 (d) 36

Unit 26 Trigonometric ratios

Calculations using the tangent ratio (page 77)

1 (a) 0.466 (b) 1.23 (c) 2.75 (d) 0.900 (e) 0.416 (f) 0.778 (g) 0.164 (h) 2.01
2 (a) 24.2° (b) 53.7° (c) 63.9° (d) 44.5° (e) 71.7° (f) 10.9°
3 (a) 4.81 cm (b) 6.37 cm (c) 1.79 cm (d) 10.9 cm
4 (a) 51.8° (b) 54.2° (c) 47.9° (d) 58.0°
5 42.5° 6 36.6° 7 4.62 cm
8 20.8 cm

Calculations using the sine ratio (page 78)

1 (a) 0.292 (b) 0.656 (c) 0.934 (d) 0.956 (e) 0.550 (f) 0.754 (g) 0.889 (h) 0.988
2 (a) 12.9° (b) 21.6° (c) 26.8° (d) 30.4° (e) 46.2° (f) 62.1°
3 (a) 3.01 cm (b) 4.71 cm (c) 1.99 cm (d) 5.98 cm
4 (a) 44.4° (b) 28.7° (c) 55.1° (d) 18.7°
5 2.77 cm 6 7.35 cm 7 54.0°
8 3.06 cm

Calculations using the cosine ratio (page 79)

1 (a) 0.616 (b) 0.777 (c) 0.326 (d) 0.588 (e) 0.775 (f) 0.884 (g) 0.399 (h) 0.922
2 (a) 76.5° (b) 55.9° (c) 39.5° (d) 28.9° (e) 26.1° (f) 24.2°
3 (a) 13.4 cm (b) 19.3 cm (c) 2.29 cm (d) 6.60 cm
4 (a) 38.9° (b) 33.8° (c) 47.2° (d) 54.0°
5 8.48 cm 6 5.07 cm 7 34.4°
8 41.4°

Unit 27 Problems involving trig. ratios

Angles of elevation and depression (page 81)

1 20.2 m 2 115.47 m 3 1169.5 m 4 16 354 m
5 18.4° 6 11.3° 7 5.85 m

Bearings (page 82)

1 (a) 8.60 km (b) 12.29 km
2 (a) 54.38 km (b) 25.36 km
3 050.2° 4 209.7° 5 141.6°
6 (a) 47.55 km east of Ship *Y* (b) 20.55 km south of Ship *Y*

Trig. problems (page 83)

1 31.0° 2 42.9° 3 47.2° 4 23.14 cm
5 12 cm 6 $\widehat{X}=106.2°$ $\widehat{Y}=\widehat{Z}=36.9°$ 7 160.4 m
8 60.8 m 9 15.45 km 10 73.7° and 106.3°

Unit 28 Three-dimensional trigonometry

3-D trig., problems involving cubes and cuboids (page 84)

1 (a) 11.31 cm (b) 13.86 cm (c) 35.3° (d) 45° (e) 54.7°
2 (a) 13 cm (b) 10.3 cm (c) 15 cm (d) 15.81 cm (e) 29.1° (f) 22.6° (g) 18.4° (h) 18.4°

3-D trig., problems involving pyramids and cones (page 84)

1 (a) 14.14 cm (b) 13.9 cm (c) 59.5° (d) 61°
2 (a) 25.0 cm (b) 20.3 cm (c) 60.5° (d) 52° (e) 43.4° (f) 59° (g) 76°
3 (a) 7.21 cm (b) 56.3° (c) 67.4° (d) 33.7°
4 (a) 2.5 m (b) 5.22 m (c) 5.59 m (d) 21.0°
5 $VD=VB=31.2$ cm, $VC=37.1$ cm, $V\widehat{B}A=V\widehat{D}A=50.2°$, $V\widehat{C}A=40.3°$
6 $VK=15$ cm, $VM=21.2$ cm, $VL=23.0$ cm, $V\widehat{K}J=53.1°$, $V\widehat{L}J=49.4°$, $V\widehat{M}J=55.5°$
7 $AB=82.7$ m
8 (a) 20.9 cm (b) 41.8 cm (c) 16°

Unit 29 Gradients

The gradient of a line (page 86)

1 $AB=\frac{2}{3}, CD=-\frac{1}{4}, EF=2, GH=0, IJ=\infty, KL=-3$
2 (a) 5 (b) 10 (c) 0 (d) −2 (e) $2\frac{1}{2}$ (f) ∞
3 (a) $\tan\theta=\frac{2}{1}$ (b) $\tan\theta=\frac{3}{1}$ (c) $\tan\theta=\frac{1}{2}$ (d) $\tan\theta=\frac{1}{2}$
4 (a) $\frac{1}{3}$ (b) $-\frac{1}{3}$ (c) $\frac{1}{4}$ (d) $-\frac{1}{2}$ (e) $-\frac{2}{7}$ (f) −1 (g) $-\frac{1}{2}$ (h) 3

The gradient of a curve at a particular point (page 87)

1 gradient at $P=1$ 2 gradient at $P=\frac{13}{10}$; gradient at $Q=-\frac{11}{10}$
3 (b) at $x=2$, gradient $=1$; at $x=4$, gradient $=2$
4 at $x=2$, gradient $=-5$; at $x=4$, gradient $=-1.25$

Unit 30 Congruent triangles (page 88)

1 (a) Yes (S.S.S.) (b) Yes (S.A.S.) (c) Yes (S.A.S.) (d) No (e) Yes (A.S.A.) (f) No (g) Yes (S.S.S.)

Unit 31 Similar triangles (page 89)

1 (a) $AY=9$ cm (b) $AB=20$ cm (c) $AX=3.2$ cm
2 (a) $AB=7.5$ cm, $AC=6$ cm (b) 9:4
3 (a) $DE=1.6$ cm, $EF=1.2$ cm (b) 16:25
4 (a) 73° (b) 50° (c) 57°

Unit 32 Angle properties of a circle (page 91)

1 **(a)** 35° **(b)** 122° **(c)** $a = 42°, b = 42°$
(d) $c = 79°, d = 125°$ **(e)** $a = 99°, b = 81°$
(f) $a = 28°, b = 58°, c = 32°$ **(g)** $p = 41°, q = 41°, r = 49°$
(h) $a = 64°, b = 74°, c = 42°$ **(i)** $e = 97°, f = 97°, g = 46°$
(j) $a = 40°, b = 50°$ **(k)** $c = 97°, d = 67°$
(l) $a = 91°, b = 92°, c = 88°$

2 **(a)** $A\widehat{C}D = 44°$ **(b)** $B\widehat{D}C = 44°$ **(c)** $B\widehat{A}C = 44°$

3 $C\widehat{D}B = 70°, D\widehat{C}B = 20°, C\widehat{B}A = 20°$

Unit 33 Geometric transformations

Reflections (page 92)

1 **(a)**

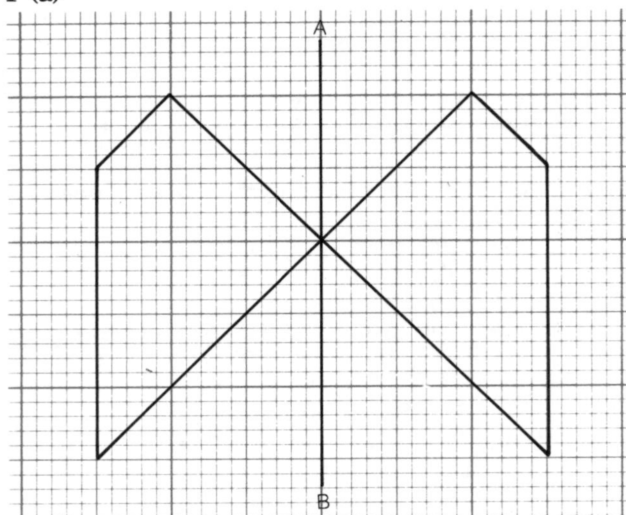

Fig. A33.1

(b)

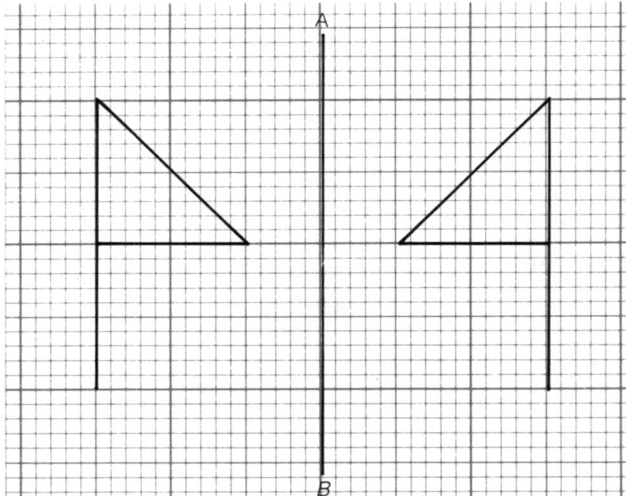

Fig. A33.2

2 **(a)**

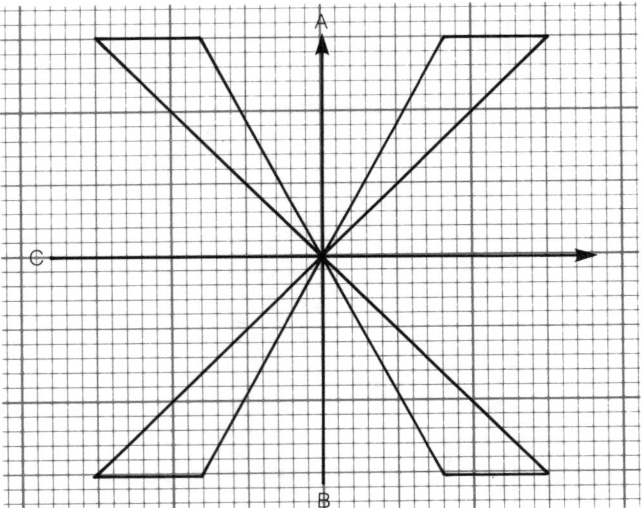

Fig. A33.3

(b)

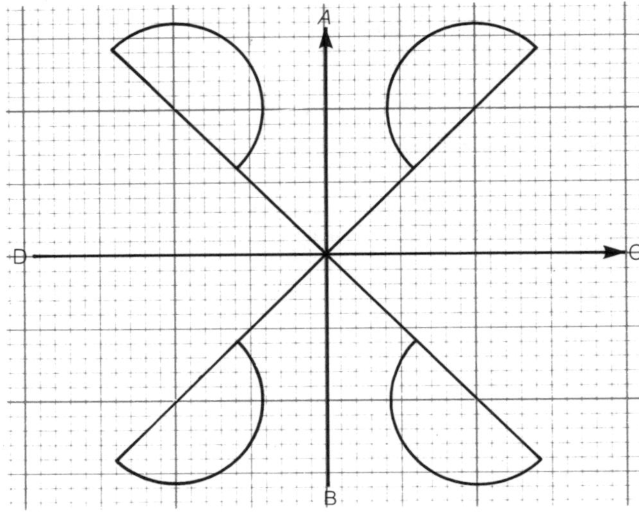

Fig. A.33.4

(c)

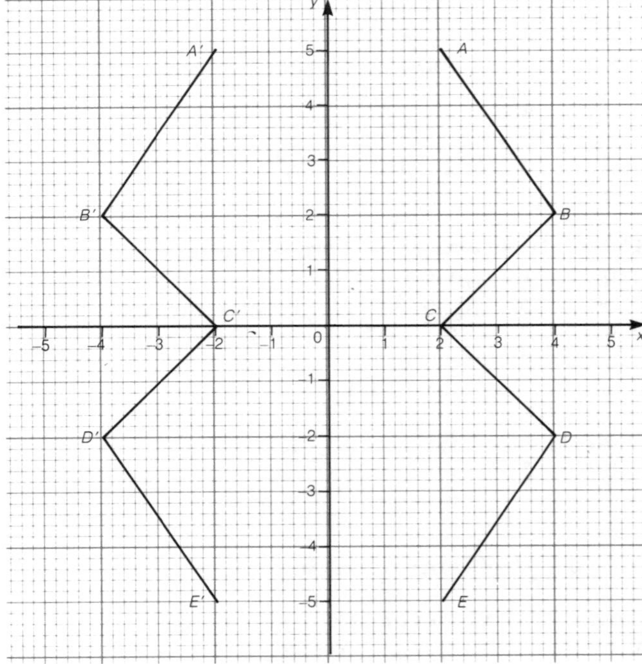

Fig. A33.5

4

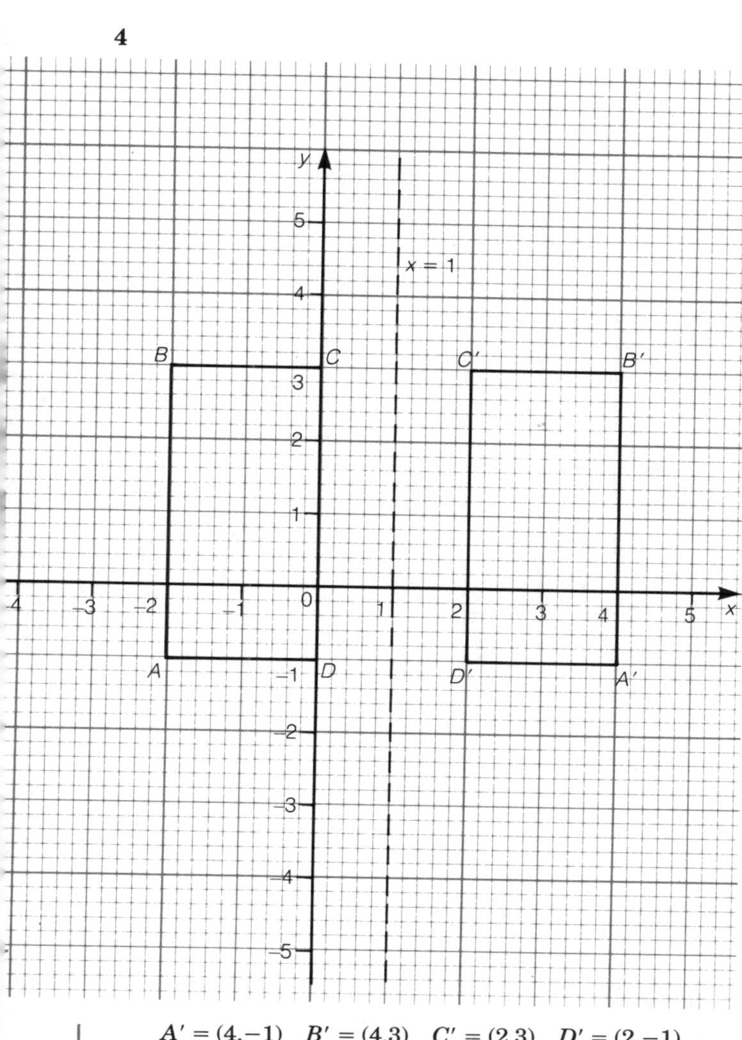

$A' = (4,-1)$ $B' = (4,3)$ $C' = (2,3)$ $D' = (2,-1)$

Fig. A33.6

5 **(a)** (2,−3) **(b)** (−5,−6) **(c)** (3,4) **(d)** (0,−7)
6 **(a)** (2,−1) **(b)** (4,0) **(c)** (0,6) **(d)** (−1,3)

Rotations (page 94)

1 **(a)**

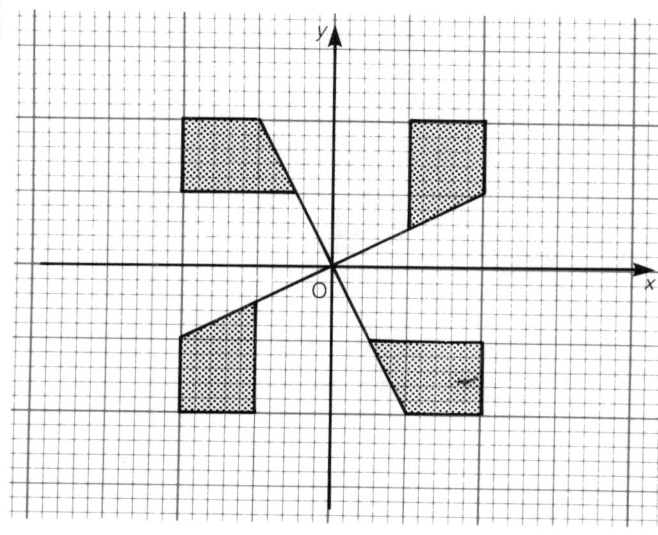

Fig. A33.7

(b)

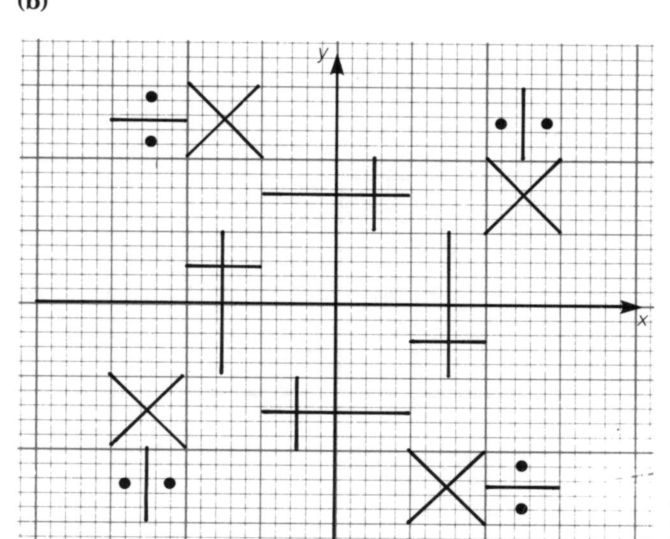

Fig. A33.8

2

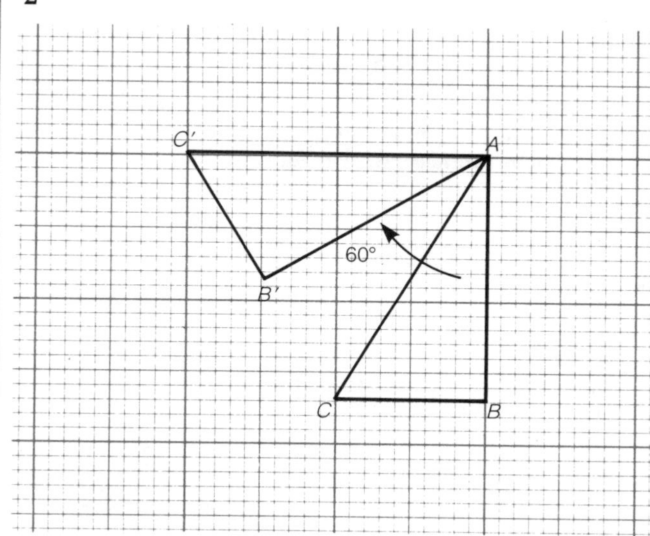

Fig. A33.9

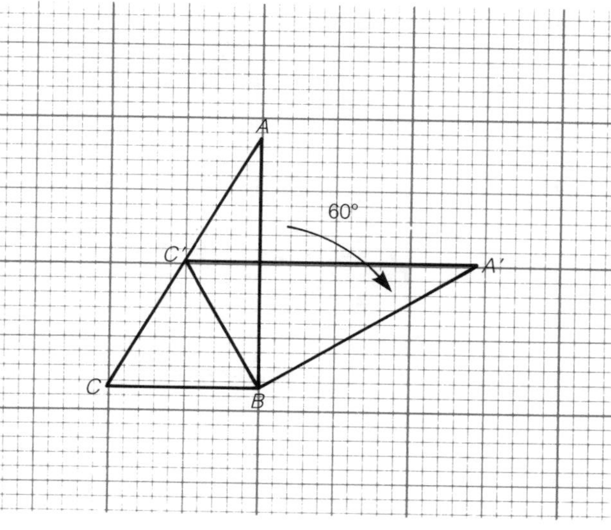

Fig. A33.10

3

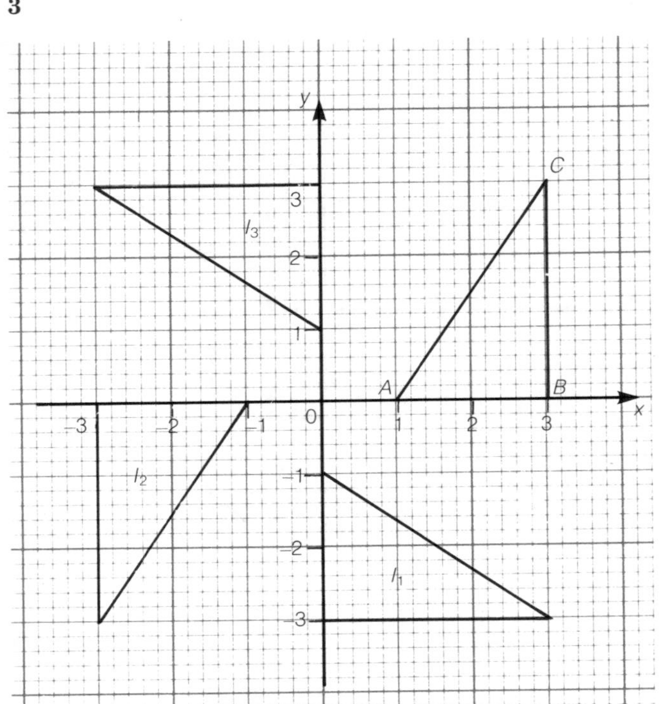

Fig. A33.11

(a) rotation 90° clockwise about O
(b) rotation 90° anticlockwise about O.

4

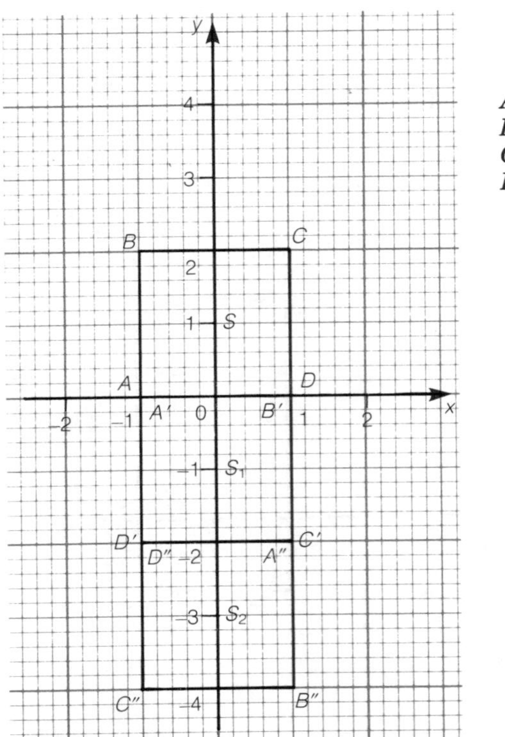

Fig. A33.12

$A' = (-1,0)$
$B' = (1,0)$
$C' = (1,-2)$
$D' = (-1,-2)$

Point of rotation for S_1 moving to S_2 is D' $(-1,-2)$; angle of rotation is 90° clockwise.

Enlargements (page 95)

1

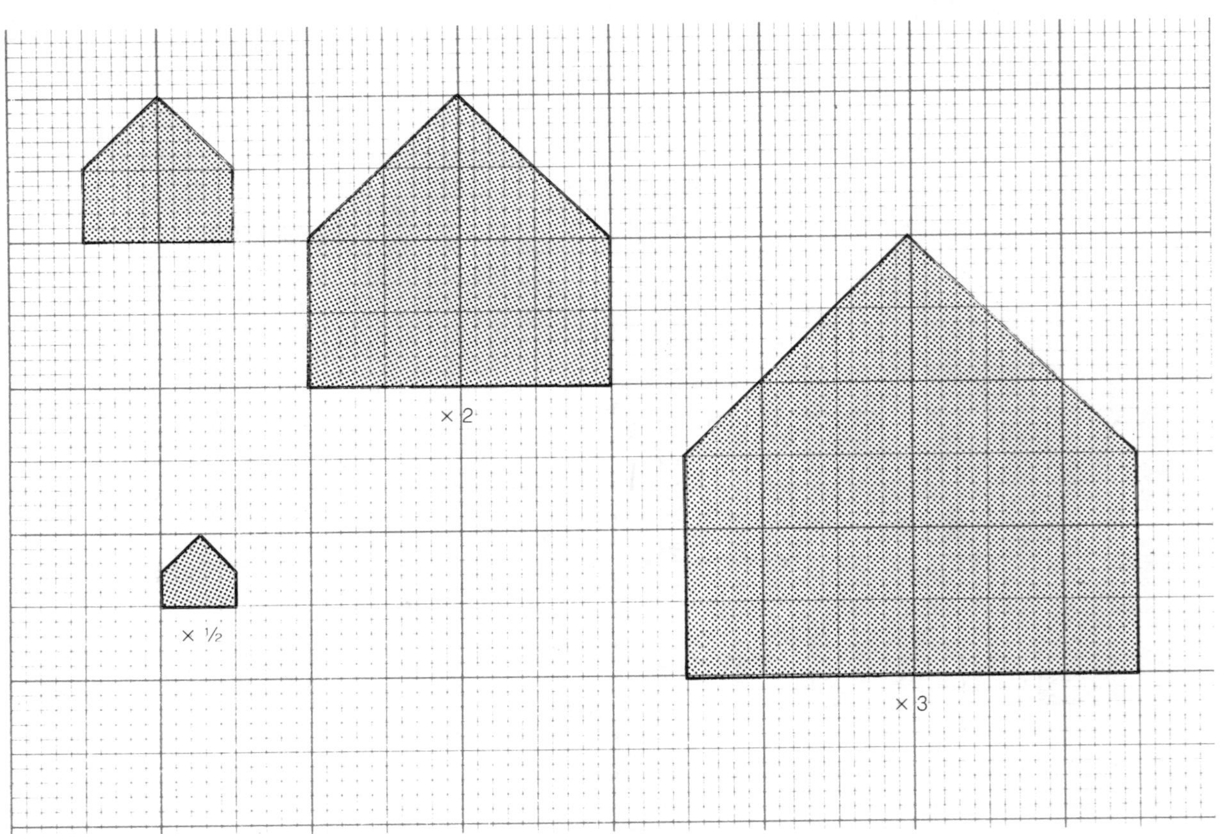

Fig. A33.13

2
(a)

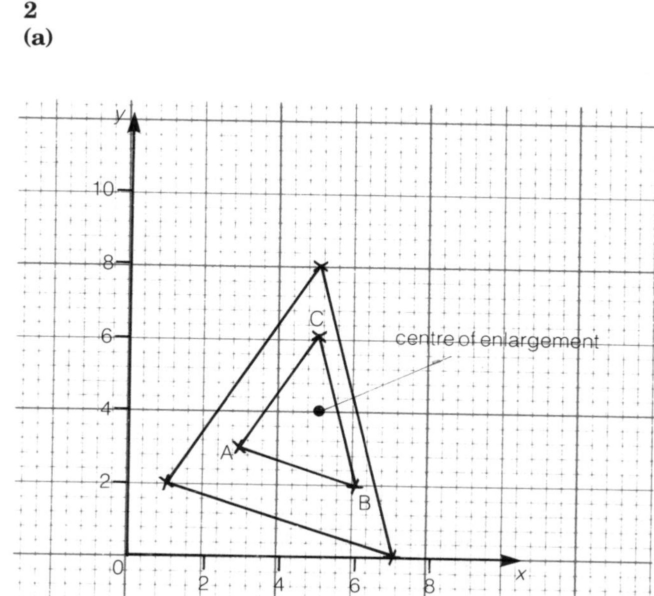

Fig. A33.14

(b)

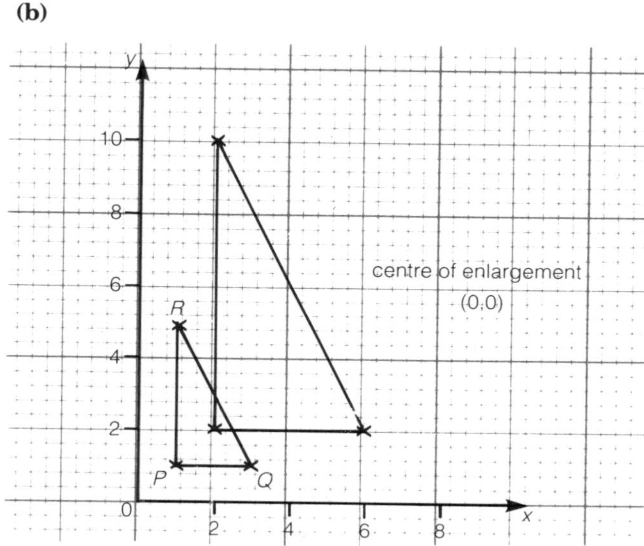

Fig. A33.15

(c)

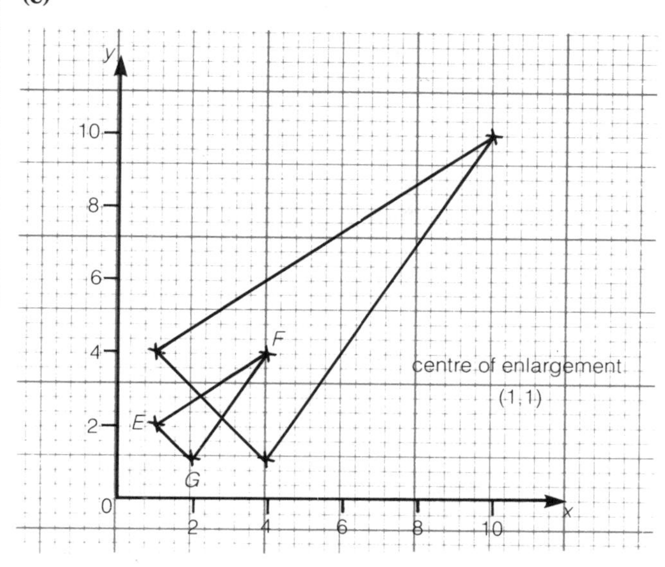

Fig. A33.16

Translations (page 96)

1

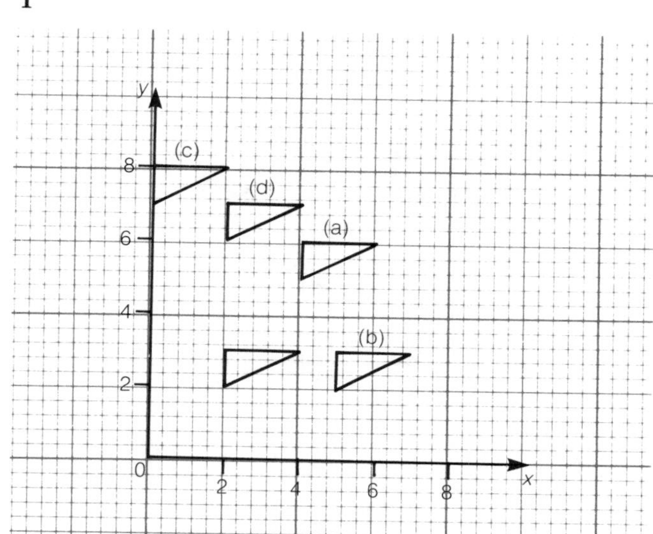

Fig. A33.17

2 A' (−2,4), B' (0,5), C' (−1,7)
3 A (0,4), B (−2, 2), C (−1,3)

Unit 34 Transformation matrices (page 97)

1 A' (2,−3), B' (3,−5) reflection in x-axis
2 P' (−1,3), Q' (−5,2) reflection in y-axis
3 F' (−3,2), G' (−1, 4) rotation 90° anticlockwise about O.
4 (a)

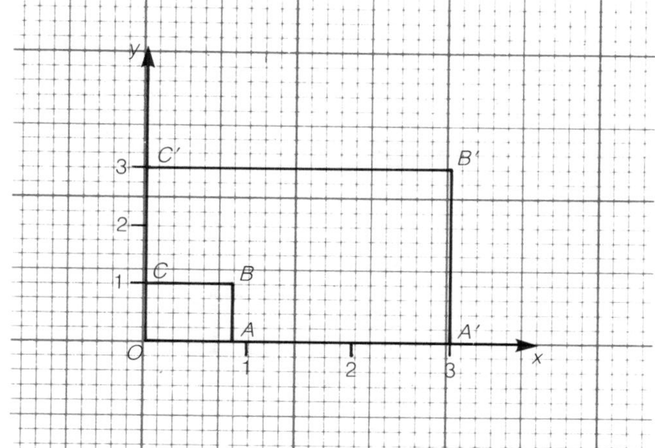

Fig. A34.1

(b)

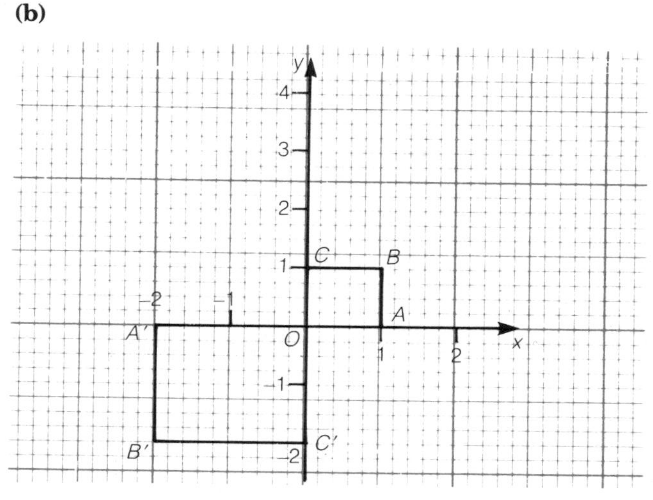

Fig. A34.2

(c)

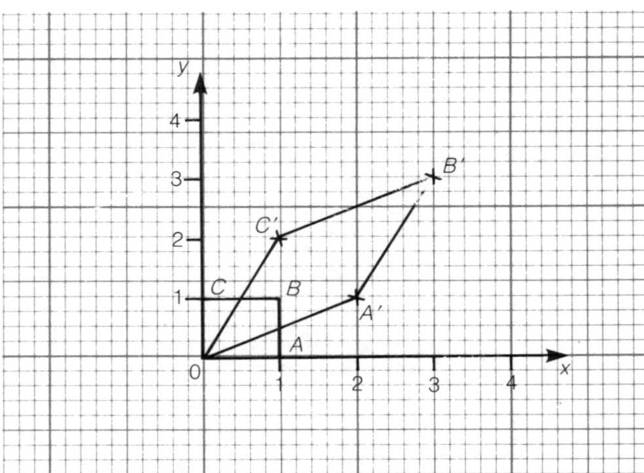

Fig. A34.3

5 (a) $\begin{pmatrix}2 & 0\\0 & 2\end{pmatrix}$ is enlargement of scale factor 2

(b) $\begin{pmatrix}5 & 0\\0 & 5\end{pmatrix}$ is enlargement of scale factor 5

(c) $\begin{pmatrix}\frac{1}{2} & 0\\0 & \frac{1}{2}\end{pmatrix}$ is enlargement of scale factor $\frac{1}{2}$

6 $A'(-6,-3), B'(20,10), C'(4,2)$

7 $P_1 = (-2,4), Q_1 = (-2,8), R_1 = (-6,8), S_1 = (-6,8)$

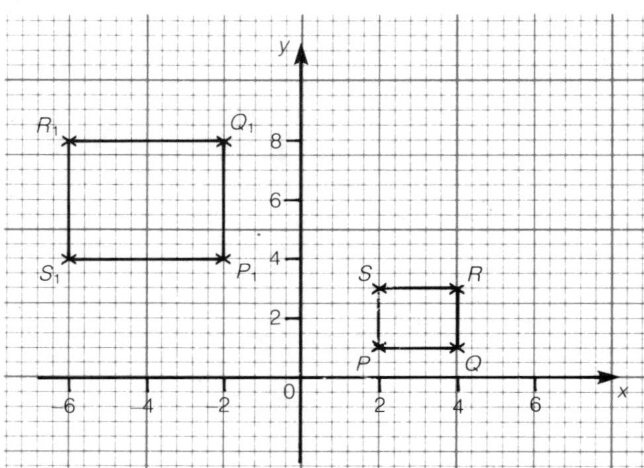

Fig. A34.4

8 $\begin{pmatrix}0 & -1\\1 & 0\end{pmatrix}\begin{pmatrix}2 & 0\\0 & 2\end{pmatrix} = \begin{pmatrix}0 & -2\\2 & 0\end{pmatrix}$

and $\begin{pmatrix}2 & 0\\0 & 2\end{pmatrix}\begin{pmatrix}0 & -1\\1 & 0\end{pmatrix} = \begin{pmatrix}0 & -2\\2 & 0\end{pmatrix}$

Hence it makes no difference in which order the transformations are performed.

$\begin{pmatrix}2 & 0\\0 & 2\end{pmatrix}$ is an enlargement of scale factor 2, and

$\begin{pmatrix}0 & -1\\1 & 0\end{pmatrix}$ is an anticlockwise rotation of 90° about the origin (0,0).

9 (a) $O_1 = (0,0),\ A_1 = (-2,0),\ B_1 = (-4,4),\ C_1 = (-2,4)$
(b) $O_2 = (0,0),\ A_2 = (0,-2),\ B_2 = (-4,-4),\ C_2 = (-4,-2)$

10 $O_1 = (0,0),\ A_1 = (0,-4),\ B_1 = (6,-2)$

Unit 35 Cumulative frequency

Cumulative frequency tables (page 99)

1

Height (less than)	Cumulative Frequency
145.5	2
146.5	3
147.5	6
148.5	11
149.5	18
150.5	22
151.5	25
152.5	27
153.5	27
154.5	30

Table A35.1

2

Mass (g) (less than)	Cumulative Frequency
650	3
750	13
850	37
950	59
1050	72
1150	78
1250	80

Table A35.2

3

Marks (less than)	Cumulative Frequency
1.5	1
2.5	3
3.5	10
4.5	31
5.5	66
6.5	101
7.5	122
8.5	129
9.5	130

Table A35.3

4 (a) Frequency distribution table, Table A35.4.

Score	65	66	67	68	69	70	71	72	73	74	7
Frequency	1	2	2	8	7	7	5	2	2	2	2

Table A35.4

(b)

Score (less than)	Cumulative Frequency
66	1
67	3
68	5
69	13
70	20
71	27
72	32
73	34
74	36
75	38
76	40

Table A35.5

(c) Number of rounds of less than 71 scored = 27
(d) Number of rounds of more than 72 scored = 6

5 (a)

Time (seconds) (less than)	Cumulative Frequency
20.5	1
40.5	3
60.5	6
80.5	12
100.5	21
120.5	46
140.5	67
160.5	82
180.5	91
200.5	98
220.5	100

Table A35.6

(b) 6 calls (c) 54 calls (d) 21% (e) 88%

6

Hours (less than)	Cumulative Frequency
2.5	34
5.5	78
8.5	136
11.5	172
14.5	190
17.5	200

Table A35.7

32% (i.e. $\frac{64}{200}$) watched TV for 9 hours or more.

Further measures of dispersion (page 102)

1 (a) 28 pupils (approx.) (b) 6 pupils (c)

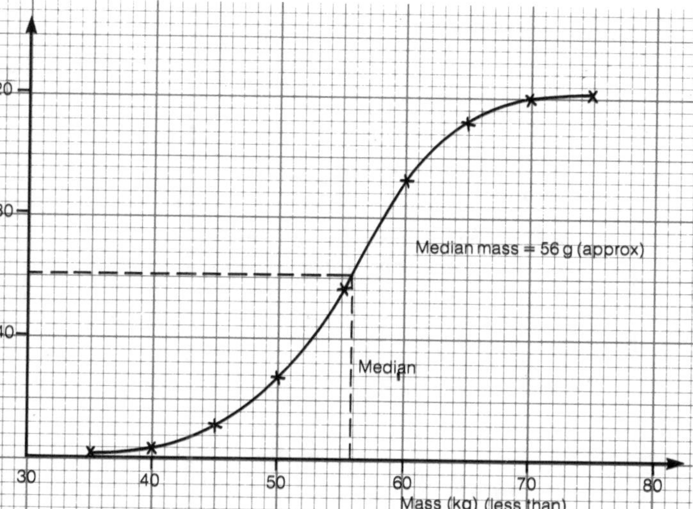

Fig. A35.1

2 (a)

Mass (g) (less than)	Cumulative Frequency
1490	6
1500	26
1510	60
1520	100
1530	120

Table A35.8

(b)

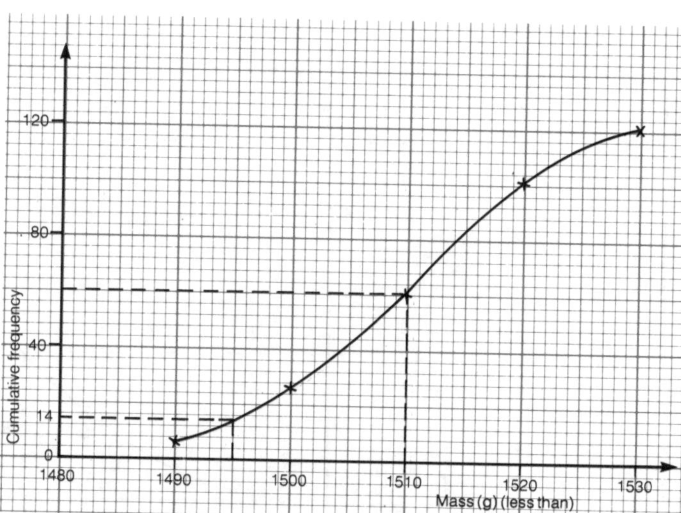

Fig. A35.2

(c) median mass = 1510 g (approx.)
(d) Number of packets having mass > 1495 g
= 120 − 14 = 106 (approx.)
(e) 1510 g is exceeded by $\frac{1}{2}$ of the packets.

3 (a)

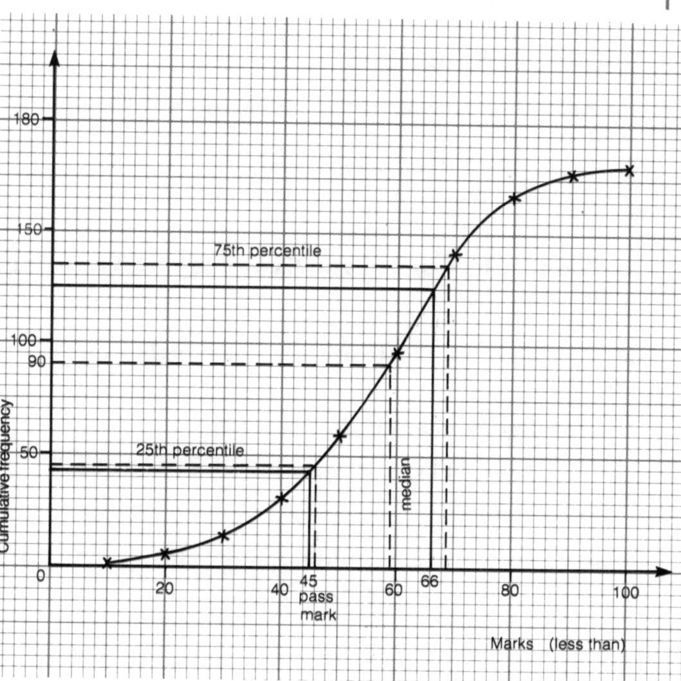

Fig. A35.3

(b) median mark is 58 (approx.)

(c) The number who failed is (approx.) 42.

(d) 30% of the candidates is 54. Hence, mark exceeded by 30% of the candidates = 180 − 54 (i.e. 126 candidates) is 66 marks (approx.).

(e) semi-interquartile range = $\frac{68-46}{2} = \frac{22}{2} = 11$ marks (approx.)

4 (a)

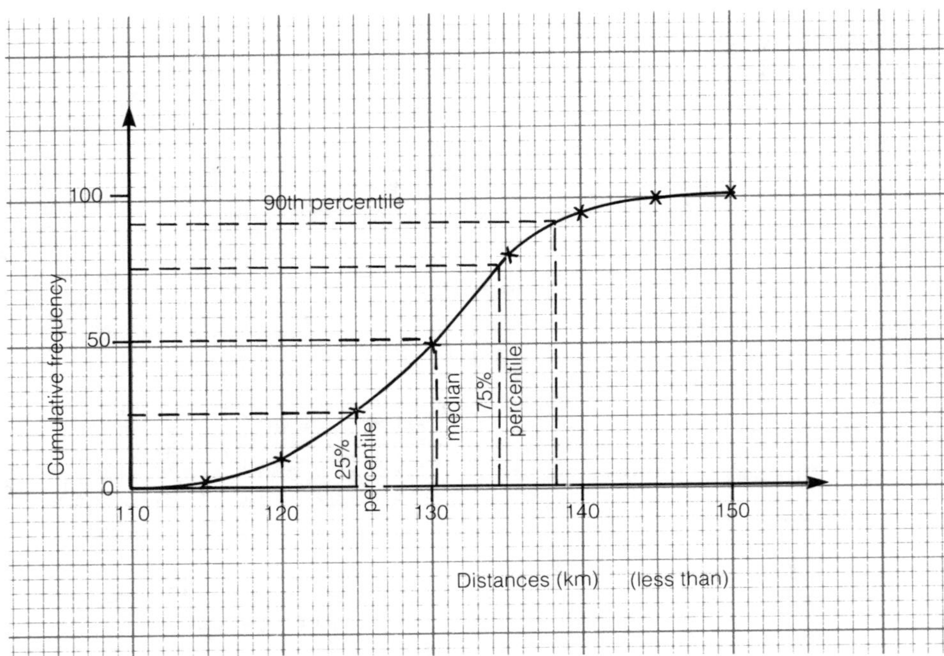

Fig. A35.4

(b) median is 131 km (approx.)

(c) semi-interquartile range $= \dfrac{134 - 125}{2} = \dfrac{9}{2} = 4.5$ km

(d) 90th percentile is approx. 138 km.

Unit 36 Probability

Probability by experiment, Experiment 1, Tossing a coin (page 104)

(a), (b), (c) Record your own results.
(d) The more results obtained, the nearer to the expected probability.

Probability by experiment, Experiment 2, Throwing a die (page 105)

(a), (b), (c) Record your own results.
(d) The more results obtained, the nearer to the expected probability.

Probability by calculation (page 105)

1 (a) $\frac{4}{52} = \frac{1}{13}$ (b) $\frac{1}{52}$ (c) $\frac{13}{52} = \frac{1}{4}$ (d) $\frac{12}{52} = \frac{3}{13}$ (e) $\frac{0}{52} = 0$

2 (a) $\frac{4}{11}$ (b) $\frac{2}{11}$

3 (a) $\frac{8}{20} = \frac{2}{5}$ (b) $\frac{4}{20} = \frac{1}{5}$ (c) $\frac{6}{20} = \frac{3}{10}$ (d) $\frac{6}{20} = \frac{3}{10}$

4 (a) $\frac{10}{50} = \frac{1}{5}$ (b) $\frac{40}{50} = \frac{4}{5}$ (c) $\frac{0}{50} = 0$

5 6 black, 18 white

6 (a) $P(\text{red}) = \frac{7}{20}$

(b) $P(\text{green}) = \frac{8}{20} = \frac{2}{5}$

(c) $P(\text{yellow}) = \frac{5}{20} = \frac{1}{4}$

Unit 37 Complementary events (page 106)

1 $P(6) = \frac{1}{6}$; $P(\text{not } 6) = \frac{5}{6}$ 2 $\frac{7}{8}$ 3 $\frac{3}{30} = \frac{1}{10}$ 4 0.4 or $\frac{2}{5}$

5 $\frac{27}{36} = \frac{3}{4}$ 6 $\frac{7}{10}$ 7 (a) $\frac{40}{52} = \frac{10}{13}$ (b) $\frac{3}{4}$

8 (a) $\frac{1}{2}$ (b) $\frac{4}{5}$ (c) $\frac{7}{10}$ (d) 1

Unit 38 Sample spaces and combined events
(page 107)

1

	coin 1	
coin 2	*ht* *th*	*hh* *tt*

Table A38.1

Hence, $P(t \text{ and } t) = \frac{1}{4}$

2

	die					
	1	2	3	4	5	6
coin	*h*1 *t*1	*h*2 *t*2	*h*3 *t*3	*h*4 *t*4	*h*5 *t*5	*h*6 *t*6

Table A38.2

(a) $P(h \text{ and } 4) = \frac{1}{12}$

(b) $P(t \text{ and } 3) = \frac{1}{12}$

(c) $P(h \text{ and } 7) = 0$

3

		white die					
	+	1	2	3	4	5	6
	1	2	3	4	5	6	7
	2	3	4	5	6	7	8
black	3	4	5	6	7	8	9
die	4	5	6	7	8	9	10
	5	6	7	8	9	10	11
	6	7	8	9	10	11	12

Table A38.3

(a) $P(\text{score of } 5) = \frac{4}{36} = \frac{1}{9}$

(b) $P(\text{score} < 8) = \frac{21}{36} = \frac{7}{12}$

(c) $P(\text{score} \geqslant 10) = \frac{6}{36} = \frac{1}{6}$

(d) Most likely sum is 7

4

+	2	4	6	8	10
5	7	9	11	13	15
7	9	11	13	15	17
9	11	13	15	17	19

Table A38.4

(a) $P(9) = \frac{2}{15}$ **(c)** $P(\text{even total}) = 0$

(b) $P(>9) = \frac{12}{15} = \frac{4}{5}$ **(d)** $P(\text{a multiple of } 3) = \frac{5}{15} = \frac{1}{3}$

5

	+	die 1 1	1	2	3	3	4
	1	2	2	3	4	4	5
	1	2	2	3	4	4	5
die 2	2	3	3	4	5	5	6
	3	4	4	5	6	6	7
	3	4	4	5	6	6	7
	4	5	5	6	7	7	8

Table A38.5

(a) $P(\text{total of } 4) = \frac{9}{36} = \frac{1}{4}$

(b) $P(\text{total of } 5) = \frac{8}{36} = \frac{2}{9}$

(c) $P(\text{even number}) = \frac{20}{36} = \frac{5}{9}$

6 (a) $P(\text{double}) = \frac{6}{36} = \frac{1}{6}$

(b) $P(\text{not a double}) = \frac{30}{36} = \frac{5}{6}$

7 (a) $\frac{2}{16} = \frac{1}{8}$ **(b)** $\frac{3}{16}$

(c) $\frac{12}{16} = \frac{3}{4}$ **(d)** $\frac{4}{16} = \frac{1}{4}$

(e) 1

8 $\frac{1}{16}$

9 (a) $P(\text{two black}) = \frac{1}{6}$

(b) $P(\text{two white}) = \frac{1}{4}$

(c) $P(\text{one of each colour}) = \frac{7}{12}$

10 $1+1+4,\ 2+1+3,\ 3+1+2,\ 4+1+1,$
$1+2+3,\ 2+2+2,\ 3+2+1,$
$1+3+2,\ 2+3+1,$
$1+4+1,$

$P(\text{total of } 6) = \frac{10}{216} = \frac{5}{108}$

11 (a) $\frac{1}{5}$ **(b)** $\frac{6}{25}$ **(c)** $\frac{12}{25}$

Unit 39 Combining probabilities

Mutually exclusive events (page 108)

1 $\frac{1}{3}$ **2** $\frac{1}{2}$ **3** $\frac{3}{13}$

4

+	1	2	3	4	5	6
1	2	3	4	5	6	7
2	3	4	5	6	7	8
3	4	5	6	7	8	9
4	5	6	7	8	9	10
5	6	7	8	9	10	11
6	7	8	9	10	11	12

Table A39.1

$P(4 \text{ or } 9) = \frac{7}{36} = P(4) + P(9)$

i.e. $\frac{3}{36} + \frac{4}{36}$

5 (a) $P(8 \text{ or double}) = \frac{10}{36} = \frac{5}{18}$

but $P(8) = \frac{5}{36}$ and $P(\text{double}) = \frac{6}{36}$. Because one of the 8s is the same as one of the doubles, i.e. 4, 4.

(b) $P(9 \text{ or double}) = \frac{10}{36} = \frac{5}{18}$

$P(9) = \frac{4}{36}$ and $P(\text{double}) = \frac{6}{36}$

6 $\frac{6}{36} = \frac{3}{36} + \frac{3}{36}$

7 $P(A \text{ or } B) = \frac{2}{5} + \frac{3}{10} = \frac{7}{10}$

8 (a) $\frac{5}{15} + \frac{6}{15} = \frac{11}{15}$

(b) $\frac{5}{15} + \frac{4}{15} = \frac{9}{15} = \frac{3}{5}$

(c) $\frac{6}{15} + \frac{4}{15} = \frac{10}{15} = \frac{2}{3}$

Independent events (page 109)

1 (a) $\frac{1}{24}$ **(b)** $\frac{1}{12}$

2 (a) $\frac{1}{16}$ **(b)** $\frac{1}{169}$

3 (a) $\frac{9}{64}$ **(b)** $\frac{15}{64}$ **(c)** $\frac{15}{64}$ **(d)** $\frac{25}{64}$

The answers add to one since **(a)**, **(b)**, **(c)** and **(d)** are the only results possible in this situation.

4 (a) $\frac{1}{216}$ **(b)** $\frac{1}{8}$ **5** $\frac{1}{16}$

6 (a) $\frac{6}{125}$ **(b)** $\frac{14}{125}$

7 (a) $\frac{5}{63}$ **(b)** $\frac{1}{21}$

Unit 40 Probability tree diagrams (page 110)

1

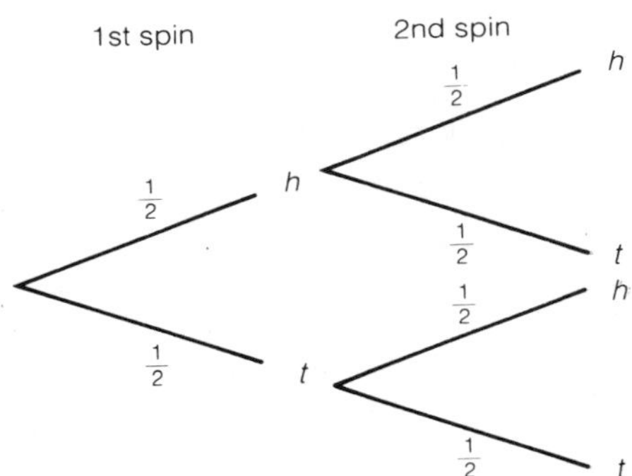

Fig. A40.1

2

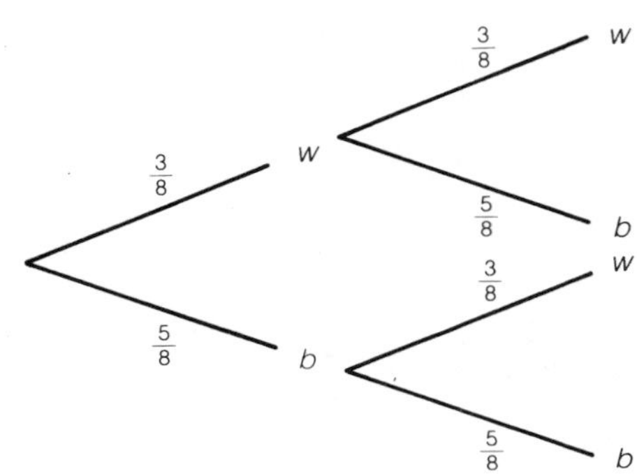

Fig. A40.2

(a) $P(w \text{ and } w) = \frac{9}{64}$ **(c)** $P(\text{one of each}) = \frac{15}{64} + \frac{15}{64} = \frac{30}{64} = \frac{15}{32}$

(b) $P(b \text{ and } b) = \frac{25}{64}$

3

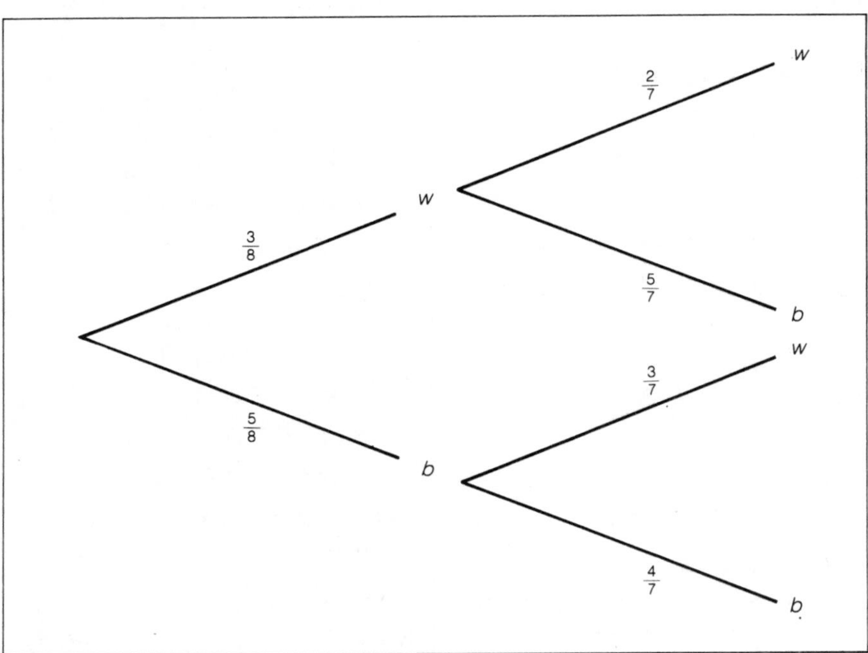

Fig. A40.3

(a) $P(w \text{ and } w) = \frac{3}{8} \times \frac{2}{7} = \frac{3}{28}$

(b) $P(b \text{ and } b) = \frac{5}{8} \times \frac{4}{7} = \frac{5}{14}$

(c) $P(\text{one of each}) = \frac{15}{56} + \frac{15}{56} = \frac{15}{28}$

4

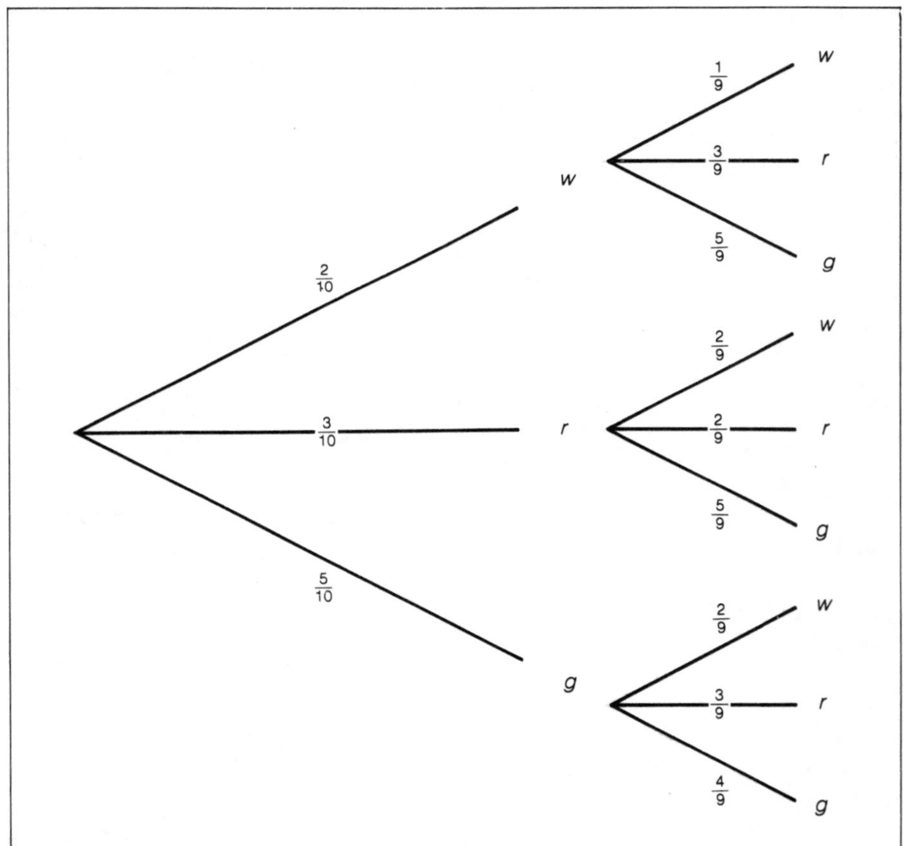

Fig. A40.4

(a) $P(w \text{ and } w) = \frac{2}{10} \times \frac{1}{9} = \frac{1}{45}$

(b) $P(g \text{ and } g) = \frac{5}{10} \times \frac{4}{9} = \frac{2}{9}$

(c) $P(r \text{ and } r) = \frac{3}{10} \times \frac{2}{9} = \frac{1}{15}$

(d) $P(g \text{ and } r)$ or $P(r \text{ and } g)$
$= (\frac{5}{10} \times \frac{3}{9}) + (\frac{3}{10} \times \frac{5}{9}) = \frac{1}{6} + \frac{1}{6} = \frac{1}{3}$

(e) $P(w \text{ and } g)$ or $P(g \text{ and } w)$
$= (\frac{2}{10} \times \frac{5}{9}) + (\frac{5}{10} \times \frac{2}{9}) = \frac{1}{9} + \frac{1}{9} = \frac{2}{9}$

5

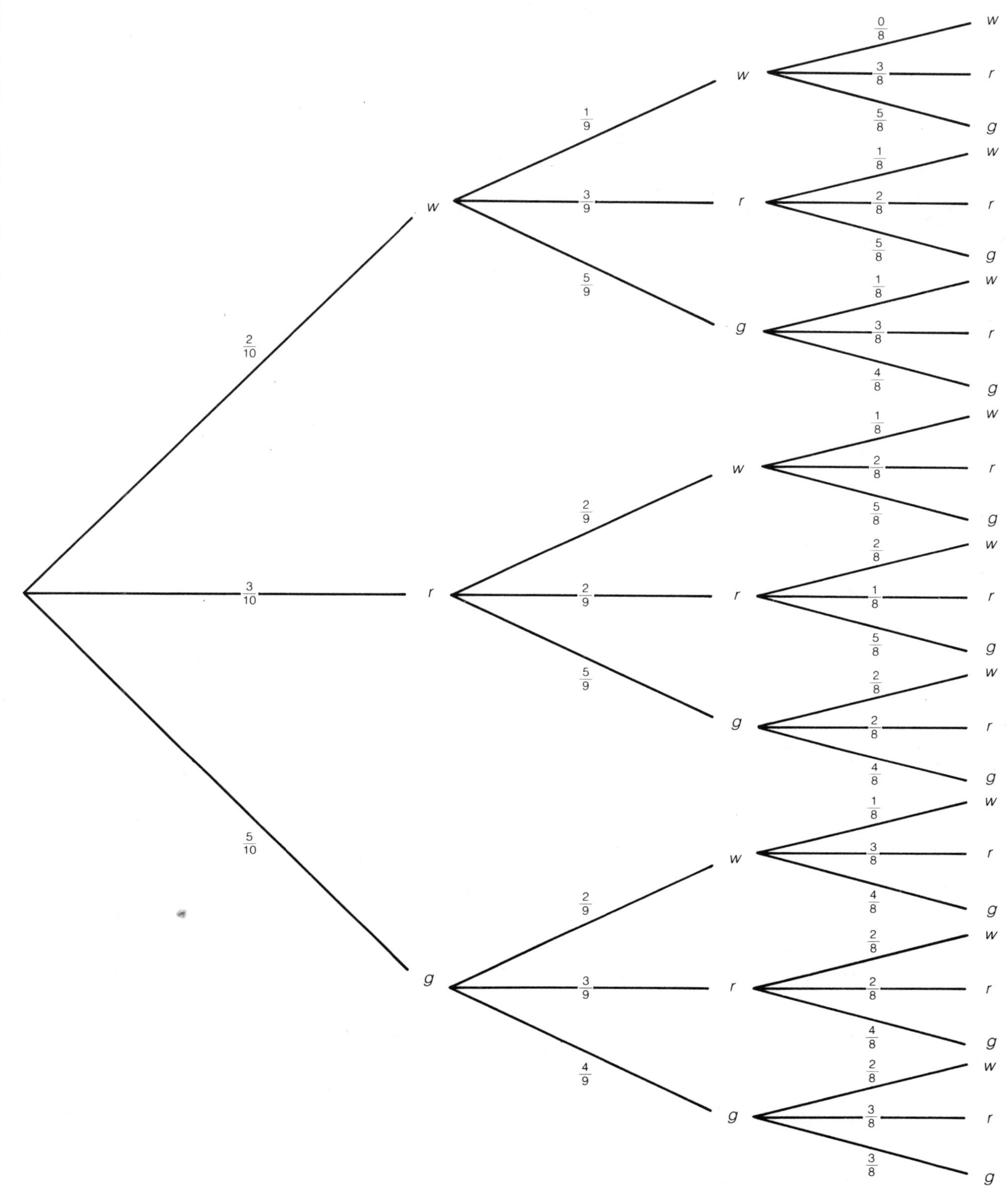

Fig. A40.5

(a) $P(\text{3 white}) = 0$

(b) $P(\text{3 green}) = \frac{5}{10} \times \frac{4}{9} \times \frac{3}{8} = \frac{1}{12}$

(c) $P(\text{3 red}) = \frac{3}{10} \times \frac{2}{9} \times \frac{1}{8} = \frac{1}{120}$

(d) $P(\text{one of each}) = P(w,r,g)$ or $P(w,g,r)$ or $P(r,w,g)$ *or*
$P(r,g,w)$ or $P(g,w,r)$ or $P(g,r,w)$
$= \frac{1}{24} + \frac{1}{24} + \frac{1}{24} + \frac{1}{24} + \frac{1}{24} + \frac{1}{24} = \frac{6}{24} = \frac{1}{4}$

6

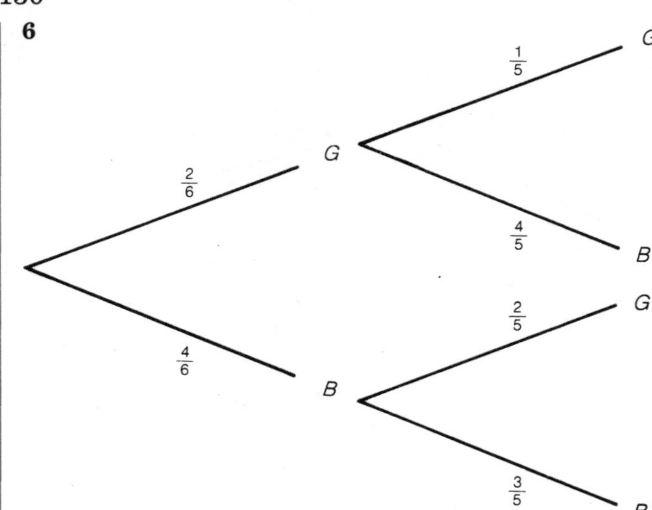

Fig. A40.6

(a) $P(\text{two of same colour}) = P(B,B) \text{ or } P(G,G)$
$= (\frac{4}{6} \times \frac{3}{5}) + (\frac{2}{6} \times \frac{1}{5})$
$= \frac{2}{5} + \frac{1}{15} = \frac{7}{15}$

(b) $P(\text{two of different colours}) = P(G,B) \text{ or } P(B,G)$
$= (\frac{2}{6} \times \frac{4}{5}) + (\frac{4}{6} \times \frac{2}{5})$
$= \frac{4}{15} + \frac{4}{15} = \frac{8}{15}$

or $1 - \frac{7}{15} = \frac{8}{15}$

7

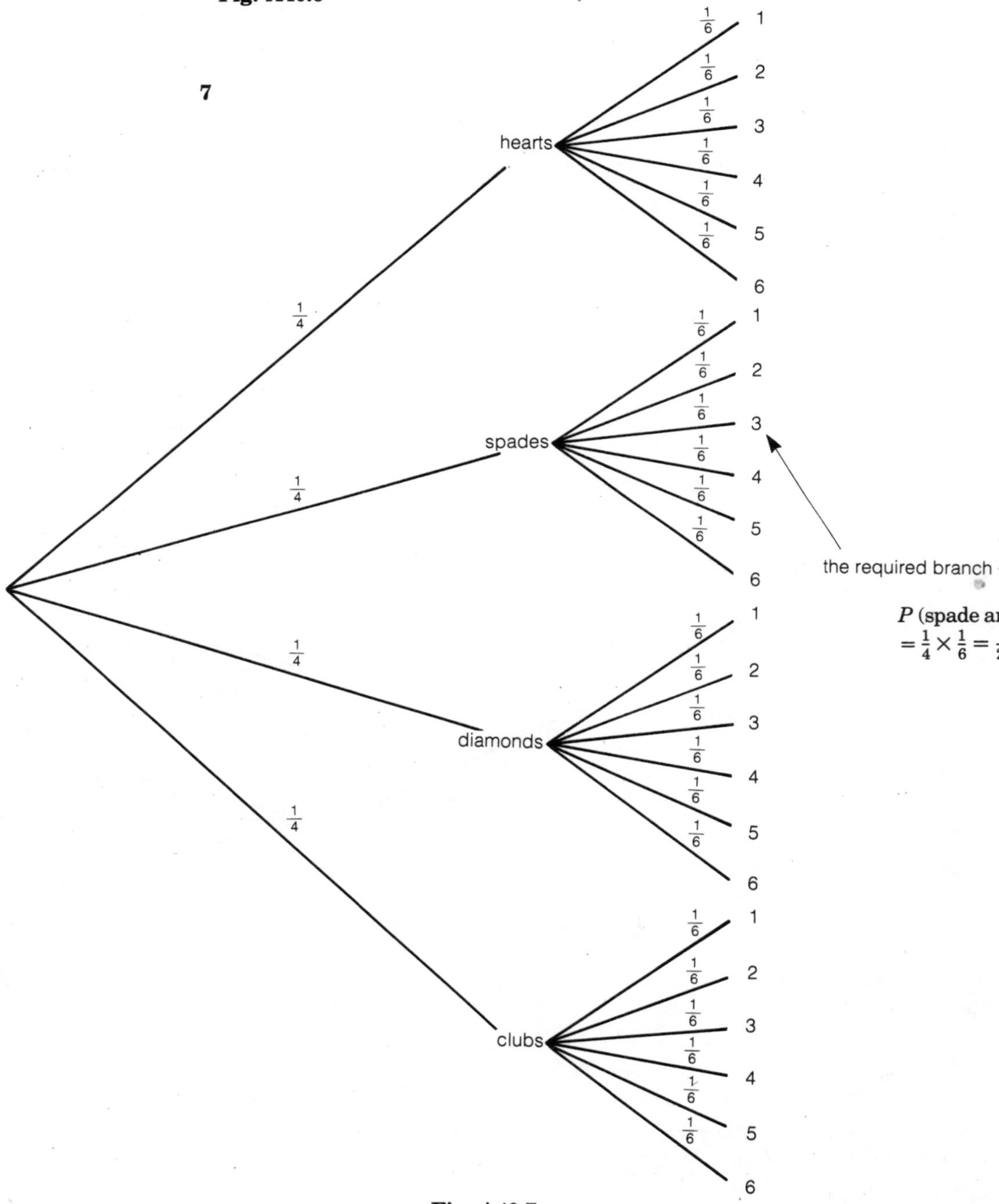

hearts: $\frac{1}{4}$ — 1, 2, 3, 4, 5, 6 (each $\frac{1}{6}$)

spades: $\frac{1}{4}$ — 1, 2, 3, 4, 5, 6 (each $\frac{1}{6}$)

diamonds: $\frac{1}{4}$ — 1, 2, 3, 4, 5, 6 (each $\frac{1}{6}$)

clubs: $\frac{1}{4}$ — 1, 2, 3, 4, 5, 6 (each $\frac{1}{6}$)

the required branch

P (spade and a3)
$= \frac{1}{4} \times \frac{1}{6} = \frac{1}{24}$

Fig. A40.7

Glossary

Acute angle An angle less than 90°
Adjacent side In a right-angled triangle, the side (other than the hypotenuse) next to the considered angle
Algebra The methods of reasoning about numbers by using letters to represent them.
Angle The measure of the amount of rotation
Angle of depression The angle through which the eye-line is lowered from the horizontal to view an object situated at a lower level
Angle of elevation The angle through which the eye-line is raised from the horizontal to view a raised object
Annulus The ring part of a circle with a hole in it
Approximation A number which is accepted as an estimate of another number
Arc Part of the circumference of a circle
Area The size of a surface (measured in square units)
Arithmetic mean The sum of a group of quantities divided by the number of quantities in the group
Associative Law $(a * b) * c = a * (b * c)$ where $* = +$ or $\times$ (in this Volume)
Average Usually refers to arithmetic mean, but also includes the median and the mode
Average speed The total distance travelled divided by the total time taken

Bar Graph A representation of a set of frequencies by a set of parallel bars of equal widths, with lengths proportional to the frequencies
Bearing Directional angle measured in a clockwise direction from North
Bias Unfair influence, weighted (or lop-sided)
Bisect To cut into two equal parts
Brackets A system of indicating terms that are to be treated collectively

Capacity The amount of space enclosed, i.e. internal volume
Characteristic The integral part of a logarithm determined by the place value of the digit with the largest place value
Chord A straight line joining any two points on the circumference of a circle
Circumference The perimeter of a circle
Class boundary (class limit) The point at which a set of data is separated from the next group
Class interval The width of the class, or the difference between the upper and lower limits
Co-domain The image or range set of a domain under a particular mapping
Coefficient The constant (number) factor in a product involving variables (e.g. 2 is the coefficient of $2x$)
Commutative law $a * b = b * a$ where $* = +$ or $\times$ (in this Volume)
Complement of a set If A is a subset of a universal set, the subset containing all the elements not in A is the complement of A
Complementary angles A pair of angles which total 90° when added
Composite shape A shape made up of two or more basic shapes
Cone The solid bounded by a conical surface and a plane circular end surface
Congruent triangles Triangles identical in every respect (i.e. angles and side lengths of each triangle correspond exactly)
Continuous data Information gained by measurement
Co-ordinates An ordered pair of numbers (x,y) which determine the precise location of a point on a graph
Cosine of an angle The ratio of the adjacent side length to the hypotenuse length of a right-angled triangle
Cross-section Normally, the shape made when a solid is cut through vertically and at right angles to line of centre (axis) of the shape
Cube A block with side lengths all of the same length and made up of 6 square faces
Cubic number The third power of a number; e.g. $8 = 2^3$
Cuboid = A rectangular-shaped block with 6 rectangular faces
Cumulative frequency A frequency distribution re-written as a running total of previous frequencies
Cylinder A geometrical solid with uniform cross-section and (in this Volume) circular ends e.g. a pipe or a tin can or a garden roller etc.

Data Given information or detail
Degree A rotation of one three-hundred-and-sixtieth ($\frac{1}{360}$th) part of one revolution
Denominator The term on the bottom line of a common fraction
Density The mass per unit volume of an object
Determinant The product of the leading diagonal elements minus the product of the elements of the other diagonal in a matrix (2×2)
Deviation Variation from the mean
Diagonal A line joining any two corners of a shape which are not next to each other
Diameter A line passing through the centre of a circle from one point on the circle to another point on the circle.
Difference The resulting number after the operation of subtraction
Dimensions Measurements of such things as length, breadth, height etc.
Directed numbers Numbers with either a positive or negative sign in front of them
Discrete data Information gained by counting
Dispersion A statistical term for the variation in, or the amount of scatter of, a set of data
Distinct sets (disjoint sets) Sets having no common elements
Distributive law A law linking the operations of addition and multiplication i.e.

$$a \times (b + c) = (a \times b) + (a \times c)$$

Dividend A term used in division; in $a \div b$, a is the dividend
Divisor A term used in division; in $a \div b$, b is the divisor
Domain The initial set of elements to which a mapping is applied

Elimination The process whereby two simultaneous equations are combined in order to remove one of the variables
Empty set A set which has no elements in it
Enlargement A transformation which increases (or possibly decreases) the size of a figure
Equation A statement of equality, written to show that two things are equal
Equilateral shape A shape with all sides of equal length
Equivalent sets Sets containing the same elements
Estimation The process of obtaining an approximate result by rounding off the numbers of the calculation
Even number An integer which has no remainder when divided by 2
Expression A symbol, or a collection of symbols which are connected by signs of operations (usually + and −)

Exterior angle An angle at a vertex of a polygon formed outside the polygon by two adjacent sides, one of which has been extended (produced)

Factorization The process by which any number or expression is broken into the parts which make it, when the parts are multiplied together
Factors When a number or expression is the product of two or more numbers or expressions, each of the latter is called a factor of the former
Finite set A set which has an end number
Frequency distribution A table of results showing how many times something occurs
Frequency polygon The shape formed, by joining with straight lines, the mid-points of the tops of the bars of a histogram, and closed by the horizontal axis
Function A one-to-one or many-to-one correspondence

Gradient The slope of a line in relation to the positive direction of the x-axis
Grouped data Statistical data put into class intervals

Histogram A statistical graph in which the area of the columns represents the data
Horizontal A line parallel to the earth's surface; a flat line
Hypotenuse The longest side of a right-angled triangle

Improper fraction A common fraction in which the top line (numerator) is bigger than the bottom line (denominator)
Independent events Events which do not affect each other in any way
Indices Positive or negative integers or fractions placed above and to the right of quantities, to express the power to which the quantity is to be raised or lowered
Inequality A statement that one quantity is greater than or less than another
Infinite set A set which goes on and on, i.e. it has no end number
Integer A whole number, either positive or negative
Intercept The point at which two lines meet (intersect)
Interior angle One of the inside angles of a shape
Intersecting set A set containing element(s) belonging to two or more sets
Inverse function If a function consists of a one-to-one correspondence, then the function may be reversed; such a reversal is known as the inverse of the original function
Inverse matrix An inverse matrix is such that the product of it and its own matrix produces the identity matrix. (Not all matrices have an inverse matrix)
Isosceles triangle A triangle with 2 equal sides and 2 equal base angles

Latitude Small circles on a sphere, having the polar axis as a common axis
Least common multiple L.C.M. is the smallest positive common multiple
Like terms Algebraic terms which can be added or subtracted
Logarithm A convenient way of converting multiplication/division problems into easier addition/ subtraction problems
Longitude Great circles on a sphere which all pass through the North and South Poles
Lowest terms A fraction cancelled down to its simplest form

Mantissa The positive fractional part of a logarithm
Mapping A correspondence or function linking each element of a set with a unique corresponding element of another set
Mass The 'quantity of matter' in a body
Matrix An array of numbers or letters, called elements, in rows and columns
Mean See Arithmetic mean
Mean deviation The arithmetic mean of all the deviations from the mean
Median The middle element of a set of measurements when arranged in order of size
Mixed number A number which has a whole number coupled to a fractional number, e.g. $2\frac{3}{4}$
Mode The most frequently occurring value in a series of measurements
Modulo arithmetic The application of fundamental operations to number systems which involve the use of numbers of these systems only
Multiple Any integer which has a given integer as a factor, is called a multiple of that factor
Mutually exclusive events Events which cannot happen at the same time

Natural numbers Positive integers; whole numbers
Negative numbers Numbers with a minus sign in front of them
Net The opened-out shape of a geometric solid
Number bases Different systems of counting, the most usual being the denary (base 10) system
Numerator The term on the top line of a common fraction

Obtuse angle An angle between 90° and 180°
Odd number An integer which has a remainder when divided by 2
Ogive A cumulative frequency curve
Opposite side In a right-angled triangle, the side (other than the hypotenuse) opposite to the considered angle
Origin The point of intersection of the axes in Cartesian co-ordinates

Parallel lines Lines which never meet, no matter how far they are extended
Parallelogram A 4-sided figure, with opposite sides equal in length, and parallel
Percentage A number expressed in fractional form as a part of 100
Percentile A statistical term for a value which divides the range of a set in such a way that a given percentage of it lies before the point of division
Perimeter The distance around the boundary of a figure
Perpendicular A line which is at right angles to another line
Pi (π) Letter of the Greek alphabet used to signify the constant value which links the circumference of any circle to its diameter
Pictogram (pictograph) A graph which uses symbols to represent frequency
Pie chart (pie graph) A circular graph in which the sectors represent the frequency (like slices of a cake)
Polygon The general name for any figure having 3 or more sides, e.g. pentagon is 5-sided, decagon is 10-sided etc
Positive numbers Numbers with a plus sign (or no sign) in front of them
Power The quantity to which a number is raised or lowered, shown by the index (see Indices)
Prime factors Factors which are prime numbers
Prime number Any integer which has only itself and 1 as factors i.e. 2, 3, 5, 7, 11, etc
Prism Any geometric solid with a uniform cross-section
Probability A numerical measure of the likelihood of an event taking place
Product The result of multiplication
Proportion A statement of the equality of two ratios
Protractor An instrument used for measuring the size of angles

Pyramid Normally a solid with a square or rectangular base, with all sides meeting at a vertical apex

Quadratic function A function with a variable of highest power 2, i.e. $ax^2 + bx + c$
Quadrilateral Any 4-sided figure
Quartile The 25th, 50th and 75th percentiles are the first, second and third quartiles
Questionnaire Inquiry for data by means of a series of questions
Quotient The result obtained by division

Radius A straight line joining the centre of a circle to any point on the circumference. It is half of the diameter
Range The spread between the lower and upper limit of any given statistical data
Ratio The relation existing between two or more quantities of the same kind
Rectangle A quadrilateral with two pairs of equal, opposite and parallel sides and 4 right angles.
Reflection A geometric transformation producing an image of a point, using a line in a similar manner to a mirror
Reflex angle An angle between 180° and 360°
Regular polygon A polygon having sides of the same length and equal interior angles
Relation A mapping linking a domain to its co-domain (or range)
Rhombus A quadrilateral with opposite sides parallel and sides all of the same length
Right angle An angle of 90°
Root of real number Denoted by $\sqrt{a}$ (square root), $\sqrt[3]{a}$ (cube root), $\sqrt[4]{a}$ (fourth root), etc
Rotation A geometrical transformation in which a point turns (clockwise or anticlockwise) about a fixed point
Rounding off The process of approximating a number; reduction in decimal places or significant figures, etc

Sample Part of a total population, used for statistical work
Sample space A list or table of all possible outcomes, which follow from a particular course of action
Sampling The process of obtaining a sample of a population for statistical purposes
Scalar quantity A number having size but without any direction
Scale A system of points placed at known intervals on a line for the purpose of measuring. It may also be used to give a comparison between a real object and a drawing or model of the object
Scalene triangle A triangle with all sides and angles unequal
Sector The part of a circle enclosed by two radii and an arc
Segment Part of a circle bounded by a chord and an arc
Semi-circle Half a circle, separated from its other half by a diameter
Semi-interquartile range Half the difference of the 25th and 75th percentiles
Sequence (series) A set of elements written consecutively
Set A collection of things called elements or members
Significant figures The specified number of figures in any number expressed as integer and/or a decimal, which serves as an approximation for the number
Similar triangles Triangles which are similar in shape but not identical
Simultaneous equations A pair of equations with 2 unknown values which are satisfied by the same values of the unknown quantities involved
Sine of an angle The ratio of the opposite side length to the hypotenuse length of a right-angled triangle
Slant height The sloping height of a triangle (as opposed to its perpendicular height)
Solution The answer when a problem is solved
Sphere A solid shape bounded by a spherical surface (e.g. a ball)
Square A quadrilateral with 4 equal sides and 4 right angles, and with opposite sides parallel
Square measure The measurement of area
Square numbers 1, 4, 9, 16, etc. (i.e. $1^2, 2^2, 3^2, 4^2$ etc)
Standard deviation The square root of the mean value of the squares of individual deviations
Standard form A way of expressing a number as a power of 10 i.e. $A \times 10^n$, where $1 \leqslant A < 10$ and n is the power of 10
Statistics The study of methods of collecting, analysing and using data
Subset If set A is part of set B, then A is a subset of B
Substitution Replacing a letter with a given number
Subtended angle An angle formed by any 2 line segments inside a circle
Suffix The small number following the main number, indicating the base of the number
Sum The result of addition
Supplementary angles A pair of angles, the sum of which is 180°
Surface area The area of the surface of a solid, either flat or curved depending on the shape of the solid
Symmetry The state of a shape, being the same either side of an axis drawn through it, or about its central point

Tally A method of counting frequency in 'bunches' of five
Tangent of an angle The ratio of the opposite side length to the adjacent side length of a right-angled triangle
Trailing zeros Zeros in an integer or decimal number, which are not significant
Translation A transformation which simply moves one point to another point
Trapezium A quadrilateral with just one pair of parallel sides
Trend A statistical term for a general tendency in the data
Triangle A polygon with 3 straight sides and 3 interior angles which total 180°
Triangular numbers Numbers which can be represented by a triangle of dots e.g. 3, 6, 10, etc
Trigonometry The study of angles and side lengths of right-angled triangles
Trigonometric ratios The ratios of the lengths of the sides in a right-angled triangle (see Sine, Cosine and Tangent of an angle)

Union of sets A set containing all the elements of two or more combined sets (but having no repeated elements)
Universal set The set of all those elements under consideration

Variable Any symbol for any member of a set of numbers, points, values etc, which may change in value
Variance The mean value of the squares of individual deviations
Venn diagram A diagram used to represent sets
Vertical line A line in the direction towards or away from the centre of the earth (at right angles to a horizontal line)
Volume The measure of the space occupied by a geometric solid

***x*-axis** The horizontal axis of a Cartesian graph
***y*-axis** The vertical axis of a Cartesian graph